SYMBOLIC LOGIC

An Introduction

By

FREDERIC BRENTON FITCH

PROFESSOR OF PHILOSOPHY
YALE UNIVERSITY

THE RONALD PRESS COMPANY · NEW YORK

3

VR-VR

Library of Congress Catalog Card Number: 52-6196
PRINTED IN THE UNITED STATES OF AMERICA

PREFACE

This book is intended both as a textbook in symbolic logic for undergraduate and graduate students and as a treatise on the foundations of logic. Much of the material was developed in an undergraduate course given for some years in Yale University. The course was essentially a first course in logic for students interested in science. Many alternative devices and methods of presentation were tried. Those included here are the ones that seemed most successful.

The early sections of the book present rules for working with implication, conjunction, disjunction, and negation. In connection with negation, there is a discussion of Heyting's system of logic and the law of excluded middle. Following this, various modal concepts such as necessity, possibility, and strict implication are introduced. The theory of identity and the general theory of classes and relations are presented. The theory of quantifiers is then developed. Finally, operations on classes and relations are defined and discussed. The book provides a novel way for avoiding Russell's paradox and other similar paradoxes. No theory of types is required. The system of logic employed is shown to be free from contradiction. There are three appendices: Appendix A shows how classes can be defined by means of four operators using techniques similar to those of Curry's combinatory logic. Appendix B shows in outline how the system can be further extended so as to form a consistent foundation for a large part of mathematics. Appendix C discusses an important kind of philosophical reasoning and indicates why the system of logic of the book is especially well suited for handling it.

The student not acquainted with symbolic logic can omit Sections 20 and 27 which are of a more difficult nature than the other sections. The three appendices are also of a somewhat advanced nature. These appendices and the Foreword are addressed mainly to readers who already have some knowledge of symbolic logic.

The sections concerned with modal logic, namely, 11, 12, 13, and 23, can be omitted if desired, since the other sections do not depend essentially on them.

I am greatly indebted to my past teachers and to my present colleagues and students for their inspiring interest in logic and philosophy and for their helpful insights and suggestions. I am also, of course, greatly indebted to many contemporary writers in logic and allied fields. In some ways my debt is greatest to Professor Filmer S. C. Northrop, since he made clear to me the importance of modern logic and guided my first work in it.

Some of the fundamental ideas of this system of logic were conceived during the tenure of a John Simon Guggenheim Memorial Fellowship in 1945–1946.

Thanks are due to Miss Erna F. Schneider for her careful reading of a large part of the manuscript. She made numerous useful suggestions. I am also very grateful to Dr. John R. Myhill for studying some of the more difficult portions of the manuscript, for pointing out some logical and typographical errors, and for making various constructive criticisms. I wish to thank Mr. I. Sussmann for calling my attention to typographical errors, and Miss Mabel R. Weld for her help in typing the manuscript. Various members of the Yale philosophy department also made helpful suggestions regarding the general scheme of the book. I am indebted to Mr. Herbert P. Galliher and Mr. Abner E. Shimony for valuable comments on the manuscript.

FREDERIC B. FITCH

New Haven, Conn.
February, 1952

FOREWORD

Five outstanding characteristics of the system of logic of this book are as follows:

(1) It is a system that can be proved free from contradiction, so there is no danger of any of the standard logical paradoxes arising in it, such as Russell's paradox or Burali-Forti's paradox. In Sections 20 and 27 a proof will be given of the consistency of as much of the system as is presented in the present volume. In Appendix B a proof of the consistency of the rest of the system is outlined.

(2) The system seems to be adequate for all of mathematics essential to the natural sciences. The main principles of mathematical analysis will be derived in a subsequent volume. Apparently no other system of logic, adequate for as large a portion of standard mathematics, is now known to be free from contradiction.

(3) The system is not encumbered by any "theory of types". The disadvantage of a theory of types is that it treats as "meaningless" all propositions that are concerned with attributes or classes in general. A logic with a theory of types is of little or no use in philosophy, since philosophy must be free to make completely general statements about attributes and classes. A theory of types also has the disadvantage of ruling out as "meaningless" some philosophically important types of argument which involve propositions that have the character of referring directly or indirectly to themselves. In Appendix C there is a discussion of the nature and importance of these self-referential propositions. Furthermore, a theory of types, if viewed as applying to all classes, cannot itself even be stated without violating its own principles. Such a statement would be concerned with all classes and so would be meaningless according to the principles of such a theory of types itself. This point has been made by Paul Weiss [1] and myself.[2]

[1] Paul Weiss, "The Theory of Types", *Mind*, n.s., vol. 37 (1928), pp. 338–48.
[2] F. B. Fitch, "Self-Reference in Philosophy", *Mind*, n.s., vol. 55 (1946), pp. 64–73. This article is reprinted in Appendix C.

(4) The system employs the "method of subordinate proofs", a method that vastly simplifies the carrying out of complicated proofs and that enables the reader to gain rapidly a real sense of mastery of symbolic logic.

(5) The system is a "modal logic"; that is, it deals not only with the usual concepts of logic, such as conjunction, disjunction, negation, abstraction, and quantification, but also with logical necessity and logical possibility.

No great stress is laid on the contrast between syntax and semantics, or on the finer points concerning the semantical use of quotation marks. The reason for this is that such emphasis very often produces unnecessary difficulties in the mind of a person first approaching the subject of symbolic logic, and inhibits his ability to perform the fundamental operations with ease. The use of quotation marks will be found to be rather informal. This is done deliberately for pedagogical convenience. The semantical paradoxes, incidentally, are avoided by this system of logic in the same way that it avoids the purely logical and mathematical paradoxes.

Numerous exercises have been provided. Even the logically sophisticated reader will get a better understanding of the material by doing some of the exercises.

In comparing this system with some other well-known systems, it can be said to appear to be superior to the Whitehead-Russell system,[3] at least with respect to its demonstrable consistency and its freedom from a theory of types. In place of Russell's "vicious circle principle" [4] for avoiding paradoxes, my system uses a weakened law of excluded middle (see 10.16 and 10.19) and the following novel principle: A proposition p is not to be regarded as validly proved by a proof that makes essential use of the fact that some proposition other than p follows logically from p. This principle is reminiscent of the classical prohibition against treating a proposition as true simply because it implies another proposition that *is* true. My principle, however, makes no stipulation about the truth or falsity of the proposition implied by p. (See 18.6 for a technical statement of this principle.)

The demonstrable consistency of the present system is also an

---

[3] A. N. Whitehead and Bertrand Russell, *Principia Mathematica*, 3 vols., Cambridge, England, 1910, 1912, 1913. Second edition, 1925, 1927. Reprinted 1950.
[4] *Principia Mathematica*, Chapter II of the Introduction to the first edition.

important point in its favor when compared with the "set-theoretical" logics proposed by Zermelo,[5] Fraenkel,[6] von Neumann,[7] and Bernays.[8] These logics are widely used by mathematicians but are not known to be free from contradiction. Even these systems, in their most fully developed forms, employ what is almost a theory of types. For example, in Gödel's reformulation [9] of the Bernays system, the distinction between "set", "class", and "notion" is very much like the distinction between three successively higher "types" or "orders".

Quine [10] has constructed various interesting and elegant systems that bear close affiliations with the Whitehead-Russell logic and with the set-theoretic logics just mentioned.

All these systems with which the present system is being compared are characterized by the fact that none of them permits the formation of attributes or classes with the ease and freedom allowed by the rules stated in Section 17. (See in particular 17.4 and 17.5.) The restrictions imposed on this freedom by other systems seem arbitrary and philosophically unconvincing.

The method of subordinate proofs was suggested by techniques due to Gentzen [11] and Jaśkowski.[12] It has various pedagogical advantages and also facilitates comparison of the theory of negation of this book with the theory of negation of the intuitionistic logic of

[5] Ernst Zermelo, "Untersuchungen über die Grundlagen der Mengenlehre I", *Math. Annalen*, vol. 65 (1908), pp. 261–81.

[6] Adolf Fraenkel, "Untersuchungen über die Grundlagen der Mengenlehre", *Math. Z.*, vol. 22 (1925), pp. 250–73.

[7] J. von Neumann, "Eine Axiomatisierung der Mengenlehre", *Jour. r. angew. Math.*, vol. 154 (1925), pp. 219–40; "Die Axiomatisierung der Mengenlehre", *Math. Z.*, vol. 27 (1928), pp. 669–752.

[8] Paul Bernays, "A System of Axiomatic Set Theory", *Journal of Symbolic Logic*, vol. 2 (1937), pp. 65–77; vol. 6 (1941), pp. 1–17; vol. 7 (1942), pp. 65–89, 133–45; vol. 8 (1943), pp. 89–106; vol. 13 (1948), pp. 65–79.

[9] Kurt Gödel, *The Consistency of the Continuum Hypothesis*, Princeton, 1940.

[10] For example, the system of W. V. Quine's book, *Mathematical Logic* (New York, 1940). See also his paper, "New Foundations for Mathematical Logic", *American Mathematical Monthly*, vol. 44 (1937), pp. 70–80. For a discussion of Quine's systems in connection with problems of consistency, see Hao Wang, "A Formal System of Logic", *Journal of Symbolic Logic*, vol. 15 (1950), pp. 25–32.

[11] Gerhard Gentzen, "Untersuchungen über das logische Schliessen", *Math. Z.*, vol. 39 (1934), pp. 176–210, 405–31.

[12] Stanisław Jaśkowski, "On the Rules of Suppositions in Formal Logic", *Studia Logica*, No. 1, Warsaw, 1934.

Heyting,[13] as is shown in Section 10. This method has been used in my teaching for the past eleven years.

The treatment of modality is very similar to that employed by Lewis and Langford [14] and by Ruth Barcan Marcus,[15] but the subordinate proof technique in this connection is an innovation.

The system of this book is closely similar to, and in certain important respects an improvement on, the system of my paper, "An Extension of Basic Logic",[16] and that of my paper, "A Further Consistent Extension of Basic Logic".[17] The improvement over both the latter systems consists in a more adequate theory of implication and the restriction of all proofs to finite length, so that the resulting logic can be said to be "finitary". Analogues of the rules [#], [∼#], [*], and [∼*] of 3.1 of "An Extension of Basic Logic" (and of the rules 3.28 and 3.29 of the other paper) are not given in the main body of this volume, but they are stated in Appendix B as rules R41–R44. These rules together with R45 complete the total of forty-five rules needed for formulating the whole system. An outline is given in Appendix B of a consistency proof for this total system. A derivation of the more important theorems of mathematical analysis from these forty-five rules can proceed along the lines of my papers, "The Heine-Borel Theorem in Extended Basic Logic" [18] and "A Demonstrably Consistent Mathematics".[19] This will be done in detail in a subsequent volume. The systems of logic of the two papers just cited are non-finitary, while the system based on the forty-five rules has the asset of being finitary.

[13] A. Heyting, "Die formalen Regeln der intuitionistischen Logik", *Sitzungsberichte der Preussischen Akademie der Wissenschaften* (Physicalisch-mathematische Klasse), 1930, pp. 42–56. See also, *ibid.*, pp. 57–71, 158–69.

[14] C. I. Lewis and C. H. Langford, *Symbolic Logic*, New York, 1932.

[15] Ruth C. Barcan (Ruth Barcan Marcus), "A Functional Calculus of First Order Based on Strict Implication", *Journal of Symbolic Logic*, vol. 11 (1946), pp. 1–16. See also, *ibid.*, pp. 115–18; vol. 12 (1947), pp. 12–15.

[16] *Journal of Symbolic Logic*, vol. 13 (1948), pp. 95–106.

[17] *Ibid.*, vol. 14, No. 4 (1950), pp. 209–18.

[18] *Ibid.*, vol. 14, No. 1 (1949), pp. 9–15.

[19] *Ibid.*, vol. 15, No. 1 (1950), pp. 17–24; vol. 16, No. 2 (1951), pp. 121–4.

CONTENTS

APPENDIX

SYMBOLIC LOGIC

Chapter 1

SYMBOLIC LOGIC AND FORMAL PROOFS

1. Introduction

1.1. Modern deductive logic, also known as "symbolic logic" or "mathematical logic", arose in the nineteenth century from earlier systems of logic, especially Aristotelian logic, and from traditional mathematics. In a sense it now embraces all these sources from which it came. The Aristotelian forms of inference appear within it as special cases of more general forms of reasoning, while the laws of mathematics are likewise derivable within it. Symbolic logic also represents an important advance beyond Aristotelian logic and ordinary mathematics. It surpasses the former in being able to deal far more adequately with complicated relational structures. It surpasses the latter in being able to deal more powerfully with non-quantitative concepts. The non-quantitative concepts handled by mathematics tend to be fairly direct generalizations from quantitative concepts, while symbolic logic can deal in addition with non-quantitative concepts that are not generalizations of this sort.

1.2. No satisfactory theory of relations is provided by Aristotelian logic. The only relations that were even partly amenable to genuine logical treatment in past centuries were the familiar numerical and geometrical relations of mathematics, together with the relation of identity and some relations of implication and class-inclusion.

1.3. When philosophers of the past attempted to exploit this fact that mathematical relations were, for them, almost the only relations that could be handled with logical precision, the tendency was toward a quantitative view of the universe. The emphasis was on geometry or on materialism, or on both. Often there was a deprecation of the unmeasurable qualitative and aesthetic factors in the world, factors which are the special concern of art, literature, and religion. One way of deprecating them was to say that they were "merely in the mind" and hence "subjective" and "unreal". This did not actually dispose of them however, because the mind and its contents are themselves part of the universe.

1.4. When identity and implication, rather than mathematical relations, were the relations most emphasized by philosophers, and when relatedness was treated as disguised or partial identity or implication, the tendency was toward monism ("All is one") and toward an exaggeration of the importance of the whole of the universe at the expense of the parts. Implication itself was often viewed as a kind of partial identity, so that one thing implied another if the latter was identical with part of the former. Thus all relatedness reduced to identity, and the final identity was identity with the final one reality. Differences tended to be treated as illusory, but there was always the residual problem of how there could be even illusory differences and how these illusory differences could be related to each other and to the one reality without becoming identical with each other and with the one reality. If such a philosophy becomes politically influential, its outcome is likely to be totalitarianism. The totalitarianism of Hitler can perhaps be regarded as derived in some degree from Hegel's monism. The totalitarianism of Stalin is clearly derived from Hegel by way of Marx, who added an element of materialism to Hegel's philosophy.

1.5. When no relations were particularly emphasized in philosophic thought, or at least none that could be easily handled by logical procedures then available, the tendency was toward a pluralism of loosely related "substances", sometimes with God or "mind" or "pre-established harmony" serving as a relating factor. Such a view, though deficient in some respects, at least would allow for the nonmathematical aspects of the world and would not tend to treat all differences as illusory and all political differences as undesirable.

1.6. These various types of philosophy, when properly and sympathetically understood, are perhaps less divergent from one another and less defective than the inadequate systems of logic, on which they had to depend, forced them to appear to be. With the extraordinary development of logic during the first half of the twentieth century, mankind for the first time finds itself in possession of a tool that is powerful enough to be of help in reasoning about relations and qualities of all sorts. There have already been applications of symbolic logic to problems in biology,[1] neurophysiology,[2] engineering,[3] psychology,[4] and philosophy.[5] Some day it may be possible for experts in symbolic logic to think as clearly and as effectively about social, moral, and aesthetic concepts as experts in mathematics have long been able to do with respect to the "colorless" ideas of physics. The full impact of the new science of logic has not yet been felt. This is partly because its theoretical development is not yet complete, and partly because it has not yet been learned by many who could most profitably use it. When its impact is felt, a richer, more human, and more rational philosophy may gradually arise. The day may come when it will be as improper to study ethics and politics without a thorough grounding in symbolic logic as it now is to study physics without a thorough grounding in mathematics. Man's ingenuity in devising a workable system of world peace may then have a chance of equaling his ingenuity in devising the atomic bomb.

1.7. If the pages of this book seem rather technical, so are the pages of any reputable book on mathematics or physics. Philosophy is no less technical than physics. It deals with even more of the world than physics does; in fact, with everything. We should not expect the logic suitable for philosophy, ethics, and aesthetics to be very much less technical than the mathematics suitable for physics and chemistry.

2. The Nature of Propositions

2.1. Certain combinations of words constitute word groups called "sentences".

2.2. Every sentence has one or more "meanings", depending on how it is interpreted. Thus the sentence, "He can put two and two

---

[1] J. H. Woodger, *The Axiomatic Method in Biology* (Cambridge: Cambridge University Press, 1937). Also, "Technique of Theory Construction", *International Encyclopedia of Unified Science* (Chicago, 1939).

[2] W. S. McCulloch and W. Pitts, "A Logical Calculus of the Ideas Immanent in Nervous Activity", *Bulletin of Mathematical Biophysics*, vol. 5 (1943), pp. 115–33.

[3] C. E. Shannon, "A Symbolic Analysis of Relay and Switching Circuits", *Transactions of the American Institute of Electrical Engineers*, vol. 57 (1938), pp. 713–23.

[4] C. L. Hull, C. I. Hovland, *et al.*, *Mathematico-Deductive Theory of Rote Learning* (New Haven, 1940).

[5] W. V. Quine, "On What There Is", *Review of Metaphysics*, vol. 2 (1948), pp. 21–38. Also, F. B. Fitch, "Actuality, Possibility, and Being", *ibid.*, vol. 3 (1949), pp. 367–84. The writings of Rudolf Carnap should also be mentioned; for example, *Meaning and Necessity* (Chicago, 1947).

together", obviously has more than one meaning. We shall restrict our attention to sentences which have only one meaning, or at least we shall assume that there is always a preferred or intended meaning which we shall call "the meaning" of the sentence. We will not attempt to discuss here the difficult problem of how meaning is communicated.

2.3. Meanings of sentences may also be called "verbalized propositions". Every verbalized proposition is the meaning of some sentence. Roughly speaking, a proposition is anything that might conceivably be the meaning of some sentence, whether or not the requisite sentence has ever been formulated or uttered, and hence whether the proposition is verbalized or not. We often have vague feelings or premonitions that we cannot easily express in words. These are unverbalized propositions.

2.4. Some sentences are true and others are false. The meaning of a true sentence is a true proposition, and the meaning of a false sentence is a false proposition. The meaning of the sentence, "The earth revolves around the sun", is the true proposition that the earth does revolve around the sun. The sentence, "Hydrogen is heavier than oxygen", has as its meaning a false proposition.

2.5. Propositions can be objects of belief and disbelief. Thus someone may believe the false proposition expressed by the sentence, "The earth is flat", while someone else may disbelieve this same proposition.

2.6. Sentences are usually referred to by writing them in quotation marks, as has been done above. A proposition may be referred to by first writing in quotation marks a sentence that means the proposition, and by then referring to the proposition as the meaning of the quoted sentence. A second method is to use a subordinate noun clause expressing the meaning of the sentence. According to the first method, we would speak of the proposition expressed by the sentence, "The earth is flat". According to the second method, we would speak of the proposition that the earth is flat. Both methods are used in paragraph 2.4. Similarly, we might say that Columbus did not believe the proposition expressed by the sentence, "The earth is flat", or we might equally well say that Columbus did not believe the proposition that the earth is flat. Still more briefly, we could say that Columbus did not believe that the earth is flat. A still different method is to say that Columbus did not believe the proposition, "The earth is flat". This is simply a shorthand way of saying that Columbus did not believe the proposition expressed by the sentence, "The earth is flat".

2.7. True propositions may also be called "facts" or "truths". Thus it is a true proposition that the earth is not flat, and it is also a truth and a fact that the earth is not flat.

2.8. False propositions may be called "untruths" or "counter-facts". It is an untruth that the earth is flat. Similarly, it is an untruth that $4 + 4 = 9$, while it is a fact (or truth) that $4 + 4 = 8$.

2.9. There are two important kinds of facts (or truths): contingent facts and non-contingent facts. Contingent facts are true without being true by logical necessity, while non-contingent facts are true by logical necessity. Thus it is true that men discovered the usefulness of fire, but this discovery was the outcome of practical necessity and not of logical necessity. Indeed, some savage tribes are said not to have made this discovery yet. So it is only a contingent fact that men discovered the usefulness of fire. On the other hand it is true by logical necessity that $1 + 1 = 2$, so $1 + 1 = 2$ is a non-contingent fact. Logic and mathematics are concerned mainly with non-contingent facts. The other special sciences and arts deal mainly with contingent facts. Philosophy deals with both kinds of facts in their interrelationships.

2.10. Some thinkers have advocated the view that all facts are contingent and that what appear to be non-contingent, logically necessary truths, are merely arbitrary conventions about the use of symbols, or are somehow merely the outcome of such conventions. Thus they might say that $2 + 2 = 4$ is necessarily true only because, and only in the sense that, we have agreed by an arbitrary convention to use the symbols "2", "+", "=", and "4" in this way. The only necessity they would find in such an equation would be the necessity of accepting conventions we have agreed to accept. This view has never been developed very satisfactorily, or in sufficient detail, in my opinion. For the purposes of this book, therefore, I shall continue to adhere to my own view that there are non-contingent truths as well as contingent truths, and that non-contingent truths are something other than the outcome of mere conventions.

2.11. We will also assume that there are propositions which, by logical necessity, are false, for example, $2 + 2 = 5$. These propositions are non-contingent untruths.

2.12. Furthermore, we shall assume that there are some propositions which are not to be asserted as true or false. Examples of these will be given later. They will be called "indefinite" propositions. Propositions which are true or false will be called "definite" propositions. The "principle of excluded middle" asserts that all propositions are true or false. This principle will not be asserted here except in the limited sense of applying to definite propositions.

2.13. The classification of propositions as so far given may be outlined as follows:

A. Definite.
  1. True.
      (a) Necessarily true.
      (b) Contingently true.
  2. False.
      (a) Necessarily false.
      (b) Contingently false.
B. Indefinite.

2.14. An example of an indefinite proposition is the proposition expressed by the sentence, "This proposition itself is false". The latter proposition cannot be assumed true without also being assumed false, nor can it be assumed false without also being assumed true. If such a proposition is regarded as satisfying the principle of excluded middle, then it must be treated as either true or false, and hence as both true and false. So we do not assert that it satisfies the principle of excluded middle.

2.15. Propositions are not to be thought of as located in space and time. Consider, for example, the true proposition, or fact, that the earth revolves around the sun. The sun has a location in space and time, and the earth has a location in space and time, but the fact that the earth revolves around the sun does not have any genuine location in space and time. If we were to try to assign this fact to some specific region of space time, the exact limits of such a region would be impossible to specify. Similarly, the fact that grass is green is not located anywhere, though grass itself and other green things do have location. Just as facts or truths have no space-time location, so also counterfacts or untruths have no location in space and time. The untruth that $2 + 2 = 5$ has no more location than the truth that $2 + 2 = 4$. It is a mistake to argue that because propositions have no location in space and time there can be no such things as propositions. The word "thing" does not have to be used in such a narrow way as to mean only "thing located in space time". Numbers themselves are in a sense "things" but are not located anywhere. Marks standing for numbers may have location, as on a blackboard, and measurements involving numbers may characterize located objects.

2.16. Propositions, finally, are not to be thought of as "merely mental" things. The fact that the earth goes around the sun is not just a mental thing. In other words, propositions are no more "located in the mind" than they are located in space and time. But the mind may be in relationship to various propositions, as when it believes or disbelieves them. The mind may also be in relationship to various objects that do have space-time location.

3. Complex If-Then Propositions

3.1. Given any two propositions, we may combine them into a compound proposition by use of such conjunctions as "and", "or", "but". Thus the proposition that roses are red and the proposition that violets are blue may be combined to give the proposition that roses are red and violets are blue. In general, if we let "p" and "q" stand for any two propositions, then "p and q" can stand for the proposition expressed by the sentence that results from writing "and" between the sentences expressing these two propositions, and "p or q" can stand for the proposition expressed by the sentence that results from writing "or" between the sentences expressing these two propositions, and so on for other conjunctions or conjunctive phrases such as "but", "if", "only if", "if and only if", "so", "therefore", and others. For greater clarity the compound proposition "p and q" will hereafter be written with square brackets as follows: [p and q]. Similarly, "p or q" will be written, [p or q]. (See 6.1 and 8.1.)

3.2. Another very important conjunctive phrase is the phrase, "if . . . then . . .". The triple dots indicate where the two sentences are to be placed which the phrase can serve to join. Thus from the proposition, "Roses are red", and the proposition, "Violets are blue", we may form the compound proposition, "If roses are red then violets are blue". This resulting proposition can be written, [If (roses are red) then (violets are blue)]. The parentheses merely serve to set off the smaller propositions out of which the larger proposition is compounded. Notice that we are simply considering methods of compounding propositions into larger and more complex propositions, regardless of the truth or falsity of the larger propositions thus obtained. Here are some further examples of propositions that have been compounded out of smaller propositions:

> If one and one make two, then one and one make three.
>
> If Socrates is a man and all men are mortal, then Socrates is mortal.
>
> If Jack loves Jill, then Jill loves Jack.
>
> If F. D. Roosevelt is elected, then Henry agrees to eat his own hat.

3.3. For purposes of symbolic logic it is desirable to build up more and more complex propositions from relatively simple ones by repeated use of the if-then phrase. In so doing, the simplest propositions will sometimes be set off by use of parentheses as was done in an example in the above paragraph, while compound propositions will be set off by use of square brackets. Thus the second proposition in the above list could be written, [If [(Socrates is a man) and (all men are mortal)] then (Socrates is mortal)]. This is doubly compound. It is of the general form, [If [p and q] then r]. Unless there is some indication to the contrary, the letters "p", "q", "r", "s", and "t" are always hereafter to be thought of as standing for propositions.

3.4. Propositions built up by repeated use of various conjunctive phrases, including the if-then phrase, are often clumsy and inelegant from a literary standpoint, but they may be very useful tools in logical analysis. The following sentence, though somewhat clumsy, expresses not only a genuine proposition but even a necessarily true one: "If Jack loves Jill, then, if Jill loves Tom, Jack loves Jill". In our special symbolism this proposition could be written, [If (Jack loves Jill) then [if (Jill loves Tom) then (Jack loves Jill)]]. The proposition can be stated in a more colloquial form somewhat as follows: "If Jack loves Jill, then even if Jill loves Tom, it is still true that Jack loves Jill". This proposition is of the general form, [If p then [if q then p]]. Any compound proposition of this form is a necessarily true proposition. This is simply the principle that if a proposition is true, it is true regardless of what else may be the case. Granted that p is true, then p is also true under the condition that q is true, no matter what the condition q may be.

3.5. Accordingly any proposition of the form, [If p then [if q then p]], will be called an **axiom**, or more specifically, an **axiom of conditioned repetition**. Every proposition which is an axiom of conditioned repetition is necessarily true.

3.6. If p and q are propositions, we will say that the proposition q is a **direct consequence** of the pair of propositions,

(1) p,
(2) [If p then q].

More specifically, we will say that it is a direct consequence by the **rule of modus ponens.** Clearly, if propositions (1) and (2) are both true, then q itself is true. Furthermore, if (1) and (2) are both necessarily true, and not merely contingently true, then q must also be a necessary truth. For example, the propositions (3) and (4) below are necessarily true. Therefore (5), which is a direct consequence of them by modus ponens, is also a necessarily true proposition.

(3) $a + b = b + a$.
(4) If $a + b = b + a$, then $c + (a + b) = c + (b + a)$.
(5) $c + (a + b) = c + (b + a)$.

3.7. We regard modus ponens as a **rule of direct consequence** according to which one proposition is a direct consequence of a pair of other propositions. Another rule of direct consequence will now be presented, **the rule of distribution.** We will say that if p, q, and r are propositions, then the compound proposition (7) below is a direct consequence of the compound proposition (6) by distribution.

(6) [If p then [if q then r]].
(7) [If [if p then q] then [if p then r]].

Suppose, for example, that p is the proposition, $x = 2y$, and q is the proposition, $3y = z$, and r is the proposition, $3x = 2z$. Then (6) and (7) are (8) and (9) as follows:

(8) [If $x = 2y$ then [if $3y = z$ then $3x = 2z$]].

(9) [If [if $x = 2y$ then $3y = z$] then [if $x = 2y$ then $3x = 2z$]].

Here (9) is a direct consequence of (8) by distribution. In general, a proposition that is a direct consequence of a true proposition by distribution is, itself, true; and a proposition that is a direct consequence of a necessarily true proposition by distribution is, itself, necessarily true. In particular, (8) is a necessary truth, so (9) is also necessarily true. Even if p, q, and r in (6) and (7) are so chosen that (6) is not true, it is still the case that (7) is a direct consequence of (6) by distribution.

3.8. In what follows we shall deal with propositions in very much the way that algebra deals with numbers, not always mentioning them explicitly, but rather representing them by letters.

4. Formal Proofs

4.1. In logic, as in mathematics, it is desirable to carry out proofs of theorems on the basis of various axioms which are supposed to be logically true. The axioms can be chosen in various different ways, and also the rules of direct consequence whereby steps are taken from axioms to theorems or from theorems to other theorems. Some of these differences of choice are extreme enough to give rise to different systems of logic. Other differences of choice merely represent alternative techniques for formulating one and the same system or equivalent systems. We say that two systems of logic are **equivalent** if every theorem of one is a theorem of the other, and vice versa. A system of logic may be said to be **valid** if every one of its theorems is a necessarily true proposition. Two systems of logic, incidentally, could not both be valid and also be such that some theorems of one contradict some theorems of the other. But two valid systems could differ in the sense that some theorems of one are not theorems of the other. Results due to Gödel [6] seem to indicate that no consistent system,

---

[6] K. Gödel, "Über formal unentscheidbare Sätze der Principia Mathematica und verwandter Systeme I", *Monatshefte für Mathematik und Physik*, vol. 38 (1931), pp. 173–98.

formulated in the usual way, can encompass all logical truths among its theorems.   Thus we can formulate systems of logic that are more and more adequate, but never one that is adequate for all of logical truth.   Indeed, it is often very difficult to know whether or not some complicated proposition is to be regarded as logically true.   The decision often has to be made only in a tentative way and in the light of a careful study of many different systems of logic.

4.2. The system of logic of the present book is defined relatively to a set of propositions which we will call the **axioms** of the system. The set of axioms will not be completely specified at first, but it has already been partially specified in the sense that we have asserted in 3.5 that every axiom of conditioned repetition is one of our axioms. The system of logic of the present book is defined also relatively to a set of **rules of direct consequence.** These rules, also, will not be completely listed at first, but two of them have already been described, the rule of modus ponens and the rule of distribution.   Finally, the system of logic of the present book is defined relatively to a set of things which we will call **items.**   For the present we can say that all propositions are items.   Later some things other than propositions will be treated as items.

4.3. By a **formal proof** will be meant a finite sequence of items (usually written as a vertical column or list) such that each item of the sequence satisfies at least one of the following two conditions:

(1) It is an axiom of the system.
(2) It is a direct consequence of preceding items of the sequence.

4.4. If every axiom is a necessarily true proposition, and if every rule of direct consequence is such that a direct consequence of necessarily true items is itself necessarily true, then clearly each item of a formal proof must be necessarily true.   A formal proof will be said to be a formal proof of each of its items.   In particular, it will be said to be a formal proof of its last item.

4.5. An example of a formal proof will be given in 4.6 below.   The letters "p", "q", "r" are used, as usual, to stand for any propositions. The steps of the formal proof are numbered on the left, and a vertical line is drawn between these numbers and the list of items.   To the right of each item is written the "reason" or "justification" for its inclusion in the formal proof, namely, the kind of axiom it is if it is an axiom, or the rule of direct consequence according to which it is a direct consequence of preceding items. In the latter case the numbers of the relevant preceding items should be stated.

4.6.

1	[If p then [if p then p]]	ax cond rep
2	[If p then [if [if p then p] then p]]	ax cond rep
3	[If [if p then [if p then p]] then [if p then p]]	2, dist
4	[If p then p]	1, 3, m p

4.7. Observe that each of the four items of the above formal proof is necessarily true. In particular, the last item is rather easily recognized as being necessarily true. The abbreviations "ax cond rep", "dist", and "m p" mean, respectively, "axiom of conditioned repetition", "rule of distribution", and "rule of modus ponens". Item 4, for example, is a direct consequence of items 2 and 3 by the rule of modus ponens. The formal proof 4.6 is a formal proof of the proposition, [If p then p].

4.8. The notion of formal proof will now be extended in such a way that we will allow a formal proof to possess items called **hypotheses**. A formal proof that has no hypothesis is still correctly described as in 4.3 and will be known as a **categorical proof**. Formal proofs that possess one or more hypotheses will be known as **hypothetical proofs.** Such a formal proof is, by definition, a finite sequence of items (usually written as a vertical column or list) such that the items which are the hypotheses precede all the others, and such that each item satisfies at least one of the following three conditions:

(1) It is an axiom of the system.
(2) It is a direct consequence of preceding items of the sequence.
(3) It is a hypothesis of the sequence.

A proposition might appear as a hypothesis of the sequence and also appear subsequently in the sequence. In its later appearance in the sequence, it could still be said to satisfy condition (3) above. It will be customary to use the same notation in writing hypothetical proofs as in writing formal proofs that have no hypotheses, except that the hypotheses will be listed at the beginning and will be separated from the subsequent items by a short horizontal line or dash. After each hypothesis we will write "hyp" to indicate its status. Any finite number of items may be chosen to serve as the hypotheses of a hypothetical proof, but they must all be carefully listed and designated as such. It is permissible for a hypothetical proof to have just a single proposition as its hypothesis. The items of a hypothetical proof will not all be true unless the hypotheses are all true, and the items will not all be necessarily true unless the hypotheses are all necessarily true. This is on the supposition that all our axioms are necessarily true and that our rules of direct consequence never provide a transition from items that are necessarily true to items that are not necessarily true, or from items that are true to items that are not true. Some examples of hypothetical proofs will now be given.

4.9.

1	p	hyp
2	[If p then [if q then p]]	ax cond rep
3	[If q then p]	1, 2, m p

4.10.

1	[If q then r]	hyp
2	[If [if q then r] then [if p then [if q then r]]]	ax cond rep
3	[If p then [if q then r]]	1, 2, m p
4	[If [if p then q] then [if p then r]]	3, dist

4.11. For convenience and brevity, a more concise notation will now be introduced. An expression of the form, "[If p then q]", will hereafter be written as "[$p \supset q$]". The horseshoe symbol can be read as "implies", but a more accurate reading is the *if-then* reading. Thus the proposition, [(It is raining) $\supset$ (the ground is wet)], can be read as, "If it is raining, then the ground is wet", or less accurately but often more conveniently as, "It is raining implies that the ground is wet". Using the horseshoe notation, we now rewrite 4.6, 4.9, 4.10, respectively, as 4.12, 4.13, 4.14. It will be customary to omit the outermost pair of square brackets from each item of a formal proof. In general, when propositions are displayed separately or are written in a list, we omit outermost square brackets. We will call 4.12 the principle of **reflexivity of implication** ("refl imp"). Strictly speaking, this principle is illustrated by the last step of 4.12 rather than by the whole of 4.12.

4.12.
1 $\quad p \supset [p \supset p]$ $\hfill$ ax cond rep

2 $\quad p \supset [[p \supset p] \supset p]$ $\hfill$ ax cond rep

3 $\quad [p \supset [p \supset p]] \supset [p \supset p]$ $\hfill$ 2, dist

4 $\quad p \supset p$ $\hfill$ 1, 3, m p

4.13.
1 $\quad p$ $\hfill$ hyp

2 $\quad p \supset [q \supset p]$ $\hfill$ ax cond rep

3 $\quad q \supset p$ $\hfill$ 1, 2, m p

4.14.
1 $\quad q \supset r$ $\hfill$ hyp

2 $\quad [q \supset r] \supset [p \supset [q \supset r]]$ $\hfill$ ax cond rep

3 $\quad p \supset [q \supset r]$ $\hfill$ 1, 2, m p

4 $\quad [p \supset q] \supset [p \supset r]$ $\hfill$ 3, dist

4.15. We will say that 4.13 is a hypothetical proof of $[q \supset p]$ on the hypothesis p, and we will say that 4.14 is a hypothetical proof of $[[p \supset q] \supset [p \supset r]]$ on the hypothesis $[q \supset r]$. A similar way of speaking will be used with respect to other hypothetical proofs.

4.16. Observe that steps 1 through 3 of 4.14 are exactly like steps 1 through 3 of 4.13 except that $[q \supset r]$ and p, respectively, take the places of p and q. Since these steps are just the same (with the exception noted), it would be more convenient in 4.14 simply to refer back to 4.13 instead of repeating something which has, in effect, already been done in 4.13. Thus 4.14 could be written more briefly as follows:

4.17.
1 $\quad q \supset r$ $\hfill$ hyp

2 $\quad p \supset [q \supset r]$ $\hfill$ 1, 4.13

3 $\quad [p \supset q] \supset [p \supset r]$ $\hfill$ 2, dist

4.18. Observe that the notation "1, 4.13", at the right of step 2 in 4.17, indicates that step 2 is obtainable from step 1 by the same method used to obtain the last step of 4.13 from the hypothesis of 4.13. In other words, there are missing steps in 4.17 which the reader can supply by referring to 4.13. Actually 4.17 is not, as written, a formal proof in the sense of 4.8, unless the missing steps are inserted.

We can think of 4.17, as written, as being an abbreviation for the full formal proof given in 4.14.

4.19. A very useful hypothetical proof will next be presented. It is seen to possess two hypotheses. The formal proof will first be presented in full as 4.20, and then in abbreviated form as 4.21. This formal proof will be called the principle of the **transitivity of implication** ("trans imp"). The reasons for the various steps in 4.20 and 4.21 are purposely omitted so that the reader may insert them as an exercise.

4.20. 1 | $p \supset q$
      2 | $q \supset r$
      3 | $[q \supset r] \supset [p \supset [q \supset r]]$
      4 | $p \supset [q \supset r]$
      5 | $[p \supset q] \supset [p \supset r]$
      6 | $p \supset r$

4.21. 1 | $p \supset q$
      2 | $q \supset r$
      3 | $[p \supset q] \supset [p \supset r]$
      4 | $p \supset r$

4.22. Observe that the order of hypotheses does not make any difference. Thus 4.21 could equally well have been written as follows:

4.23. 1 | $q \supset r$
      2 | $p \supset q$
      3 | $[p \supset q] \supset [p \supset r]$
      4 | $p \supset r$

4.24. Another useful hypothetical proof will next be presented. It will be called the principle of **conditioned modus ponens** ("cond m p").

4.25. 1 | $s \supset p$ hyp
      2 | $s \supset [p \supset q]$ hyp
      3 | $[s \supset p] \supset [s \supset q]$ 2, dist
      4 | $s \supset q$ 1, 3, m p

4.26. In addition to those propositions which are axioms of conditioned repetition, some further propositions will now be counted as being axioms of this system. These further propositions are all those of the form, $[p_1 \supset p_2]$, where p_1 and p_2 have so been chosen that p_2 is a direct consequence of p_1 by distribution. Such axioms will be called **distributive axioms** ("ax dist"). Thus every proposition of the form, $[[p \supset [q \supset r]] \supset [[p \supset q] \supset [p \supset r]]]$, is a distributive axiom. Such an axiom is used in step 2 of 4.27 below. We will call 4.27 the principle of **conditioned distribution** ("cond dist").

4.27.

$$
\begin{array}{lll}
1 & s \supset [p \supset [q \supset r]] & \text{hyp} \\
2 & [p \supset [q \supset r]] \supset [[p \supset q] \supset [p \supset r]] & \text{ax dist} \\
3 & s \supset [[p \supset q] \supset [p \supset r]] & \text{1, 2, trans imp (4.20)}
\end{array}
$$

4.28. If we wished, we could now dispense entirely with the rule of distribution, since the same results can always be obtained by using the requisite distributive axiom together with the rule of modus ponens. Thus we can make the transition from $[p \supset [q \supset r]]$ to $[[p \supset q] \supset [p \supset r]]$ as in 4.29.

4.29.

$$
\begin{array}{lll}
1 & p \supset [q \supset r] & \text{hyp} \\
2 & [p \supset [q \supset r]] \supset [[p \supset q] \supset [p \supset r]] & \text{ax dist} \\
3 & [p \supset q] \supset [p \supset r] & \text{1, 2, m p}
\end{array}
$$

4.30. The two following categorical proofs will be referred to subsequently in 5.21.

4.31.

$$
\begin{array}{lll}
1 & p \supset [q \supset p] & \text{ax cond rep} \\
2 & s \supset [p \supset [q \supset p]] & \text{1, 4.13}
\end{array}
$$

4.32.

$$
\begin{array}{lll}
1 & [p \supset [q \supset r]] \supset [[p \supset q] \supset [p \supset r]] & \text{ax dist} \\
2 & s \supset [[p \supset [q \supset r]] \supset [[p \supset q] \supset [p \supset r]]] & \text{1, 4.13}
\end{array}
$$

4.33. The theorems of the present system of logic are all those propositions for which there are categorical proofs. For example, every proposition of the form, $[p \supset p]$, is a theorem of this system, and so is every proposition of the form, $[[s \supset p] \supset [s \supset [r \supset r]]]$.

$$\begin{array}{ll} | \quad s \supset t & \text{hyp} \\ | \quad \cdot \\ | \quad \cdot \\ | \quad \cdot \\ | \quad s \supset [r \supset t] \end{array}$$

...ppose that the last step is obtained by implication introduction. ...hen the required proof must have the general form,

$$\begin{array}{lll} 1 & | \quad s \supset t & \text{hyp} \\ 2 & | \quad | \quad s & \text{hyp (of the subordinate proof)} \\ & | \quad | \quad \cdot \\ & | \quad | \quad \cdot \\ & | \quad | \quad r \supset t \\ & | \quad s \supset [r \supset t] & \text{imp int} \end{array}$$

The problem is then resolved into that of filling in the steps of the subordinate proof. This will be facilitated by reiterating step 1 into the subordinate proof. The whole formal proof then looks as follows:

$$\begin{array}{lll} 1 & | \quad s \supset t & \text{hyp} \\ 2 & | \quad | \quad s & \text{hyp} \\ 3 & | \quad | \quad s \supset t & \text{1, reit} \\ & | \quad | \quad \cdot \\ & | \quad | \quad \cdot \\ & | \quad | \quad r \supset t \\ & | \quad s \supset [r \supset t] & \text{imp int} \end{array}$$

We see at once that modus ponens can be used in the subordinate proof, and so we get:

$$\begin{array}{lll} 1 & | \quad s \supset t & \text{hyp} \\ 2 & | \quad | \quad s & \text{hyp} \\ 3 & | \quad | \quad s \supset t & \text{1, reit} \\ 4 & | \quad | \quad t & \text{2, 3, m p} \\ & | \quad | \quad \cdot \\ & | \quad | \quad \cdot \\ & | \quad | \quad \cdot \\ & | \quad | \quad r \supset t \\ & | \quad s \supset [r \supset t] & \text{imp int} \end{array}$$

EXERCISES

1. Give a categorical proof of $[p \supset [q \supset q]]$.

2. Give a categorical proof of $[[s \supset p] \supset [s \supset [r \supset r]]]$.

3. Give a hypothetical proof of $[q \supset [r \supset p]]$ on the hypothesis p.

4. Give a hypothetical proof of $[p \supset r]$ on the hypotheses q and $[p \supset [q \supset r]]$.

5. Give a hypothetical proof of $[s \supset [r \supset p]]$ on the hypothesis $[s \supset p]$.

6. Give a hypothetical proof of $[p \supset q]$ on the hypothesis $[p \supset [p \supset q]]$.

7. Give a hypothetical proof of $[q \supset [p \supset r]]$ on the hypothesis $[p \supset [q \supset r]]$. (This exercise is more difficult than the others.)

Chapter 2

THE METHOD OF SUBORDINATE PROOFS

5. Subordinate Proofs

5.1. A new procedure will now be introduced. It consists in writing one proof as part of another, as in the following example. The "reasons" for steps 5 and 8 will be discussed and explained later.

5.2.

1	$p \supset s$	hyp
2	$[p \supset s] \supset [p \supset [p \supset r]]$	hyp
3	$p \supset [p \supset r]$	1, 2, m p
4	p	hyp
5	$p \supset [p \supset r]$	3, reiteration
6	$p \supset r$	4, 5, m p
7	r	4, 6, m p
8	$p \supset r$	4–7, implication introduction

5.3. The inner or subordinate proof in 5.2 has its own hypothesis, namely, the proposition p, and it has three other items, namely, the three propositions to the right of the numbers 5, 6, and 7. It also has its own vertical line to indicate its exact extent. The main proof, of which the subordinate proof is a part, has exactly two hypotheses, and it has exactly three other items: first, the proposition to the right of the number 3; second, the whole subordinate proof to the right of the numbers 4–7; third, the proposition to the right of the number 8. Hereafter it will be permissible to use subordinate proofs as items of other proofs. We will even permit subordinate proofs to have other subordinate proofs as items in them, and so on.

5.4. Subordinate proofs must satisfy all the same requirements laid down in 4.3 and 4.8 for formal proofs, except that a subordinate proof may have one or more items that are repetitions of items of

the proof to which it is subordinate. Thus item of item 3. Such a repetition of an item from a subordinate to it is called a **reiteration.** Thus we tion of item 3, and hence we write "3, reitera Hereafter, in proofs, the word "reiteration" will "reit". It is not permissible to reiterate from one proof unless the latter is subordinate to the former. one proof is **subordinate** to another only if it is an item or an item of an item of that other (as when we have proofs within other subordinate proofs), or an item of item of that other, and so on. We can never, of course, of a subordinate proof into a proof to which the subordin subordinate.

5.5. The notion of formal proof given in 4.3 and 4.8 may be of as extended, so that any item which is itself a subordinate now permitted to be an item of a formal proof. We could wished, treat subordinate proofs as being axioms of a very kind. Then they would automatically satisfy condition (1) and 4.8, and so for this reason would be admissible as items formal proof.

5.6. A further rule of direct consequence will now be state Suppose that a subordinate proof has a proposition p as its onl hypothesis and has a proposition q as its last item (or as any one of its items, for that matter). Then the proposition $[p \supset q]$ will be said to be a direct consequence of that subordinate proof by the **rule of implication introduction.** Step 8 in 5.2, for example, is a direct consequence of the subordinate proof 4–7 by the rule of implication introduction. Hereafter in proofs we will write "imp int" to mean implication introduction.

5.7. The great value of the rule of implication introduction lies in the fact that it gives us a fairly direct way for proving a proposition of the form, $[p \supset q]$. We merely "set up" a subordinate proof that has p as its hypothesis and q as its conclusion, fill in the steps leading from p to q (using reiterations if needed), and then write $[p \supset q]$ as following from the whole subordinate proof by implication introduction. For example, suppose that we wish to prove $[s \supset [r \supset t]]$ on the hypothesis $[s \supset t]$. That means we require a formal proof of the form,

Finally, we can get from t to $[r \supset t]$ by the method used in 4.13.   The required formal proof then has the following appearance after all numerical references have been inserted:

1	$s \supset t$	hyp
2	s	hyp
3	$s \supset t$	1, reit
4	t	2, 3, m p
5	$t \supset [r \supset t]$	ax cond rep
6	$r \supset t$	4, 5, m p
7	$s \supset [r \supset t]$	2–6, imp int

5.8. The same general method will now be illustrated in solving the more difficult problem of giving a hypothetical proof of $[q \supset [p \supset r]]$ on the hypothesis $[p \supset [q \supset r]]$.   The required formal proof has the form,

1	$p \supset [q \supset r]$	hyp
	$\cdot$	
	$\cdot$	
	$\cdot$	
	$q \supset [p \supset r]$	

We suppose that the last step follows by implication introduction. Then the proof must be more specifically as follows:

1	$p \supset [q \supset r]$	hyp
2	q	hyp (of subordinate proof)
	$\cdot$	
	$\cdot$	
	$\cdot$	
	$p \supset r$	
	$q \supset [p \supset r]$	imp int

Wherever an implication is to be obtained, we can suppose it to be obtained by implication introduction.   Let us suppose that $[p \supset r]$ at the end of the subordinate proof is obtained by implication introduction.   Then there must be a still further subordinate proof which immediately precedes $[p \supset r]$ and is of the form,

$$
\begin{array}{ll}
p & \text{hyp} \\
\quad\cdot & \\
\quad\cdot & \\
\quad\cdot & \\
r &
\end{array}
$$

The whole formal proof then looks as follows, with a subordinate proof within a subordinate proof:

$$
\begin{array}{lll}
1 & p \supset [q \supset r] & \text{hyp} \\
2 & \quad q & \text{hyp} \\
3 & \quad\quad p & \text{hyp} \\
  & \quad\quad\quad\cdot & \\
  & \quad\quad\quad\cdot & \\
  & \quad\quad\quad\cdot & \\
  & \quad\quad r & \\
  & \quad\; p \supset r & \text{imp int} \\
  & q \supset [p \supset r] & \text{imp int}
\end{array}
$$

The problem is now resolved into that of deriving r from p in the innermost subordinate proof. This is not a difficult problem if we make full use of possible reiterations. We can reiterate steps 1 and 2 directly into the innermost subordinate proof, since the latter proof is subordinate to both the proofs from which these reiterations are made. After these two reiterations have been inserted, the result looks like this:

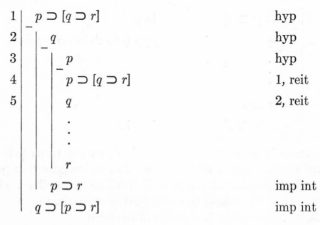

$$
\begin{array}{lll}
1 & p \supset [q \supset r] & \text{hyp} \\
2 & \quad q & \text{hyp} \\
3 & \quad\quad p & \text{hyp} \\
4 & \quad\quad p \supset [q \supset r] & 1, \text{reit} \\
5 & \quad\quad q & 2, \text{reit} \\
  & \quad\quad\quad\cdot & \\
  & \quad\quad\quad\cdot & \\
  & \quad\quad\quad\cdot & \\
  & \quad\quad r & \\
  & \quad\; p \supset r & \text{imp int} \\
  & q \supset [p \supset r] & \text{imp int}
\end{array}
$$

The missing steps in the innermost subordinate proof can now easily be filled in by two uses of modus ponens. The final result, with numerical references all inserted, is as follows:

5.9.

1	$p \supset [q \supset r]$		hyp
2	q		hyp
3	p		hyp
4	$p \supset [q \supset r]$		1, reit
5	q		2, reit
6	$q \supset r$		3, 4, m p
7	r		5, 6, m p
8	$p \supset r$		3–7, imp int
9	$q \supset [p \supset r]$		2–8, imp int

5.10. Some rules of direct consequence will be called **introduction rules** and others will be called **elimination rules.** We will regard implication introduction as being an introduction rule, and we will regard modus ponens as being an elimination rule. The rule of distribution will not be treated as being in either group. Nor will reiteration be regarded as being an introduction rule or an elimination rule. In fact, reiteration is not really a rule of direct consequence at all. This is because it is concerned with the fact that some item of a proof is also an item of some other proof, rather than with a relation among items of one and the same proof. If a proof and all its subordinate proofs (if any) use no rules of direct consequence, except introduction rules and elimination rules, and use no axioms (except some that will later be specified as being introduction axioms), such a proof will be said to be an **introduction-elimination proof,** or, more briefly, an **intelim proof.** Hypotheses and subordinate proofs are permissible in an intelim proof, and so are reiterations, uses of modus ponens, and uses of implication introduction. For example, 5.9 is an intelim proof. On the other hand, the proof at the end of 5.7 is not an intelim proof, since it makes use of an axiom of conditioned repetition. It is not permissible in an intelim proof to make use of any axiom of conditioned repetition or any distributive axiom, or to use the rule of distribution. But this is no hardship, since an intelim proof can be given of each axiom of conditioned repetition and of each distributive axiom, as we show in 5.11 and 5.12 below. The rule of distribution, furthermore, is superfluous in the presence of distributive axioms, as was pointed out in 4.28.

5.11. An intelim proof of an axiom of conditioned repetition.

1	p	hyp
2	q	hyp
3	p	1, reit
4	$q \supset p$	2–3, imp int
5	$p \supset [q \supset p]$	1–4, imp int

5.12. An intelim proof of a distributive axiom.

1	$p \supset [q \supset r]$	hyp
2	$p \supset q$	hyp
3	p	hyp
4	$p \supset [q \supset r]$	1, reit
5	$p \supset q$	2, reit
6	q	3, 5, m p
7	$q \supset r$	3, 4, m p
8	r	6, 7, m p
9	$p \supset r$	3–8, imp int
10	$[p \supset q] \supset [p \supset r]$	2–9, imp int
11	$[p \supset [q \supset r]] \supset [[p \supset q] \supset [p \supset r]]$	1–10, imp int

5.13. There is nothing that excludes a formal proof from possessing only a single item. The following single-item proof is a hypothetical proof of p on the hypothesis p. It is a proof of p in the sense that p is the last (and only) item of the proof. It is a proof that has only one hypothesis, p itself. It is also an intelim proof.

5.14. 1 | p hyp

5.15. Since 5.14 has p as its only hypothesis, and since it has p as its last (and only) item, we may, by the rule of implication introduction (5.6), regard the proposition $[p \supset p]$ as a direct consequence of it. Hence the proof of $[p \supset p]$ given below as 5.16 is correct, though somewhat strange looking. The notation "1–1" is to be understood as referring to the subordinate proof that has p as its only item.

5.16. An intelim proof of the reflexivity of implication.

1	p	hyp
2	$p \supset p$	1–1, imp int

5.17. An intelim proof of the transitivity of implication.

1	$p \supset q$	hyp
2	$q \supset r$	hyp
3	p	hyp
4	$p \supset q$	1, reit
5	$q \supset r$	2, reit
6	q	3, 4, m p
7	r	5, 6, m p
8	$p \supset r$	3–7, imp int

5.18. Hereafter "refl imp" will refer to 5.16 rather than to 4.12, and "trans imp" will refer to 5.17 rather than to 4.20. Thus we can often write an intelim proof in shorter form by referring to 5.16 or to 5.17, just as, for example, 4.27 was written in shorter form by making reference to 4.20. The use of "refl imp" and "trans imp" as "reasons" in a proof does not keep the proof from being an intelim proof, because 5.16 and 5.17 are themselves intelim proofs, so that when missing steps are inserted by referring to the steps of 5.16 and 5.17, the missing steps thus inserted will all be permissible in an intelim proof. In fact, in any intelim proof, we can refer to some previous intelim proof to indicate how missing steps can be inserted. This sort of short-cut method is used in 5.19. The way 5.19 would look if written out in full, with all missing steps inserted, is shown by 5.20.

5.19.	1	$r \supset s$	hyp
	2	$[p \supset p] \supset [q \supset r]$	hyp
	3	$p \supset p$	refl imp (5.16)
	4	$q \supset r$	2, 3, m p
	5	$q \supset s$	4, 1, trans imp (5.17)

5.20.

1	$r \supset s$	hyp
2	$[p \supset p] \supset [q \supset r]$	hyp
3	p	hyp
4	$p \supset p$	3–3, imp int
5	$q \supset r$	2, 4, m p
6	q	hyp
7	$q \supset r$	5, reit
8	$r \supset s$	1, reit
9	r	6, 7, m p
10	s	8, 9, m p
11	$q \supset s$	6–10, imp int

5.21. It can be shown that all formal proofs that involve sub-ordinate proofs, or refer back to other formal proofs that do, can be transformed into proofs that make no use of subordinate proofs, although the resulting proof will not in general be an intelim proof. Suppose the original formal proof is written out in full with no missing steps and has only one subordinate proof subordinate to it, and suppose that this subordinate proof is also written out in full without missing steps. We are not necessarily supposing the original proof to be an intelim proof. It might be, for example, the proof at the end of 5.7. In order to transform the original proof into one that does not involve a subordinate proof, we proceed as follows: Let p be the only hypothesis of the subordinate proof. (We do not need to consider subordinate proofs with no hypotheses or with more than one hypothesis, since such subordinate proofs cannot be used for implication introduction and so can be omitted anyway without any loss.) Restore the outermost brackets of each step of the subordinate proof and write "$p \supset$" in front of each such step. Delete the vertical line and the horizontal dash associated with the subordinate proof, so that the steps of the subordinate proof, modified in the way indicated, become steps of the main proof. In particular, the hypothesis of the subordinate proof becomes a step of the main proof written, "$p \supset p$". The "reasons" originally attached to the steps of the subordinate proof must now be changed as follows:

> "hyp" to "4.12",
> "reit" to "4.13",
> "m p" to "4.25" or "cond m p",
> "ax cond rep" to "4.31",
> "ax dist" to "4.32",
> "dist" to "4.27" or "cond dist".

The step of the main proof that originally followed by the rule of implication introduction must now be given a different reason. This step, fortunately, is exactly like the proposition into which the last step of the subordinate proof has been transformed, and it can therefore be assigned exactly the same reason, whatever that reason may be. In fact, this step could be dropped altogether, since it is now a mere repetition of the proposition into which the last step of the subordinate proof has been transformed. The resulting proof will not be a proof that is written out in full, but it can subsequently be written out in full by making use of the references in it to 4.12, 4.13, 4.25, 4.31, 4.32, and 4.27. Following the method outlined above, we now write the result of transforming the proof at the end of 5.7 into a proof from which the subordinate proof has been removed:

5.22.

1	$s \supset t$	hyp
2	$s \supset s$	4.12
3	$s \supset [s \supset t]$	1, 4.13
4	$s \supset t$	2, 3, cond m p
5	$s \supset [t \supset [r \supset t]]$	4.31
6	$s \supset [r \supset t]$	4, 5, cond m p
7	$s \supset [r \supset t]$	4, 5, cond m p

5.23. Notice that steps 4 and 7 in 5.22 are redundant and could be omitted. If a proof contains subordinate proofs within subordinate proofs, this same method can be used to remove the innermost subordinate proofs first, then the next-to-innermost ones, and so on, until all are removed. In such a case, however, the original proof and its subordinate proofs must not only be written out in full, but each reiteration must be from a proof into an item of that proof (rather than directly into an item of an item of the proof). For example, 5.12 would have to rewritten in such a way that step 1 is first reiterated into the next-to-innermost subordinate proof, and then reiterated from there into the innermost subordinate proof.

5.24. Suppose that it is possible to find a proof of q on the hypothesis p. Then it is also possible to find a categorical proof for the proposition $[p \supset q]$, and, indeed, a categorical proof that involves no subordinate proofs. We simply set up a proof of the following form,

and then by the method of 5.21 we transform it into a categorical proof from which the subordinate proof has been removed. The fact that a categorical proof of $[p \supset q]$ can be found, given a proof of q on the hypothesis p, is sometimes called the **deduction theorem.** By essentially the same method, a stronger form of the deduction theorem can also be proved. It is to the effect that a proof of $[p \supset q]$ on the hypotheses $r_1, r_2, \cdots, r_n$ can be found, given a proof of q on the hypotheses $r_1, r_2, \cdots, r_n, p$. (For $n = 0$, this is to be understood as the same as the previously stated form of the deduction theorem, the proof of $[p \supset q]$ then being categorical.)

5.25. We will not hereafter be interested in removing subordinate proofs or in making use of the deduction theorem. On the contrary, we will make even greater use of subordinate proofs in connection with further rules of deduction not yet stated. Suffice it to say that even after these further deduction rules have been included in the system, it would still be possible to remove subordinate proofs if we were to choose suitable further axioms that play a role analogous to that played by axioms of conditioned repetition and distributive axioms, and it would still be possible to establish the deduction theorem.

5.26. In the usual presentations of systems of symbolic logic, subordinate proofs do not appear at all. Much greater flexibility is provided by allowing subordinate proofs, and much greater efficiency in solving specific problems. (For example, compare 5.9 with Exercise 7 of Section 4.) In 5.21–5.24 the relationship of the method of subordinate proofs to the more usual method that does not use subordinate proofs was shown, and the more usual method itself was described in Sections 3 and 4.

5.27. Hereafter we shall be concerned only with formal proofs that are intelim proofs. This is because all proofs we need can be put into the form of intelim proofs, because of the great flexibility and convenience of intelim proofs, and finally, because the whole system can most easily be shown to be consistent if no proofs but intelim proofs are used.

5.28. It is often desirable in an intelim proof to make a transition from q to $[p \supset q]$. This can always be done as follows:

1	q	hyp
2	p	hyp
3	q	1, reit
4	$p \supset q$	2–3, imp int

5.29. The above proof can be referred to as the principle of **added condition** ("add cond"). It is reminiscent of the axiom of conditioned repetition, $[p \supset [q \supset p]]$, especially when rewritten as $[q \supset [p \supset q]]$.

EXERCISES

1. Give an intelim proof of $[[p \supset [p \supset q]] \supset q]$ on the hypothesis p.

2. Give an intelim proof of r on the two hypotheses p and $[[q \supset p] \supset [p \supset r]]$.

3. Change the formal proof at the end of 5.7 so that it becomes an intelim proof, but with the same hypothesis $[s \supset t]$ and the same conclusion $[s \supset [r \supset t]]$.

4. Give an intelim proof of $[[p \supset [s \supset q]] \supset [s \supset r]]$ on the two hypotheses $[s \supset p]$ and $[q \supset r]$.

5. Give an intelim proof of $[q \supset [[r \supset p] \supset [r \supset s]]]$ on the hypothesis $[p \supset [q \supset [r \supset s]]]$.

6. Give a categorical intelim proof of $[[p \supset q] \supset [[q \supset r] \supset [s \supset [[s \supset p] \supset r]]]]$.

7. Give an intelim proof of $[s \supset [r \supset [s \supset [q \supset [p \supset t]]]]]$ on the hypothesis $[p \supset [q \supset [r \supset [s \supset t]]]]$.

8. Using the method of 5.21, transform 5.2 into a proof that has no subordinate proofs.

9. Give an intelim proof of $[p \supset [q \supset [r \supset s]]]$ on the hypothesis $[[[p \supset q] \supset r] \supset s]$.

10. Give a categorical intelim proof of $[[p \supset q] \supset [[r \supset s] \supset [[q \supset r] \supset [p \supset s]]]]$.

6. Conjunction

6.1. From any two propositions, such as "The sun is shining" and "The grass is green", we can form a compound proposition by joining them by the idea expressed by the word "and". Thus we obtain the proposition, "The sun is shining and the grass is green". In symbolic logic the symbol "**&**" may be used to take the place of the word "and" between propositions. The above proposition may therefore be written, [(The sun is shining) **&** (the grass is green)]. We will say that the latter proposition is the **conjunction of** the two propositions of which it is made up, and we will say that the symbol "**&**" denotes **conjunction.** Thus for any two propositions p and q, it is the case that $[p \,\&\, q]$, the conjunction of p with q, is also a proposition. Observe that if p and q are both true, then the proposition $[p \,\&\, q]$ is true. Conversely, if $[p \,\&\, q]$ is true, so are the propositions p and q. If either p or q is false, then $[p \,\&\, q]$ must be regarded as false, since $[p \,\&\, q]$ can be true only if p and q are *both* true.

6.2. The proposition $[p \,\&\, q]$ is not regarded as being the same proposition as $[q \,\&\, p]$, though it is clearly the case that $[p \,\&\, q]$ implies and is implied by $[q \,\&\, p]$. Similarly, $[[p \,\&\, q] \,\&\, r]$ is not regarded as being the same proposition as $[p \,\&\, [q \,\&\, r]]$, though $[[p \,\&\, q] \,\&\, r]$ implies and is implied by $[p \,\&\, [q \,\&\, r]]$. For each p, we regard $[p \,\&\, p]$ as being a proposition that is different from p but which implies and is implied by p. These various implications will later be seen to be derivable.

6.3. We now provide a rule of direct consequence that is concerned with conjunction. This rule is an elimination rule (see 5.10) and is called the **rule of conjunction elimination** ("conj elim"). It has two forms. The first form asserts that p is a direct consequence of $[p \,\&\, q]$. The second form asserts that q is a direct consequence of $[p \,\&\, q]$. Thus the two following hypothetical proofs are valid intelim proofs and we may think of them as embodying the rule of conjunction elimination:

6.4. 1 | $p \,\&\, q$ hyp
      2 | p 1, conj elim

6.5. 1 | p & q hyp
    2 | q 1, conj elim

6.6. Another rule of direct consequence that is concerned with conjunction will now be stated. This rule is an introduction rule (see 5.10) and is called the **rule of conjunction introduction** ("conj int"). It asserts that the proposition [p & q] is a direct consequence of the pair of propositions, p and q. It therefore permits us to write [p & q] as an item in any proof if p and q (in any order) are preceding items of that proof. Thus the following two hypothetical proofs are valid intelim proofs and we may think of them as embodying the rule of conjunction introduction:

6.7. 1 | p hyp
    2 | q hyp
    3 | p & q 1, 2, conj int

6.8. 1 | q hyp
    2 | p hyp
    3 | p & q 1, 2, conj int

6.9. The following two proofs make use of the rule of conjunction introduction and the rule of conjunction elimination.

6.10. 1 | p & q hyp
     2 | p 1, conj elim
     3 | q 1, conj elim
     4 | q & p 2, 3, conj int

The above result may be called the **commutative law for conjunction** ("comm conj") or the **rule of symmetry of conjunction**.

6.11. 1 | [p & q] & r hyp
     2 | p & q 1, conj elim
     3 | p 2, conj elim
     4 | q 2, conj elim
     5 | r 1, conj elim
     6 | q & r 4, 5, conj int
     7 | p & [q & r]   3, 6, conj int

In a similar way we can derive $[[p \mathbin{\&} q] \mathbin{\&} r]$ from $[p \mathbin{\&} [q \mathbin{\&} r]]$. These two results constitute the **associative law for conjunction** ("ass conj").

6.12. From 6.10 and the rule of implication introduction we can prove $[[p \mathbin{\&} q] \supset [q \mathbin{\&} p]]$. Clearly, we can also prove the two implications $[[[p \mathbin{\&} q] \mathbin{\&} r] \supset [p \mathbin{\&} [q \mathbin{\&} r]]]$ and $[[p \mathbin{\&} [q \mathbin{\&} r]] \supset [[p \mathbin{\&} q] \mathbin{\&} r]]$.

6.13. Let "$[p \mathbin{\&} q \mathbin{\&} r]$" be an abbreviation for "$[[p \mathbin{\&} q] \mathbin{\&} r]$", and let "$[p \mathbin{\&} q \mathbin{\&} r \mathbin{\&} s]$" be an abbreviation for "$[[[p \mathbin{\&} q] \mathbin{\&} r] \mathbin{\&} s]$", and so on.

6.14. It is easy to give proofs of such propositions as $[[p \mathbin{\&} q \mathbin{\&} r] \supset [q \mathbin{\&} p \mathbin{\&} r]]$, $[[p \mathbin{\&} q \mathbin{\&} r \mathbin{\&} s] \supset [r \mathbin{\&} p \mathbin{\&} s \mathbin{\&} q]]$, and $[[p \mathbin{\&} q \mathbin{\&} r \mathbin{\&} s] \supset [r \mathbin{\&} s \mathbin{\&} q \mathbin{\&} p]]$.

6.15.

1	$p \supset [q \supset r]$	hyp
2	$p \mathbin{\&} q$	hyp
3	p	2, conj elim
4	q	2, conj elim
5	$p \supset [q \supset r]$	1, reit
6	$q \supset r$	3, 5, m p
7	r	4, 6, m p
8	$[p \mathbin{\&} q] \supset r$	2–7, imp int

6.16.

1	$[p \mathbin{\&} q] \supset r$	hyp
2	p	hyp
3	q	hyp
4	p	2, reit
5	$p \mathbin{\&} q$	3, 4, conj int
6	$[p \mathbin{\&} q] \supset r$	1, reit
7	r	5, 6, m p
8	$q \supset r$	3–7, imp int
9	$p \supset [q \supset r]$	2–8, imp int

6.17. In a way which is similar to that used in 6.15, we can prove $[[p \mathbin{\&} q \mathbin{\&} r] \supset s]$ on the hypothesis $[p \supset [q \supset [r \supset s]]]$. In a way which is similar to that used in 6.16 we can prove $[p \supset [q \supset [r \supset s]]]$ on the hypothesis $[[p \mathbin{\&} q \mathbin{\&} r] \supset s]$. An analogous result can be obtained for $[p \supset [q \supset [r \supset [s \supset t]]]]$ and $[[p$ & q & r & $s] \supset t]$, and so on.

6.18.	1		$[p \supset q]$ & $[q \supset r]$	hyp
	2		$p \supset q$	1, conj elim
	3		$q \supset r$	1, conj elim
	4		$p \supset r$	2, 3, trans imp (5.17)
	5		$[[p \supset q]$ & $[q \supset r]] \supset [p \supset r]$	1–4, imp int

6.19. The rule for conjunction introduction, we know, asserts that the proposition $[p$ & $q]$ is a direct consequence of the pair of propositions, p and q. In case p and q are the same proposition, the rule for conjunction introduction is to be understood as asserting that $[p$ & $p]$ is a direct consequence of the proposition p.

6.20.	1		p	hyp
	2		p & p	1, conj int (6.19)
	3		$p \supset [p$ & $p]$	1–2, imp int

6.21.	1		p & p	hyp
	2		p	1, conj elim
	3		$[p$ & $p] \supset p$	1–2, imp int

6.22. It is often convenient to be able to repeat some item of a proof as a later item of the same proof. This is always permissible, since if a proposition occurs as an item of a proof and also as a later item of the same proof, we can give the same "reason" for it in its later occurrence as in its earlier occurrence. We can merely write "rep" after the second occurrence, together with a numerical reference to the first occurrence, and this will be taken to mean that the reason for the second occurrence is the same as for the first occurrence. Repetition, in this sense, is not the same as reiteration, since there is no transference of a proposition into a subordinate proof, but merely a restatement of it as a later item of the same proof. Using this notion of repetition, we can give an alternative form of 6.20:

6.23.	1		p	hyp
	2		p	1, rep (6.22)
	3		p & p	1, 2, conj int
	4		$p \supset [p$ & $p]$	1–3, imp int

6.24. When a proposition is written in an abbreviated form, it is often clarifying to repeat it in unabbreviated form. We write "rep, def" after such a repetition, together with a numerical reference to the original occurrence of the proposition. In general, when use is being made of some abbreviated way of writing a proposition, this fact may be indicated by writing "def".

6.25.

1	$p \& q \& r$	hyp
2	$[p \& q] \& r$	1, rep, def (6.13, 6.24)
3	$p \& q$	2, conj elim
4	p	3, conj elim
5	q	3, conj elim
6	r	2, conj elim

6.26. Often when a proposition appears in unabbreviated form, we may wish to repeat it in abbreviated form. In this case, also, we write "rep, def" after the repetition.

6.27.

1	p	hyp
2	q	hyp
3	r	hyp
4	$p \& q$	1, 2, conj int
5	$[p \& q] \& r$	3, 4, conj int
6	$p \& q \& r$	5, rep, def (6.13, 6.26)

6.28. Hereafter a proof like 6.25 will be written in a shortened or abbreviated form as follows:

1	$p \& q \& r$	hyp
2	p	1, conj elim
3	q	1, conj elim
4	r	1, conj elim

6.29. Similarly, 6.27 can be written in a shortened or abbreviated form as follows:

1	p	hyp
2	q	hyp
3	r	hyp
4	$p \& q \& r$	1, 2, 3, conj int

6.30. The shorthand techniques illustrated in 6.28 and 6.29 are both also illustrated in the following proof:

6.31.

1	p & q & $[p \supset r]$	hyp
2	p	1, conj elim
3	q	1, conj elim
4	$p \supset r$	1, conj elim
5	r	2, 4, m p
6	$[p \supset r]$ & r & q & p	2, 3, 4, 5, conj int

EXERCISES

Give an intelim proof of each of the following:

1. $[p \supset q] \supset [[r$ & $p] \supset q]$.
2. $[p$ & $[p \supset q]] \supset q$.
3. $[p$ & $q] \supset [[[p$ & $q] \supset r] \supset [q$ & $r]]$.
4. $[[p \supset q]$ & $[p \supset r]] \supset [p \supset [q$ & $r]]$.
5. $[p \supset [q$ & $r]] \supset [[p \supset q]$ & $[p \supset r]]$.
6. $[[p$ & $q]$ & $[p \supset r]$ & $[q \supset s]] \supset [r$ & $s]$.
7. $[p \supset [q \supset [r \supset s]]] \supset [[p$ & q & $r] \supset s]$.
8. $[[p$ & q & $r] \supset s] \supset [p \supset [q \supset [r \supset s]]]$.
9. $[[p \supset q]$ & $[r \supset s]] \supset [[p$ & $r] \supset [q$ & $s]]$.
10. $[[p \supset q] \supset [r \supset s]] \supset [[p$ & $r] \supset [q \supset s]]$.

7. Coimplication

7.1. From any two propositions, p and q, we can form a proposition $[[p \supset q]$ & $[q \supset p]]$ that asserts that if p then q, and if q then p. More briefly, this proposition may be taken to assert, "p if and only if q". This notion of "if and only if" will be expressed by the triple bar, "$\equiv$", and will be referred to as **coimplication**. Thus "$[p \equiv q]$" is to be understood as an abbreviation for "$[[p \supset q]$ & $[q \supset p]]$" and may be read as "p if and only if q" or as "p coimplies q". To say that p coimplies q amounts to saying that p and q imply each other. Thus coimplication is a sort of equivalence, and sometimes it is convenient to read "$[p \equiv q]$" as "p is equivalent to q".

7.2. Some rules for coimplication will now be derived from rules already available.

7.3. Modus ponens for coimplication ("m p c") is the principle that q may be an item of a proof if p and $[p \equiv q]$ are preceding items of that proof, and also that q may be an item of a proof if p and $[q \equiv p]$ are preceding items of that proof. This principle or rule is established by the following two proofs:

1	p	hyp
2	$p \equiv q$	hyp
3	$[p \supset q]$ & $[q \supset p]$	2, rep, def
4	$p \supset q$	3, conj elim
5	q	1, 4, m p

1	p	hyp
2	$q \equiv p$	hyp
3	$[q \supset p]$ & $[p \supset q]$	2, rep, def,
4	$p \supset q$	3, conj elim
5	q	1, 4, m p

7.4. Coimplication introduction ("coimp int") is the principle that $[p \equiv q]$ may be an item of a proof if there are two preceding items of that proof, one of which is a subordinate proof with p as its hypothesis and q as its conclusion, and the other of which is a subordinate proof with q as its hypothesis and p as its conclusion. This principle is clearly valid, since we can obtain $[p \supset q]$ from the first subordinate proof by implication introduction, and we can obtain $[q \supset p]$ from the second subordinate proof by implication introduction, and finally we can obtain $[[p \supset q]$ & $[q \supset p]]$ by conjunction introduction. The latter proposition is, of course, the same as $[p \equiv q]$. Schematically the steps are as follows:

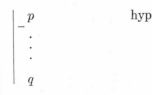

p	hyp
.	
.	
.	
q	

$$
\begin{array}{ll}
\quad\underline{q} & \text{hyp} \\
\quad\cdot \\
\quad\cdot \\
\quad\cdot \\
\quad p \\
p \supset q & \text{imp int (from first subproof)} \\
q \supset p & \text{imp int (from second subproof)} \\
[p \supset q] \ \& \ [q \supset p] & \text{conj int} \\
p \equiv q & \text{rep, def}
\end{array}
$$

7.5. In virtue of 7.3, we may infer q from the pair of propositions, p and $[p \equiv q]$, or from the pair of propositions, p and $[q \equiv p]$, giving the reason as "m p c". In virtue of 7.4 we may infer $[p \equiv q]$ from two subordinate proofs, one having p as its hypothesis and q as its conclusion, the other having q as its hypothesis and p as its conclusion. In this case the reason given is "coimp int". Notice also that we may infer the propositions $[p \supset q]$ and $[q \supset p]$ from $[p \equiv q]$ by conjunction elimination, since $[p \equiv q]$ is really $[[p \supset q] \ \& \ [q \supset p]]$. Similarly, the proposition $[p \equiv q]$ follows by conjunction introduction from the pair of propositions, $[p \supset q]$ and $[q \supset p]$.

7.6. Reflexivity of coimplication, first proof.   ("refl coimp")

$$
\begin{array}{lll}
1 & p \supset p & \text{refl imp (5.16)} \\
2 & [p \supset p] \ \& \ [p \supset p] & \text{1, conj int (6.19)} \\
3 & p \equiv p & \text{2, rep, def}
\end{array}
$$

We could also regard $[p \equiv p]$ as following directly from $[p \supset p]$ by conjunction introduction.

7.7. Reflexivity of coimplication, second proof.   ("refl coimp")

$$
\begin{array}{lll}
1 & \quad\underline{p} & \text{hyp} \\
2 & \quad p & \text{1, rep} \\
3 & \quad\underline{p} & \text{hyp} \\
4 & \quad p & \text{3, rep} \\
5 & p \equiv p & \text{1–2, 3–4, coimp int}
\end{array}
$$

7.8. **Symmetry of coimplication** (or **commutative law for coimplication**), first proof.   ("sym coimp")

1	$p \equiv q$	hyp
2	$[p \supset q]$ & $[q \supset p]$	1, rep, def
3	$q \supset p$	2, conj elim
4	$p \supset q$	2, conj elim
5	$[q \supset p]$ & $[p \supset q]$	3, 4, conj int
6	$q \equiv p$	5, rep, def

7.9. **Symmetry of coimplication** (or **commutative law for coimplication**), second proof.   ("sym coimp")

1	$p \equiv q$	hyp
2	q	hyp
3	$p \equiv q$	1, reit
4	p	2, 3, m p c
5	p	hyp
6	$p \equiv q$	1, reit
7	q	5, 6, m p c
8	$q \equiv p$	2–4, 5–7, coimp int

7.10. Notice that the first subproof (subordinate proof) in 7.9 is like the second subproof, but with the steps in reverse order. When two subproofs are thus alike except that one is the reverse of the other, it will be convenient to write them as a single subproof which read downward gives the first subproof and read upward gives the second subproof. A second list of reasons is then required for the case where the subproof is read upward, and an additional horizontal dash to separate off the hypothesis in this case. As a result 7.9 would appear thus:

7.11.

1	$p \equiv q$	hyp	
2	q	hyp	4, 3, m p c
3	$p \equiv q$	1, reit	1, reit
4	p	2, 3, m p c	hyp
5	$q \equiv p$	2–4, coimp int	

7.12. Transitivity of coimplication, first proof.   ("trans coimp")

1	$p \equiv q$	hyp
2	$q \equiv r$	hyp
3	$p \supset q$	1, def, conj elim
4	$q \supset p$	1, def, conj elim
5	$q \supset r$	2, def, conj elim
6	$r \supset q$	2, def, conj elim
7	$p \supset r$	3, 5, trans imp (5.17)
8	$r \supset p$	4, 6, trans imp
9	$p \equiv r$	7, 8, conj int, def

7.13. Transitivity of coimplication, second proof.   ("trans coimp")

1	$p \equiv q$	hyp	
2	$q \equiv r$	hyp	
3	p	hyp	5, 4, m p c
4	$p \equiv q$	1, reit	1, reit
5	q	3, 4, m p c	7, 6, m p c
6	$q \equiv r$	2, reit	2, reit
7	r	5, 6, m p c	hyp
8	$p \equiv r$	3–7, coimp int	

7.14. The subordinate proof 3–7 in 7.13 might be called a "double" subordinate proof, since by 7.10 it is a device for expressing two subordinate proofs. A further use of this sort of device will be made in 7.15.

7.15.

1	$p \equiv q$	hyp	
2	$r \equiv s$	hyp	
3	$p \,\&\, r$	hyp	5, 4, conj int
4	p	3, conj elim	8, 6, m p c
5	r	3, conj elim	9, 7, m p c
6	$p \equiv q$	1, reit	1, reit
7	$r \equiv s$	2, reit	2, reit

8	q	4, 6, m p c	10, conj elim
9	s	5, 7, m p c	10, conj elim
10	$q \mathbin{\&} s$	8, 9, conj int	hyp
11	$[p \mathbin{\&} r] \equiv [q \mathbin{\&} s]$	3–10, coimp int	

7.16.

1	$p \equiv q$	hyp
2	$r \equiv s$	hyp
3	$p \supset r$	hyp
4	q	hyp
5	$p \equiv q$	1, reit
6	p	4, 5, m p c
7	$p \supset r$	3, reit
8	r	6, 7, m p
9	$r \equiv s$	2, reit
10	s	8, 9, m p c
11	$q \supset s$	4–10, imp int
12	$[p \supset r] \supset [q \supset s]$	3–11, imp int

7.17.

1	$p \equiv q$	hyp
2	$r \equiv s$	hyp
3	$[p \supset r] \supset [q \supset s]$	1, 2, 7.16
4	$q \equiv p$	1, sym coimp (7.9)
5	$s \equiv r$	2, sym coimp
6	$[q \supset s] \supset [p \supset r]$	4, 5, 7.16
7	$[p \supset r] \equiv [q \supset s]$	3, 4, conj int, def

EXERCISES

1. Prove $[p \supset [q \supset [p \supset r]]] \equiv [[q \mathbin{\&} p] \supset r]$.
2. Prove $[[p \supset q] \supset [p \supset r]] \equiv [p \supset [[p \supset q] \supset r]]$.
3. Prove $[p \equiv [p \mathbin{\&} q]] \equiv [p \supset q]$.
4. Prove $[p \equiv q] \supset [[r \mathbin{\&} p] \equiv [r \mathbin{\&} q]]$.
5. Prove $[p \equiv q] \supset [[r \supset p] \equiv [r \supset q]]$.
6. Prove $[p \supset r]$ on the hypotheses $[q \equiv p]$ and $[q \supset r]$.

7. Prove $[p \equiv [q \And s \And t]]$ on the hypotheses $[p \equiv [q \And r]]$ and $[r \equiv [s \And t]]$.

8. Prove $[[[p \And q] \supset s] \And [[p \And s] \supset q]] \equiv [p \supset [s \equiv q]]$.

9. Prove $[q \equiv [p \supset p]]$ on the hypothesis q.

10. Prove $[[p \equiv r] \equiv [q \equiv s]]$ on the hypotheses $[p \equiv q]$ and $[r \equiv s]$.

8. Disjunction

8.1. From any two propositions, p and q, we can form a proposition that asserts that p or q is true, meaning that at least one of the propositions p and q is true. This meaning of the word "or" is said to be "non-exclusive", since the two alternatives are not asserted to exclude each other. This sense of the word "or", when used for constructing compound propositions, will be expressed by the symbol "v". Thus the proposition, $[p$ or $q]$, can be written as $[p \lor q]$, just as $[p$ and $q]$ can be written as $[p \And q]$. We will say that $[p \lor q]$ is the **disjunction of** the propositions p and q, and we will say that the symbol "v" denotes **disjunction.** The letter "v" is also the first letter of the Latin word "vel", which means "or" in the non-exclusive sense. Observe that $[p \lor q]$ is false if and only if p and q both are false.

8.2. If p is the proposition, "The moon is round", and if q is the proposition, "I'll eat my hat", then the disjunction of p with q is the proposition, "The moon is round or I'll eat my hat", written also as $[($The moon is round$) \lor ($I'll eat my hat$)]$.

8.3. There is also an "exclusive" meaning of the word "or", corresponding to the Latin "aut" rather than to "vel". The exclusive "or", instead of asserting that *at least one* of the two alternatives is true, asserts that *exactly one* of the two alternatives is true. This meaning of "or" is of less importance and we will not at present be concerned with it. It is easily definable in terms of the non-exclusive "or" and other concepts we shall be working with. The non-exclusive "or", as has been pointed out, is used to assert that at least one of two alternatives is true, rather than to assert that one and only one of them is true. Since we adhere to the non-exclusive meaning of "or", we do not regard the proposition, "The moon is round or I'll eat my hat", as making its two component propositions exclusive of each other. It would be a true proposition if "The moon is round" and "I'll eat my hat" were both true.

8.4. Introduction and elimination rules for disjunction will now be presented. The **rule of disjunction introduction** ("dis int") has two forms. The first form asserts that $[p \vee q]$ is a direct consequence of p. The second form asserts that $[p \vee q]$ is a direct consequence of q. Thus the two following hypothetical proofs are valid intelim proofs and we may think of them as embodying the rule of disjunction introduction:

8.5. 1 | p hyp
     2 | $p \vee q$ 1, dis int

8.6. 1 | q hyp
     2 | $p \vee q$ 1, dis int

8.7. Another disjunction rule is the **rule of disjunction elimination** ("dis elim"). It asserts that r is a direct consequence of the following set of three things: the proposition $[p \vee q]$, a subordinate proof having p as its hypothesis and r as its conclusion, a subordinate proof having q as its hypothesis and r as its conclusion. Thus the following hypothetical proof can be thought of as embodying this rule, supposing, of course, that p, q, and r have been chosen in such a way that the subordinate proofs could actually be somehow completed. (For example, we could choose p as $[s \,\&\, r]$ and we could choose q as $[t \,\&\, r]$.) Notice that the reason for the last step requires mention of $[p \vee q]$ as well as mention of the two subordinate proofs. There are thus *three* references normally required in connection with disjunction elimination, one to a disjunctive proposition and two to subordinate proofs.

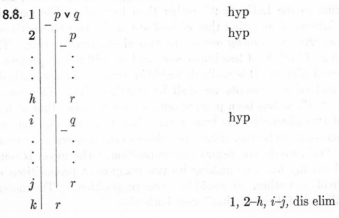

8.8. 1 | $p \vee q$ hyp
     2 | | p hyp
     · | | ·
     · | | ·
     · | | ·
     h | | r
     i | | q hyp
     · | | ·
     · | | ·
     · | | ·
     j | | r
     k | r 1, 2–h, i–j, dis elim

8.9. Some proofs using these disjunction rules will now be presented. These proofs are of course intelim proofs, as are all the proofs we are now concerned with.

8.10.

1	$p \vee q$	hyp
2	p	hyp
3	$q \vee p$	2, dis int (second form, like 8.6)
4	q	hyp
5	$q \vee p$	4, dis int (first form, like 8.5)
6	$q \vee p$	1, 2–3, 4–5, dis elim (8.7, 8.8)

Notice that just as the first form of disjunction introduction (8.4) makes $[p \vee q]$ a direct consequence of p, so also it makes $[q \vee p]$ a direct consequence of q, that is, it makes the disjunctive proposition a direct consequence of its left-hand component. This is relevant to step 5 above. In a similar way, the second form of disjunction introduction makes the disjunctive proposition a direct consequence of its right-hand component. This is relevant to step 3 above. The above derivation of $[q \vee p]$ from $[p \vee q]$ will be called the **commutative law for disjunction** ("comm dis") or the **rule of symmetry of disjunction**.

8.11.

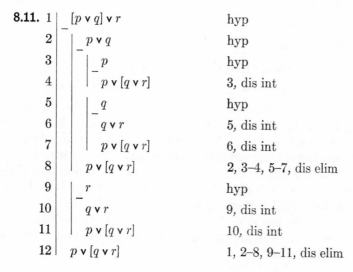

1	$[p \vee q] \vee r$	hyp
2	$p \vee q$	hyp
3	p	hyp
4	$p \vee [q \vee r]$	3, dis int
5	q	hyp
6	$q \vee r$	5, dis int
7	$p \vee [q \vee r]$	6, dis int
8	$p \vee [q \vee r]$	2, 3–4, 5–7, dis elim
9	r	hyp
10	$q \vee r$	9, dis int
11	$p \vee [q \vee r]$	10, dis int
12	$p \vee [q \vee r]$	1, 2–8, 9–11, dis elim

In a similar way we can derive $[[p \lor q] \lor r]$ from $[p \lor [q \lor r]]$. These two results constitute the **associative law for disjunction** ("ass dis").

8.12. From 8.10 and the rule of implication introduction, we can prove $[[p \lor q] \supset [q \lor p]]$. Clearly, we can also prove the two implications $[[[p \lor q] \lor r] \supset [p \lor [q \lor r]]]$ and $[[p \lor [q \lor r]] \supset [[p \lor q] \lor r]]$. The corresponding coimplications can also be proved.

8.13. Let "$[p \lor q \lor r]$" be an abbreviation for "$[[p \lor q] \lor r]$", and let "$[p \lor q \lor r \lor s]$" be an abbreviation for "$[[[p \lor q] \lor r] \lor s]$", and so on. It is not hard to give proofs for such propositions as $[[p \lor q \lor r] \supset [r \lor p \lor q]]$, $[[p \lor q \lor r \lor s] \supset [r \lor p \lor q \lor s]]$, $[[p \lor q \lor r \lor s] \supset [r \lor s \lor q \lor p]]$, and so forth.

8.14.

1	$p \ \& \ [q \lor r]$	hyp
2	p	1, conj elim
3	$q \lor r$	1, conj elim
4	q	hyp
5	p	2, reit
6	$p \ \& \ q$	4, 5, conj int
7	$[p \ \& \ q] \lor [p \ \& \ r]$	6, dis int
8	r	hyp
9	p	2, reit
10	$p \ \& \ r$	8, 9, conj int
11	$[p \ \& \ q] \lor [p \ \& \ r]$	10, dis int
12	$[p \ \& \ q] \lor [p \ \& \ r]$	3, 4–7, 8–11, dis elim

8.15. Similarly it is possible to prove $[p \ \& \ [q \lor r]]$ on the hypothesis $[[p \ \& \ q] \lor [p \ \& \ r]]$. Hence, by using coimplication introduction, we can prove $[[p \ \& \ [q \lor r]] \equiv [[p \ \& \ q] \lor [p \ \& \ r]]]$. This may be called the **distributive law of conjunction into disjunction.** This law is analogous to the familiar algebraic distributive law of multiplication into addition: $a(b + c) = ab + ac$. There is also a **distributive law of disjunction into conjunction,** $[[p \lor [q \ \& \ r]] \equiv [[p \lor q] \ \& \ [p \lor r]]]$. The derivation of the left side of this coimplication from the right side is given in 8.16. The derivation in the reverse direction is left to the reader as an exercise.

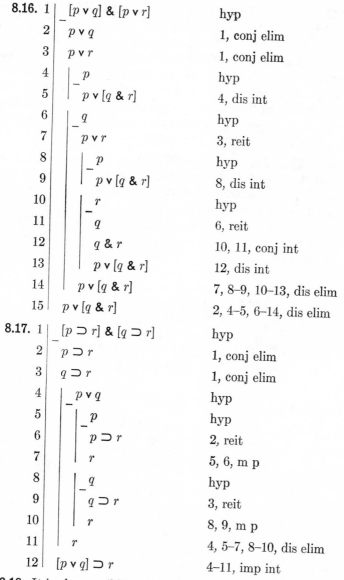

8.16.

1	$[p \lor q] \mathbin{\&} [p \lor r]$	hyp
2	$p \lor q$	1, conj elim
3	$p \lor r$	1, conj elim
4	p	hyp
5	$p \lor [q \mathbin{\&} r]$	4, dis int
6	q	hyp
7	$p \lor r$	3, reit
8	p	hyp
9	$p \lor [q \mathbin{\&} r]$	8, dis int
10	r	hyp
11	q	6, reit
12	$q \mathbin{\&} r$	10, 11, conj int
13	$p \lor [q \mathbin{\&} r]$	12, dis int
14	$p \lor [q \mathbin{\&} r]$	7, 8–9, 10–13, dis elim
15	$p \lor [q \mathbin{\&} r]$	2, 4–5, 6–14, dis elim

8.17.

1	$[p \supset r] \mathbin{\&} [q \supset r]$	hyp
2	$p \supset r$	1, conj elim
3	$q \supset r$	1, conj elim
4	$p \lor q$	hyp
5	p	hyp
6	$p \supset r$	2, reit
7	r	5, 6, m p
8	q	hyp
9	$q \supset r$	3, reit
10	r	8, 9, m p
11	r	4, 5–7, 8–10, dis elim
12	$[p \lor q] \supset r$	4–11, imp int

8.18. It is also possible to establish the converse of 8.17, that is, it is possible to prove $[[p \supset r] \mathbin{\&} [q \supset r]]$ on the hypothesis $[[p \lor q] \supset r]$. Hence, using coimplication introduction, we can establish the law,

$[[[p \lor q] \supset r] \equiv [[p \supset r] \And [q \supset r]]]$. It may seem odd to the reader that the left side of the above coimplication implies the right side. He might argue as follows: "Given that p or q implies r, we have no right to conclude that p implies r and that q also implies r". This objection, however, is based on a misunderstanding of the proposition $[[p \lor q] \supset r]$. If we read it as "p or q implies r", we must realize that it does not mean that "p implies r, or q implies r". Rather, it means, "If p or q is true, so is r". Once the wrong interpretation is replaced by the correct one, there should be no difficulty.

8.19. As a kind of short cut, we will permit a disjunction introduction rule that gives triple disjunctions, quadruple disjunctions, and so on, as well as the ordinary double disjunctions. Thus it will be permissible to make a transition directly to $[p \lor q \lor r]$ from p, instead of first making a transition to $[p \lor q]$ from p, and then making a transition to $[[p \lor q] \lor r]$ from $[p \lor q]$, and finally rewriting $[[p \lor q] \lor r]$ as $[p \lor q \lor r]$. It will also be permissible to use a disjunction elimination rule that applies to a triple disjunction and uses three subordinate proofs, and one that applies to a quadruple disjunction and uses four subordinate proofs, and so on. These more complex kinds of disjunction introduction and disjunction elimination, however, are merely short cuts and do not, in the end, provide any results that cannot be obtained by the ordinary disjunction rules at the expense of a few extra steps. They are illustrated in 8.20.

8.20.

1	$[p \lor q \lor r] \And s$	hyp
2	$p \lor q \lor r$	1, conj elim
3	s	1, conj elim
4	p	hyp
5	s	3, reit
6	$p \And s$	4, 5, conj int
7	$[p \And s] \lor [q \And s] \lor [r \And s]$	6, dis int (8.19)
8	q	hyp
9	s	3, reit
10	$q \And s$	8, 9, conj int
11	$[p \And s] \lor [q \And s] \lor [r \And s]$	10, dis int (8.19)

12	r	hyp
13	s	3, reit
14	r & s	12, 13, conj int
15	$[p$ & $s]$ v $[q$ & $s]$ v $[r$ & $s]$	14, dis int
16	$[p$ & $s]$ v $[q$ & $s]$ v $[r$ & $s]$	2, 4–7, 8–11, 12–15, dis elim (8.19)

8.21. If we wish to derive p from $[p$ v $q]$, the rule for disjunction elimination demands that we set up subordinate proofs in one of which we derive p from p and in the other of which we derive p from q. Since, however, the derivation of p from p is trivial, this subordinate proof will hereafter be omitted in such cases. This is merely another short cut, and one that is useful and clearly justified. Similar remarks apply to deriving q from $[p$ v $q]$. This kind of short cut is illustrated in 8.22.

8.22.	1	$[r$ & $s]$ v r	hyp
	2	r & s	hyp
	3	r	2, conj elim
	4	r	1, 2–3, dis elim (8.21)
8.23.	1	p v q	hyp
	2	$p \supset r$	hyp
	3	$q \supset s$	hyp
	4	p	hyp
	5	$p \supset r$	2, reit
	6	r	4, 5, m p
	7	r v s	6, dis int
	8	q	hyp
	9	$q \supset s$	3, reit
	10	s	8, 9, m p
	11	r v s	10, dis int
	12	r v s	1, 4–7, 8–11, dis elim

8.24. If the propositions p, q, r, and s have been so chosen that it is possible to derive r from p in a subordinate proof and also possible to derive s from q in a subordinate proof, then, using those two subordinate proofs, we can derive [r ∨ s] from [p ∨ q] in the following way:

$$
\begin{array}{lll}
1 & \quad p \lor q & \text{hyp} \\
2 & \quad\quad p & \text{hyp} \\
  & \quad\quad \vdots & \\
h & \quad\quad r & \\
i & \quad p \supset r & 2\text{–}h,\ \text{imp int} \\
j & \quad\quad q & \text{hyp} \\
  & \quad\quad \vdots & \\
k & \quad\quad s & \\
l & \quad q \supset s & j\text{–}k,\ \text{imp int} \\
m & \quad r \lor s & 1,\ i,\ l,\ 8.23
\end{array}
$$

8.25. In virtue of 8.24, it is seen that [r ∨ s] can always be obtained if [p ∨ q] and subordinate proofs | _p and | _q have been established

as previous items of the formal proof. Thus we can, for convenience, treat [r ∨ s] as following from [p ∨ q] and these two subordinate proofs by a rule which we will call the principle of the **complex constructive dilemma** ("cnst dil"). This is a *derived* rule rather than a fundamental or underived rule. It is simply a short-cut way of using the method of 8.24. As in 8.21, if one of the subordinate proofs is merely a derivation of p from p, we may omit it. We now give a proof illustrating the use of this rule.

8.26.
$$
\begin{array}{lll}
1 & [r\ \&\ p] \lor [q\ \&\ s] & \text{hyp} \\
2 & \quad r\ \&\ p & \text{hyp} \\
3 & \quad r & 2,\ \text{conj elim} \\
4 & \quad q\ \&\ s & \text{hyp} \\
5 & \quad s & 2,\ \text{conj elim} \\
6 & r \lor s & 1,\ 2\text{–}3,\ 4\text{–}5,\ \text{cnst dil (8.25)}
\end{array}
$$

8.27. The principle of the complex constructive dilemma can always be avoided in favor of the simpler principle of disjunction elimination if we are willing to add an extra step to each subordinate proof by disjunction introduction. If this change is made in 8.26, we have the following proof:

8.28.	1	$[r \mathbin{\&} p] \mathbin{\vee} [q \mathbin{\&} s]$	hyp
	2	$r \mathbin{\&} p$	hyp
	3	r	2, conj elim
	4	$r \mathbin{\vee} s$	3, dis int
	5	$q \mathbin{\&} s$	hyp
	6	s	5, conj elim
	7	$r \mathbin{\vee} s$	6, dis int
	8	$r \mathbin{\vee} s$	1, 2–4, 5–7, dis elim

EXERCISES

1. Prove $[p \mathbin{\&} [q \mathbin{\vee} r]]$ on the hypothesis $[[p \mathbin{\&} q] \mathbin{\vee} [p \mathbin{\&} r]]$.
2. Prove $[[p \mathbin{\vee} p] \equiv p]$.
3. Prove $[[p \mathbin{\vee} q] \mathbin{\&} [p \mathbin{\vee} r]]$ on the hypothesis $[p \mathbin{\vee} [q \mathbin{\&} r]]$.
4. Prove $[[p \supset r] \mathbin{\&} [q \supset r]]$ on the hypothesis $[[p \mathbin{\vee} q] \supset r]$.
5. Prove $[[[p \mathbin{\vee} q] \equiv q] \equiv [p \supset q]]$.
6. Prove $[p \supset q]$ on the hypotheses $[[p \mathbin{\&} r] \supset q]$ and $[p \supset [q \mathbin{\vee} r]]$.
7. Prove $[[[p \mathbin{\&} q] \mathbin{\vee} q] \equiv q]$.
8. Prove $[r \mathbin{\vee} s]$ on the hypotheses $[p \mathbin{\vee} q]$, $[p \supset r]$, and $[q \supset r]$.
9. Prove $[q \mathbin{\&} p]$ on the hypotheses p and $[q \mathbin{\vee} [p \supset q] \mathbin{\vee} [p \supset [p \supset q]]]$.
10. Prove $[[[p \mathbin{\&} q] \mathbin{\vee} [q \mathbin{\&} r] \mathbin{\vee} [r \mathbin{\&} p]] \equiv [[p \mathbin{\vee} q] \mathbin{\&} [q \mathbin{\vee} r] \mathbin{\&} [r \mathbin{\vee} p]]]$.

9. Recapitulation of the Rules

9.1. The following table summarizes the introduction and elimination rules so far used. Notice that modus ponens is treated as being the elimination rule for implication, while modus ponens for coimplication is treated as being the elimination rule for coimplication. Each of the four concepts, implication, conjunction, coimplication, and disjunction, has an introduction rule and an elimination rule. Intelim proofs use only these introduction and elimination rules, together with hypotheses, reiteration, and correctly formed subordinate proofs.

The coimplication rules are really derived from the other rules, but we can, if we wish, count them as fundamental rules in forming intelim proofs. The same is true of the various "short-cut" rules permitted by 6.28, 6.29, 8.19, and 8.21.

	Implication	Conjunction	Coimplication	Disjunction
Introduction Rule	p · · · q $p \supset q$	p q $p \,\&\, q$	p · · · q q · · · p $p \equiv q$	p $p \lor q$ q $p \lor q$
Elimination Rule	p $p \supset q$ q	$p \,\&\, q$ p $p \,\&\, q$ q	p $p \equiv q$ q p $q \equiv p$ q	$p \lor q$ p · · · r q · · · r r

9.2. From the rules in the above table, it is possible to derive fairly directly the rules for the reflexivity and transitivity of implication and coimplication, and the rule for the symmetry of coimplication. These derived rules, as well as the various short-cut rules, may there-

fore be used freely in addition to those of the table when intelim proofs are being constructed. In particular the principle of the complex constructive dilemma may be so used.

9.3. If an intelim proof involves no introduction or elimination rules other than implication introduction and implication elimination (modus ponens) and rules derivable from them, such a proof will be said to be a proof "in the pure theory of implication". Similarly for conjunction, coimplication, and disjunction. Reiteration is permitted in all such proofs. For example, 5.2 and 5.9 are proofs in the pure theory of implication, 6.25 and 6.27 are proofs in the pure theory of conjunction, 7.9 and 7.13 (but not 7.8 or 7.12) are proofs in the pure theory of coimplication, and 8.10 and 8.11 are proofs in the pure theory of disjunction. In the pure theory of implication we can permit employment of the reflexivity and transitivity rules for implication, since these rules are derivable in the pure theory of implication anyhow. Similarly, we can permit employment of the reflexivity, symmetry, and transitivity rules of coimplication in the pure theory of coimplication.

EXERCISES

1. Give a proof of $[[[p \supset p] \supset p] \supset p]$ in the pure theory of implication.

2. Give a proof of $[[[p \equiv p] \equiv p] \equiv p]$ in the pure theory of coimplication.

3. Give a proof of $[r \vee [q \vee p]]$ on the hypothesis $[[r \vee p] \vee [r \vee q]]$ in the pure theory of disjunction.

10. Negation

10.1. Every proposition has a **negate** or **contradictory**, just as every number has a negative. The negate of the proposition, "The sun is shining", is the proposition, "The sun is not shining". The latter proposition may also be read as, "It is false that the sun is shining", or as, "It is not the case that the sun is shining". The symbol "$\sim$" will be taken to mean, "It is false that", or, "It is not the case that". Thus "$\sim$(the sun is shining)" expresses the negate of the proposition, "The sun is shining". In general, $\sim p$ is the negate of p. Sometimes $\sim p$ may be referred to as the **denial** of p.

10.2. In any system of logic it is desirable to insure that there is no proposition p such that p and its denial $\sim p$ are both provable in the system; in other words, to insure that the system is consistent (free from contradiction). Many well-known systems of logic have never been shown to be consistent. The system being presented here, however, can be proved to be free from contradiction.

10.3. Three rules for negation will now be presented. These three rules are concerned only with negation. Subsequently some further rules will be added, relating negation to conjunction and disjunction.

10.4. Rule of negation elimination ("neg elim"). Every proposition q is a direct consequence of the pair of propositions p and $\sim p$. Thus from a pair of contradictory propositions every proposition may be regarded as following. This rule may seem odd to the reader unfamiliar with symbolic logic. He would perhaps wish to contend that we should assume that *nothing* follows from contradictory results, instead of assuming that *everything* follows. This rule, however, is probably best interpreted as meaning, "Anything is true if a contradiction is true". (See also 10.12 below.)

10.5. Rule of double negation introduction ("neg$_2$ int"). The proposition $\sim\sim p$ is a direct consequence of p.

10.6. Rule of double negation elimination ("neg$_2$ elim"). The proposition p is a direct consequence of $\sim\sim p$.

10.7. These three negation rules may be represented schematically by hypothetical proofs as follows:

1	p	hyp	1	p	hyp	1	$\sim\sim p$	hyp
2	$\sim p$	hyp	2	$\sim\sim p$	1, neg$_2$ int	2	p	1, neg$_2$ elim
3	q	1, 2, neg elim						

Some proofs using the above rules will now be presented.

10.8.

1	p	hyp
2	$\sim p$	hyp
3	p	1, reit
4	q	2, 3, neg elim
5	$\sim p \supset q$	2–4, imp int
6	$p \supset [\sim p \supset q]$	1–5, imp int

10.9.

1	p	hyp
2	$\sim\sim p$	1, neg$_2$ int
3	$\sim\sim p$	hyp
4	p	3, neg$_2$ elim
5	$p \equiv \sim\sim p$	1–2, 3–4, coimp int

10.10.

1	$p \vee q$	hyp
2	$\sim p$	hyp
3	p	hyp
4	$\sim p$	2, reit
5	q	3, 4, neg elim
6	q	hyp
7	q	1, rep
8	q	1, 3–5, 6–7, dis elim

10.11. Using the short-cut method described in 8.21, we can write 10.10 in abbreviated form as follows:

1	$p \vee q$	hyp
2	$\sim p$	hyp
3	p	hyp
4	$\sim p$	2, reit
5	q	3, 4, neg elim
6	q	1, 3–5, dis elim (8.21)

In a similar way, it is of course possible to derive p from the hypotheses $[p \vee q]$ and $\sim q$. Also we can similarly derive q from $[\sim p \vee q]$ and p, and we can derive p from $[p \vee \sim q]$ and q. We will call these results the principle of **modus tollendo ponens** ("m t p").

10.12. We now show how to obtain the effect of negation elimination by combining the use of modus tollendo ponens with that of disjunction introduction. Thus if we do not wish to accept as valid the principle that "if contradictory propositions are true then any proposition is true", we must reject either modus tollendo ponens or disjunction introduction.[1]

---

[1] This was pointed out to me by Miss Erna F. Schneider.

1	p	hyp
2	$\sim p$	hyp
3	$p \vee q$	1, dis int
4	q	2, 3, m t p (10.11)

10.13. The following proof is of importance in connection with a kind of reasoning called "reduction to absurdity" or "reductio ad absurdum". According to this method of reasoning, a proposition p is false if it implies mutually contradictory (and hence absurd) results.

1	$p \vee \sim p$	hyp
2	$p \supset q$	hyp
3	$p \supset \sim q$	hyp
4	p	hyp
5	$p \supset q$	2, reit
6	$p \supset \sim q$	3, reit
7	q	4, 5, m p
8	$\sim q$	4, 6, m p
9	$\sim p$	7, 8, neg elim
10	$\sim p$	1, 4–9, dis elim (8.21)

10.14. In the following proof we are assuming that p and q have been so chosen that the subordinate proof can be completed. This same sort of assumption is to be made elsewhere wherever incomplete subordinate proofs appear.

10.15.

1	$p \vee \sim p$	hyp
2	p	hyp
.	.	
.	.	
.	.	
3	q	
4	$\sim q$	
5	$p \supset q$	2–3, imp int (5.6)
6	$p \supset \sim q$	2–4, imp int
7	$\sim p$	1, 5, 6, 10.13

10.16. We will call 10.15 the **restricted principle of negation introduction** ("res neg int") or restricted reductio ad absurdum. It enables us to derive $\sim p$ from the proposition $[p \vee \sim p]$ and a subordinate proof that has hypothesis p and contradictory items q and $\sim q$. Intuitively, this principle may be taken to mean that if p is true or false and if p implies contradictory results, then p is false. The unrestricted form of the principle of negation introduction (or reductio ad absurdum) would treat $\sim p$ as a consequence of a subordinate proof having p as its hypothesis and having contradictory items q and $\sim q$, but would not require the proposition $[p \vee \sim p]$. In other words, the unrestricted principle of negation introduction would make it possible to derive step 7 of 10.15 from the subordinate proof 2–4 without use of step 1. This unrestricted principle says, in effect, that if p implies contradictory results, then p is false. In many systems of logic the proposition $[p \vee \sim p]$ is provable for every p, and so need not appear as a hypothesis anyway. A system of logic for which $[p \vee \sim p]$ is provable for every proposition p is said to possess the "principle of excluded middle". This principle asserts that every proposition is true or false. The system we are now elaborating does not possess the principle of excluded middle. (See 2.12–2.14.) It may seem contrary to our logical intuition to fail to include the principle of excluded middle among the principles of logic that we assert. This is perhaps because by "propositions" most people seem to mean "propositions that are true or false", that is, "definite" propositions in the sense of 2.12–2.14. In other words, most people seem to mean by "propositions" those propositions which *are* true or false. In this book we take the view that there are other propositions too, and we call them "indefinite propositions". The reason for holding this view is that we thereby avoid the kind of difficulty pointed out in 2.14 and at the same time avoid all sorts of more complicated contradictions in a fairly simple way. The present system lacks the unrestricted principle of negation introduction (unrestricted reductio ad absurdum) for essentially the same reason that it lacks the principle of excluded middle, since either one of these principles would give rise to the other in this system. We do, however, have the restricted form of reductio ad absurdum, 10.15, requiring the hypothesis $[p \vee \sim p]$.

10.17. There is a different theory of negation, the intuitionistic **theory of Heyting,**[2] which allows the unrestricted form of negation introduction, but does not possess the rule of double negation elimination. Heyting's system, like the present one, also lacks a principle of excluded middle. On the other hand, Heyting does not need to assume a rule of double negation introduction, since it is derivable by use of the unrestricted principle of negation introduction ("neg int"). This is seen as follows:

$$
\begin{array}{ll}
1 \quad \underline{p} & \text{hyp} \\
2 \quad \underline{\sim p} & \text{hyp} \\
3 \quad \underline{p} & \text{1, reit} \\
4 \quad \sim\sim p & \text{2-3, neg int}
\end{array}
$$

10.18. We repeat that the unrestricted principle of negation introduction is not permitted in the present system, so step 4 of the above proof is invalid from our standpoint. If this principle were added, the system, in its later development, not only could no longer be proved to be consistent, but it could even be shown to be inconsistent.

10.19. Although $[p \lor \sim p]$ is not provable in the present system for every proposition p, there are some propositions p for which it is provable in the present system. For example, if p itself is provable, then certainly $[p \lor \sim p]$ is provable by use of disjunction introduction. Similarly, if $\sim p$ is provable, so is $[p \lor \sim p]$. Later on we will employ a rule to the effect that $[p \lor \sim p]$ is true for every proposition p of the form $[a = b]$. Propositions p for which $[p \lor \sim p]$ is true will be said to "satisfy the principle of excluded middle". They are "definite" in the sense of 2.12.

10.20. In the well-known **two-valued propositional calculus,** all the negation principles here discussed are regarded as permissible, including those rejected by the present system and those rejected by Heyting's system. The unrestricted principle of negation introduction and the principle of double negation introduction together

---

[2] See footnote 13 of the Foreword.

give rise to the principle of excluded middle, as shown in the following proof (not valid in our system):

1	$\sim[p \vee \sim p]$	hyp
2	p	hyp
3	$p \vee \sim p$	2, dis int
4	$\sim[p \vee \sim p]$	1, reit
5	$\sim p$	2–4, neg int
6	$p \vee \sim p$	5, dis int
7	$\sim\sim[p \vee \sim p]$	1–6, neg int
8	$p \vee \sim p$	7, neg₂ elim

Notice that all but the last step of the above proof is valid in Heyting's system. Thus he can prove the double denial of $[p \vee \sim p]$ for every p, but he cannot prove $[p \vee \sim p]$ itself for every p. The contradictory steps in the subordinate proof 1–6 are steps 1 and 6.

10.21. In the two-valued calculus and in the Heyting logic it is possible to derive $[\sim q \supset \sim p]$ from $[p \supset q]$, but in the present system the closest we can come to this is to derive $[\sim q \supset \sim p]$ from the two hypotheses $[p \supset q]$ and $[p \vee \sim p]$. This is done as follows:

10.22.

1	$p \supset q$	hyp
2	$p \vee \sim p$	hyp
3	$\sim q$	hyp
4	$p \vee \sim p$	2, reit
5	p	hyp
6	$p \supset q$	1, reit
7	q	5, 6, m p
8	$\sim q$	3, reit
9	$\sim p$	4, 5–8, res neg int (10.15)
10	$\sim q \supset \sim p$	3–9, imp int

10.23. The same result can be obtained in a slightly different way:

1	$p \supset q$	hyp
2	$p \lor \sim p$	hyp
3	$\sim q$	hyp
4	$p \lor \sim p$	2, reit
5	p	hyp
6	$p \supset q$	1, reit
7	q	5, 6, m p
8	$\sim q$	3, reit
9	$\sim p$	7, 8, neg elim
10	$\sim p$	4, 5–9, dis elim
11	$\sim q \supset \sim p$	3–10, imp int

10.24. Further rules for negation for the present system of logic will now be stated.

10.25. Rule of negative conjunction introduction ("neg conj int"). The proposition $\sim[p \ \& \ q]$ is a direct consequence of $[\sim p \lor \sim q]$.

10.26. Rule of negative conjunction elimination ("neg conj elim"). The proposition $[\sim p \lor \sim q]$ is a direct consequence of $\sim[p \ \& \ q]$.

10.27. Rule of negative disjunction introduction ("neg dis int"). The proposition $\sim[p \lor q]$ is a direct consequence of $[\sim p \ \& \sim q]$.

10.28. Rule of negative disjunction elimination ("neg dis elim"). The proposition $[\sim p \ \& \sim q]$ is a direct consequence of $\sim[p \lor q]$.

10.29. The rule of double negation introduction might have been called "the rule of negative negation introduction" in conformity with the terminology used in 10.25–10.28, and similarly for the rule of double negation elimination. Some proofs using some of these rules will now be constructed.

10.30.

1	$\sim[\sim p \ \& \ q]$	hyp
2	$\sim \sim p \lor \sim q$	1, neg conj elim
3	$\sim \sim p$	hyp
4	p	3, neg₂ elim
5	$p \lor \sim q$	4, dis int

6	$\sim q$	hyp
7	$p \vee \sim q$	6, dis int
8	$p \vee \sim q$	2, 3–5, 6–7, dis elim

10.31.

1	$p \vee \sim q$	hyp
2	p	hyp
3	$\sim\sim p$	2, neg_2 int
4	$\sim\sim p \vee \sim q$	3, dis int
5	$\sim q$	hyp
6	$\sim\sim p \vee \sim q$	5, dis int
7	$\sim\sim p \vee \sim q$	1, 2–4, 5–6, dis elim
8	$\sim[\sim p \ \& \ q]$	7, neg conj int

10.32.

1	$\sim[\sim p \vee \sim q]$	hyp
2	$\sim\sim p \ \& \sim\sim q$	1, neg dis elim
3	$\sim\sim p$	2, conj elim
4	$\sim\sim q$	2, conj elim
5	p	3, neg_2 elim
6	q	4, neg_2 elim
7	$p \ \& \ q$	5, 6, conj int

10.33. By using methods similar to those used in 10.30–10.32, each proposition in the left-hand column below can be shown to be implied by and to imply the corresponding proposition in the right-hand column. In the Heyting system, the left-hand members are implied by the corresponding right-hand members, but the only left-hand member that implies the corresponding right-hand member is $\sim[p \vee q]$ which implies $[\sim p \ \& \ \sim q]$.

$\sim[p \ \& \ q]$	$\sim p \vee \sim q$
$\sim[\sim p \ \& \ q]$	$p \vee \sim q$
$\sim[p \ \& \ \sim q]$	$\sim p \vee q$
$\sim[\sim p \ \& \ \sim q]$	$p \vee q$
$\sim[p \vee q]$	$\sim p \ \& \ \sim q$

$$\sim[\sim p \lor q] \qquad\qquad p \mathbin{\&} \sim q$$

$$\sim[p \lor \sim q] \qquad\qquad \sim p \mathbin{\&} q$$

$$\sim[\sim p \lor \sim q] \qquad\qquad p \mathbin{\&} q$$

10.34. The equivalences listed above will be referred to jointly under the name, **De Morgan's theorem** ("d m"). It will be permissible hereafter to use these equivalences in proofs. Analogous equivalences for three or more propositions, such as the equivalence of $\sim[p \mathbin{\&} q \mathbin{\&} r]$ with $[\sim p \lor \sim q \lor \sim r]$, and the equivalence of $\sim[p \lor \sim q \lor r \lor s]$ with $[\sim p \mathbin{\&} q \mathbin{\&} \sim r \mathbin{\&} \sim s]$, are easily established and can also be used in subsequent proofs as instances of De Morgan's theorem.

10.35. It may be of interest to the reader to see how a couple of the De Morgan implications can be derived in Heyting's system. Since not all the De Morgan equivalences hold in Heyting's system, it will be customary in Heyting proofs to prove in detail each instance of De Morgan's theorem, rather than merely to invoke the theorem itself.

10.36. A Heyting system proof of $\sim[\sim p \mathbin{\&} q]$ on the hypothesis $[p \lor \sim q]$.

1	$p \lor \sim q$	hyp
2	$\sim p \mathbin{\&} q$	hyp
3	$\sim p$	2, conj elim
4	$p \lor \sim q$	1, reit
5	p	hyp
6	$\sim p$	3, reit
7	$\sim q$	5, 6, neg elim
8	$\sim q$	4, 5–7, dis elim (8.21)
9	q	2, conj elim
10	$\sim[\sim p \mathbin{\&} q]$	2–9, neg int (10.16, 10.17)

Notice that step 10 would not be valid in the present system of logic. The Heyting system, besides possessing the unrestricted rule of negation introduction, possesses the usual introduction and elimination rules for conjunction, disjunction, and implication, and hence also for coimplication. It also possesses the rule of negation elimination.

10.37. A Heyting system proof of $[\sim p \ \& \ \sim q]$ on the hypothesis $\sim[p \lor q]$.

1	$\sim[p \lor q]$	hyp
2	p	hyp
3	$p \lor q$	2, dis int
4	$\sim[p \lor q]$	1, reit
5	$\sim p$	2–4, neg int
6	q	hyp
7	$p \lor q$	6, dis int
8	$\sim[p \lor q]$	1, reit
9	$\sim q$	6–8, neg int
10	$\sim p \ \& \ \sim q$	5, 9, conj int

EXERCISES

1. Prove the following cases of De Morgan's theorem in the present system, and, where possible, in the Heyting system.

    a. $\sim[\sim p \ \& \ q]$ on the hypothesis $[p \lor \sim q]$, and conversely.
    b. $\sim[\sim p \ \& \ \sim q]$ on the hypothesis $[p \lor q]$, and conversely.
    c. $\sim[\sim p \lor \sim q]$ on the hypothesis $[p \ \& \ q]$, and conversely.

2. Prove the following propositions in the present system.

    a. $\sim[p \ \& \ \sim p] \equiv [p \lor \sim p]$.
    b. $\sim[p \ \& \ \sim p] \supset [[\sim p \supset \sim q] \supset [q \supset p]]$.
    c. $\sim[p \ \& \ [q \lor r]] \equiv \sim[[p \ \& \ q] \lor [p \ \& \ r]]$.
    d. $\sim\sim\sim[p \ \& \ q \ \& \ r] \equiv [\sim\sim\sim p \lor \sim\sim\sim q \lor \sim\sim\sim r]$.
    e. $[\sim p \lor q] \supset [p \supset q]$.
    f. $[p \lor \sim p] \supset [[\sim p \lor q] \equiv [p \supset q]]$.
    g. $[[p \lor \sim p] \ \& \ [q \lor \sim q]] \supset [[p \equiv q] \equiv [\sim p \equiv \sim q]]$.

Chapter 3

MODALITY

11. Necessity and Strict Implication

[The reader not interested in modal logic can omit Sections 11, 12, 13, and 23.]

11.1. The distinction between contingently true and necessarily true propositions has already been discussed in 2.9–2.13. We will use a special square-shaped symbol to express **necessary truth.** Thus the proposition, "It is necessarily true that $3 = 3$", will be expressed, $\square[3 = 3]$. In general, "$\square p$" may be read as "p is necessarily true", or, more briefly, as "p is necessary". We may also refer to $\square p$ as "the necessity of p", just as we refer to $\sim p$ as the negation of p. The proposition $\sim \square p$ asserts that p is not necessarily true, while the proposition $[p \ \& \sim \square p]$ asserts that p is true but not necessarily true; in other words, it asserts that p is contingently true. Similarly, it is easy to see that $\square \sim p$ asserts that p is necessarily false, while $[\sim p \ \& \sim \square \sim p]$ asserts that p is contingently false.

11.2. Clearly, if a proposition is necessarily true, it is true. Therefore the proposition p is said to be a direct consequence of the proposition $\square p$. This constitutes the **rule of necessity elimination** ("nec elim"), and it may be represented schematically by the following hypothetical proof:

$$
\begin{array}{r|l}
1 & \square p \\
\hline
2 & p
\end{array}
\qquad
\begin{array}{l}
\text{hyp} \\
\text{1, nec elim}
\end{array}
$$

11.3. We turn next to the **rule of necessity introduction** ("nec int"). This rule requires the use of a new kind of subordinate proof, one that has no hypothesis and that is such that a proposition q can be re-iterated into it only if q is of the general form $\square r$, or is of one of certain other forms later to be specified. Such a subordinate proof will be known as a **strict subordinate proof** and will always have a square

64

attached to the left of its vertical line, near the top, to indicate the special restriction regarding what can be reiterated into it. The rule of necessity introduction asserts that $\Box p$ is a direct consequence of any categorical strict subordinate proof that ends with p or has p as any one of its items. This rule may be expressed schematically as follows:

$$
\begin{array}{lll}
1 & \Box \quad \cdot & \\
\cdot & \quad\;\; \cdot & \\
\cdot & \quad\;\; \cdot & \\
\cdot & \quad\;\; \cdot & \\
h & \quad\;\; p & \\
i & \Box p & 1\text{--}h,\ \text{nec int}
\end{array}
$$

11.4. Examples of proofs using these rules will now be given.

11.5.

1	$\Box p$ **&** $\Box q$	hyp
2	$\Box p$	1, conj elim
3	$\Box q$	1, conj elim
4	$\Box$ $\Box p$	2, reit
5	$\Box q$	3, reit
6	p	4, nec elim
7	q	5, nec elim
8	p **&** q	6, 7, conj int
9	$\Box[p$ **&** $q]$	4–8, nec int

Notice that the reiterations into the strict subordinate proof 4–8 are valid, since each of the reiterated propositions is of the general form $\Box r$.

11.6.

1	$\Box[p$ **&** $q]$	hyp
2	$\Box$ $\Box[p$ **&** $q]$	1, reit
3	p **&** q	2, nec elim
4	p	3, conj elim
5	q	3, conj elim
6	$\Box p$	2–4, nec int
7	$\Box q$	2–5, nec int
8	$\Box p$ **&** $\Box q$	6, 7, conj int

11.7. From 11.5 and 11.6 we can, of course, prove

$$\Box[p \mathbin{\&} q] \equiv [\Box p \mathbin{\&} \Box q].$$

This result might be called the distributive law of necessity into conjunction.

11.8.

1		$\Box\Box p$	hyp
2		$\Box p$	1, nec elim
3		$\Box p$	hyp
4	$\Box$	$\Box p$	3, reit
5		$\Box\Box p$	4–4, nec int (Compare with 5.16.)
6	$\Box p \equiv \Box\Box p$		1–2, 3–5, coimp int

11.9. We will write "$[p \mathbin{\prec} q]$" as an abbreviation for "$\Box[p \supset q]$". Thus "$[p \mathbin{\prec} q]$" means "It is necessary that if p then q", or "p necessarily implies q". We may also read "$[p \mathbin{\prec} q]$" as "p strictly implies q", and the symbol "$\mathbin{\prec}$" will be said to denote **strict implication.** If the present system were strengthened by adding the principle of excluded middle, or equivalently, by adding the unrestricted principle of negation introduction, then the resulting system, as so far developed, would contain not only the two-valued propositional calculus but also C. I. Lewis's system of strict implication. In fact it would be essentially the system referred to as S4 on page 501 of Lewis and Langford's book, *Symbolic Logic*.[1]

11.10. A system almost the same as the system Lewis calls S2 is obtainable by adding the principle of excluded middle to the present system and making a restriction as follows: When reiterating into a strict subordinate proof, the first square on the left side of the reiterated proposition must be dropped and only the remaining part of the proposition written as an item of the subordinate proof. This restriction would make it impossible to prove $[\Box p \supset \Box\Box p]$ in general, and the second subordinate proof in 11.8 would be invalid. In fact, the main difference between S2 and S4 is that in S4 we can prove $[\Box p \supset \Box\Box p]$, while this cannot in general be proved in S2. This same restriction with respect to reiteration, however, would not prevent us from deriving $[\Box p \mathbin{\&} \Box q]$ and $\Box[p \mathbin{\&} q]$ from each other. We could modify 11.5 by dropping steps 4 and 5 and then

[1] See footnote 14 of the Foreword.

treat steps 6 and 7 as reiterations of the new kind. Similarly, step 2 of 11.6 could be omitted, and step 3 could be treated as a reiteration of the new kind. The system S4 seems more reasonable than S2 because the principle $[\Box p \supset \Box\Box p]$ itself seems reasonable. To deny this principle amounts to asserting that some proposition is necessarily true but not *necessarily* necessarily true.

11.11. Modus ponens for strict implication ("m p s"), first form.

1	p	hyp
2	$p \prec q$	hyp
3	$\Box[p \supset q]$	2, rep, def
4	$p \supset q$	3, nec elim
5	q	1, 4, m p

11.12. Modus ponens for strict implication ("m p s"), second form.

1	$\Box p$		hyp
2	$p \prec q$		hyp
3	$\Box$	$\Box p$	1, reit
4		p	3, nec elim
5		$\Box[p \supset q]$	2, def, reit
6		$p \supset q$	5, nec elim
7		q	4, 6, m p
8	$\Box q$		3–7, nec int

11.13. The reflexivity of strict implication ("refl s imp").

1	$\Box$	$p \supset p$	refl imp (5.16)
2	$\Box[p \supset p]$		1–1, nec int
3	$p \prec p$		2, rep, def

11.14. The transitivity of strict implication ("trans s imp").

1	$p \prec q$		hyp
2	$q \prec r$		hyp
3	$\Box$	$\Box[p \supset q]$	1, def, reit
4		$p \supset q$	3, nec elim
5		$\Box[q \supset r]$	2, def, reit

6	$q \supset r$	5, nec elim
7	$p \supset r$	4, 6, trans imp (5.17)
8	$\Box[p \supset r]$	3–7, nec int
9	$p \dashv 3 \, r$	8, rep, def

11.15. A subordinate proof of the form,

$$\Box \quad \underline{p}$$
$$\vdots$$
$$q$$

can be understood as an abbreviation for a combination of subordinate proofs of the form,

$$\Box \quad \underline{p}$$
$$\vdots$$
$$q$$
$$p \supset q$$

11.16. Strict implication introduction ("s imp int") is the principle that $[p \dashv 3 \, q]$ may be an item of a proof if the subordinate proof,

$$\Box \quad \underline{p}$$
$$\vdots$$
$$q$$

is a preceding item of the proof. Indeed, when the latter subordinate proof is written in unabbreviated form in accordance with 11.15, it is easy to see that we can obtain $\Box[p \supset q]$ from it by necessity introduction. The item $[p \supset q]$ that appears at the end of the unabbreviated form of the subordinate proof is, of course, itself obtained by implication introduction. Since $\Box[p \supset q]$ is by definition the same proposition as $[p \dashv 3 \, q]$, the rule of strict implication introduction is seen to be a consequence of the other rules of this system. This new rule is used twice in the following proof.

11.17.

1		$p \dashv [q \dashv r]$	hyp
2	$\square$	$\square q$	hyp
3		$\square$ p	hyp
4		$p \dashv [q \dashv r]$	1, def, reit
5		$q \dashv r$	3, 4, m p s
6		$\square q$	2, reit
7		$\square r$	5, 6, m p s (second form)
8		r	7, nec elim
9		$p \dashv r$	3–8, s imp int
10		$\square q \dashv [p \dashv r]$	2–9, s imp int

11.18. Notice that if step 2 in 11.17 were q instead of $\square q$, then the reiteration of q into the inner subordinate proof would not be permissible unless q itself were of the form $\square s$. As the proof is actually constructed, we may think of $\square q$ as reiterated past the vertical line 3–8 and into the strict subordinate proof 3–8. Similarly, we may think of $[p \dashv [q \dashv r]]$ as reiterated past the two vertical lines 2–9 and 3–8 and into the strict subordinate proof 3–8. This is permissible, since $[p \dashv [q \dashv r]]$ is by definition the same as $\square[p \supset [q \dashv r]]$. In general, if a vertical line has a square attached (as the lines 2–9 and 3–8 do in 11.17), no proposition can be reiterated past such a line into a subordinate proof to the right of such a line unless the proposition is of the general form $\square s$ or is of one of certain forms later to be specified. In other words, only propositions of the form $\square s$ (or of certain other forms) can be reiterated from outside a strict subordinate proof into that strict subordinate proof or into a proof subordinate to that strict subordinate proof. This discussion is meant to be a further elucidation of the meaning of the second sentence of 11.3.

11.19. It should be emphasized that the square symbol is to be understood as expressing purely logical necessity rather than the necessity of such laws of nature as the law of gravitation or the law of natural selection. Let us call the necessity of the laws of nature "natural necessity". Suppose that L is a proposition that is the infinite logical conjunction of all the laws of nature; then "p is naturally necessary" could be written as $[L \dashv p]$. It can be shown that if p is (logically) necessary, then p is naturally necessary. (See Exercise 4 below.) This means that the laws of logic are included among the laws of nature, but not vice versa.

11.20. A contingent proposition is one which is not necessarily true and also not necessarily false. Thus p is contingent if and only if the proposition $[\sim\Box p \,\&\, \sim\Box\sim p]$ is true. In other words, a proposition is contingent if neither it nor its denial is necessary. Similarly, a proposition is "naturally contingent" if neither it nor its denial is naturally necessary. Every naturally contingent proposition is contingent. On the other hand, those laws of nature which are not also laws of logic are examples of propositions which are contingent without being naturally contingent. The denial of every contingent proposition is itself contingent, and the denial of every naturally contingent proposition is itself naturally contingent. The proposition, "The earth contains radium", is an example of a true naturally contingent proposition. The denial of the same proposition is an example of a false naturally contingent proposition.

11.21.

1	$\Box$ p	hyp
2	$\sim\sim p$	1, neg$_2$ int
3	$p \prec \sim\sim p$	1–2, s imp int

11.22.

1	$\Box$ $\sim\sim p$	hyp
2	p	1, neg$_2$ elim
3	$\sim\sim p \prec p$	1–2, s imp int

EXERCISES

1. $[\Box[p \lor q] \,\&\, \Box[p \supset q]] \supset \Box q$.
2. $[\Box[p \lor q] \,\&\, \Box\sim q] \supset \Box p$.
3. $\Box[p \,\&\, \Box q] \equiv \Box[q \,\&\, \Box p]$.
4. $\Box q \supset [p \prec q]$. Also, $\Box q \prec [p \prec q]$.
5. $[[p \prec r] \lor [q \prec r]] \supset [\Box[p \,\&\, q] \supset \Box r]$.
6. $[p \prec q] \prec [\Box p \prec \Box q]$.
7. $[\Box[p \lor q \lor r] \,\&\, [q \prec s] \,\&\, [[p \lor r] \prec t]] \supset \Box[s \lor t]$.
8. $[\Box p \supset [\Box q \supset r]] \equiv [\Box[p \,\&\, q] \supset r]$.
9. $[\Box p \,\&\, \Box\sim[q \,\&\, r]] \prec [s \prec [p \,\&\, [\sim q \lor \sim r]]]$.

10. Show how a categorical proof of a proposition p can be converted into a categorical proof of $\Box p$.

12. Possibility

12.1. A proposition will be said to be "possibly true" or "possible" if its denial is not necessary. The diamond-shaped symbol "$\diamondsuit$" will be used to express **possibility,** so that "$\diamondsuit p$" may be read as "p is possibly true" or as "p is possible". The concepts possibility and necessity are used here in such a way that $\diamondsuit p$ is true if and only if $\sim\square\sim p$ is true, and in such a way that $\square p$ is true if and only if $\sim\diamondsuit\sim p$ is true.

12.2. The rule of possibility introduction ("pos int") states that $\diamondsuit p$ is a direct consequence of p. It may be expressed thus in schematic form:

$$
\begin{array}{ll}
1 \;\Big|\;\; p & \text{hyp} \\
2 \;\Big|^{-}\; \diamondsuit p & \text{1, pos int}
\end{array}
$$

12.3. The rule of possibility elimination ("pos elim") states that $\diamondsuit q$ is a direct consequence of $\diamondsuit p$ and the strict subordinate proof

$$
\square\;\Big|_{-}\begin{array}{l} p \\ \cdot \\ \cdot \\ \cdot \\ q \end{array}
$$

This rule may therefore be expressed in schematic form as follows:

$$
\begin{array}{ll}
1 \;\Big|_{-}\; \diamondsuit p & \text{hyp} \\
2 \;\;\square\;\Big|_{-}\; p & \text{hyp} \\
\cdot \qquad\quad \cdot & \\
\cdot \qquad\quad \cdot & \\
h \qquad\quad q & \\
i \;\;\;\; \diamondsuit q & \text{1, 2–}h\text{, pos elim}
\end{array}
$$

12.4. It may be argued that the possibility elimination rule seems more like an introduction rule than like an elimination rule, since "$\diamondsuit$" is certain to occur as the first symbol of any step obtained by this rule. In spite of this peculiarity, it will be convenient to use this rule and to call it an elimination rule.

12.5. Rule of negative necessity introduction ("neg nec int"). The proposition $\sim\Box p$ is a direct consequence of $\Diamond\sim p$.

12.6. Rule of negative necessity elimination ("neg nec elim"). The proposition $\Diamond\sim p$ is a direct consequence of $\sim\Box p$.

12.7. Rule of negative possibility introduction ("neg pos int"). The proposition $\sim\Diamond p$ is a direct consequence of $\Box\sim p$.

12.8. Rule of negative possibility elimination ("neg pos elim"). The proposition $\Box\sim p$ is a direct consequence of $\sim\Diamond p$.

12.9. Modus ponens for strict implication ("m p s"), third form.

1	$\Diamond p$	hyp
2	$p \prec q$	hyp
3	$\Box \quad p$	hyp
4	$p \prec q$	2, def, reit
5	q	3, 4, m p s (first form, 11.11)
6	$\Diamond q$	1, 3–5, pos elim (12.3)

12.10. In 12.11 we use a double proof to show that $\Diamond p$ and $\sim\Box\sim p$ are derivable from each other. Similarly, in 12.12 we use a double proof to show that $\Box p$ and $\sim\Diamond\sim p$ are derivable from each other. These double proofs are to be understood in the same way as the double subordinate proofs introduced in 7.10.

12.11.				
	1	$\Diamond p$	hyp	4, 3, m p s (12.9)
	2	$p \prec \sim\sim p$	11.21	11.21
	3	$\sim\sim p \prec p$	11.22	11.22
	4	$\Diamond\sim\sim p$	1, 2, m p s (12.9)	5, neg nec elim
	5	$\sim\Box\sim p$	4, neg nec int	hyp

12.12.				
	1	$\Box p$	hyp	4, 3, m p s (11.12)
	2	$p \prec \sim\sim p$	11.21	11.21
	3	$\sim\sim p \prec p$	11.22	11.22
	4	$\Box\sim\sim p$	1, 2, m p s (11.12)	neg pos elim
	5	$\sim\Diamond\sim p$	4, neg pos int	hyp

12.13. In virtue of 12.5–12.8, 12.11, 12.12, it is seen that each proposition in the left-hand column below implies and is implied by the corresponding proposition in the right-hand column.

$$\sim\square p \qquad\qquad \lozenge\sim p$$

$$\sim\square\sim p \qquad\qquad \lozenge p$$

$$\sim\lozenge p \qquad\qquad \square\sim p$$

$$\sim\lozenge\sim p \qquad\qquad \square p$$

12.14. The equivalences listed above will be referred to jointly as the **rule relating possibility and necessity** ("pos nec").

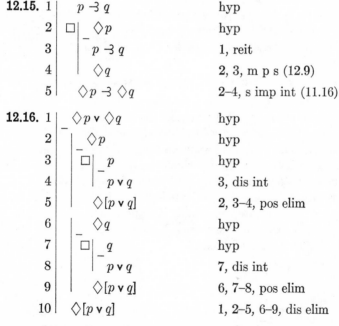

12.15.	1	$p \dashv q$	hyp
	2	$\square$ $\lozenge p$	hyp
	3	$p \dashv q$	1, reit
	4	$\lozenge q$	2, 3, m p s (12.9)
	5	$\lozenge p \dashv \lozenge q$	2–4, s imp int (11.16)
12.16.	1	$\lozenge p \lor \lozenge q$	hyp
	2	$\lozenge p$	hyp
	3	$\square$ p	hyp
	4	$p \lor q$	3, dis int
	5	$\lozenge [p \lor q]$	2, 3–4, pos elim
	6	$\lozenge q$	hyp
	7	$\square$ q	hyp
	8	$p \lor q$	7, dis int
	9	$\lozenge [p \lor q]$	6, 7–8, pos elim
	10	$\lozenge [p \lor q]$	1, 2–5, 6–9, dis elim

12.17. It is not possible in the present system to derive $[\lozenge p \lor \lozenge q]$ from $\lozenge [p \lor q]$, though a rule to this effect could be added without affecting the validity of the proof of consistency given in Section 20. Even without such a special rule, the derivation of $[\lozenge p \lor \lozenge q]$ from $\lozenge [p \lor q]$ could be carried out if the principle of excluded middle were available.

12.18.

1		$\sim\Diamond p$		hyp
2		$\Box\sim p$		1, pos nec (12.13)
3	$\Box$	$\Diamond\Diamond p$		hyp
4		$\Box$	$\Diamond p$	hyp
5			$\Box\sim p$	2, reit
6			$\sim\Diamond p$	5, pos nec
7			q	4, 6, neg elim
8		$\Diamond q$		3, 4–7, pos elim
9		$\Diamond\Diamond p \prec \Diamond q$		3–8, s imp int

Owing to the fact that we can prove $[\Diamond\Diamond p \prec \Diamond\sim[r \supset r]]$ on the hypothesis $\sim\Diamond p$ by the above method, and owing to the fact that we can prove $\sim\Diamond\sim[r \supset r]$ and hence $[\Diamond\Diamond p \prec \sim\Diamond\sim[r \supset r]]$, it is apparent that we can also prove $[\Diamond\Diamond p \prec q]$ on the hypothesis $\sim\Diamond p$.[2]

12.19. Hereafter it will be permissible to reiterate not only propositions of the form $\Box p$ into strict subordinate proofs, but also propositions of the form $\sim\Diamond p$. In permitting the reiteration of propositions of this latter kind, no results become obtainable that were not previously obtainable. This is because a proposition of the form $\sim\Diamond p$ is logically equivalent to $\Box\sim p$, which can be reiterated anyhow into strict subordinate proofs. This equivalence is made use of in 12.18 in order to get the effect of reiterating step 1 into the innermost subordinate proof as step 6. Since it is now permissible really to reiterate step 1 into the innermost subordinate proof, we can restate 12.18 in simpler form as follows:

12.20.

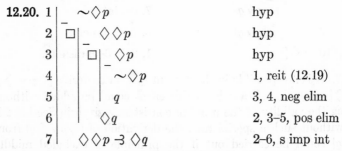

1		$\sim\Diamond p$		hyp
2	$\Box$	$\Diamond\Diamond p$		hyp
3		$\Box$	$\Diamond p$	hyp
4			$\sim\Diamond p$	1, reit (12.19)
5			q	3, 4, neg elim
6		$\Diamond q$		2, 3–5, pos elim
7		$\Diamond\Diamond p \prec \Diamond q$		2–6, s imp int

[2] This observation is due to Dr. John R. Myhill.

12.21.

1	$\sim\Diamond[p \;\&\; \sim q]$	hyp
2	$\Box\sim[p \;\&\; \sim q]$	1, pos nec
3	$\Box$ p	hyp
4	$\Box\sim[p \;\&\; \sim q]$	2, reit
5	$\sim[p \;\&\; \sim q]$	4 nec elim
6	$\sim p \lor q$	5, d m (10.34)
7	q	3, 6, m t p (10.11)
8	$p \;\dashv\; q$	3–7, s imp int

12.22. We see from 12.21 that $[\sim\Diamond[p \;\&\; \sim q] \supset [p \;\dashv\; q]]$ is provable. On the other hand, in order to prove $[[p \;\dashv\; q] \supset \sim\Diamond[p \;\&\; \sim q]]$, we need $\Box[p \lor \sim p]$, or something as strong, as a hypothesis. Similarly, $[\sim[p \;\&\; \sim q] \supset [p \supset q]]$ is provable, but in order to prove $[[p \supset q] \supset \sim[p \;\&\; \sim q]]$ we need $[p \lor \sim p]$, or something as strong, as a hypothesis. If the principle of excluded middle were added to the present system so as to give rise to C. I. Lewis's system S4, then $[p \lor \sim p]$ would be provable for every proposition p, and so would $\Box[p \lor \sim p]$. We would then have $[[p \;\dashv\; q] \equiv \sim\Diamond[p \;\&\; \sim q]]$ and $[[p \supset q] \equiv \sim[p \;\&\; \sim q]]$ as theorems. This is why Lewis is able to treat "$[p \;\dashv\; q]$" as an abbreviation for "$\sim\Diamond[p \;\&\; \sim q]$".

12.23. The concept of **consistency,** as applying to propositions, can be defined in such a way that to say that p is consistent with q is to say that the proposition $[p \;\&\; q]$ is (logically) possible. If we write "$[p \circ q]$" for "p is consistent with q", then "$[p \circ q]$" can be treated as an abbreviation for "$\Diamond[p \;\&\; q]$". No special rules will be formulated for consistency, since all statements about consistency can be regarded as statements about possibility and conjunction. We may read $[p \circ p]$ as "p is self-consistent". There is no difficulty in showing that $[p \circ p]$ and $\Diamond p$ are derivable from each other. Hence, from this standpoint, to say that p is possible is equivalent to saying that p is self-consistent.

12.24. Just as the square symbol is to be understood as expressing *logical* necessity, so also the diamond is to be understood as expressing *logical* possibility; and just as there is a difference between logical necessity and natural necessity, so also there is a difference between logical possibility and what we shall call "natural possibility". If, as in 11.19, we let L be the conjunction of all the laws of nature, then p will be said to be "naturally possible" if $[L \circ p]$ is true, that is, if p is consistent with all the laws of nature. Also, we can say that p is "naturally consistent" with q if the proposition $[p \ \& \ q]$ is naturally possible.

12.25. Contingent propositions have been described in 11.20 as propositions which are neither necessarily true nor necessarily false. They could equally well be described as propositions which are possible and which have negates that are possible. Similarly, naturally contingent propositions may be described as propositions such that they and their negates are naturally possible (i.e., consistent with all the laws of nature).

12.26. Often contrary-to-fact conditional statements may be analyzed as follows. Consider the statement, "If p were the case, then q would be the case". This can frequently be analyzed as "p is false, and the proposition, if p then q, is naturally necessary", that is, as $[\sim p \ \& \ [L \dashv 3 \ [p \supset q]]]$, where L is the conjunction of the laws of nature. Sometimes a more accurate analysis would be $[\sim p \ \& \ [[L \ \& \ r] \dashv 3 \ [p \supset q]]]$, where r would be a further premise tacitly assumed in addition to the laws of nature. Thus, suppose I say, "If I were to drop this pencil at time t, it would strike the floor". Let p be the proposition, "I drop this pencil at time t", let q be the proposition, "The pencil strikes the floor at some time later than t", and let r be the proposition that specifies that the pencil is held at a height h above the floor at time t and is free to move directly to the floor without interference when released. Then it is seen that $[\sim p \ \& \ [[L \ \& \ r] \dashv 3 \ [p \supset q]]]$ provides a logical analysis of the statement, "If I were to drop this pencil at time t, it would strike the floor".

12.27. Under this analysis, we cannot easily explain what is meant by such a proposition as: "If p were one of the laws of nature, then q would be the case". It might be argued that such a statement does not have any very clear meaning, or perhaps that it means merely that q is strictly implied by some propositions, including p, which are not all laws of nature but which are in some respects similar to laws of nature. In saying that the laws of nature "might have been different from what they are", we can apparently mean only they are "possibly false", that is to say, not true by any logical necessity. This can be expressed as $\sim \Box L$, or equally well as $\Diamond \sim L$,

and is taken for granted anyhow in saying that the laws of nature are
logically contingent.

12.28. Philosophers frequently make use of contrary-to-fact conditional statements when arguing on some subtle point. Such arguments should always be regarded with some suspicion or at least
very critically. It is often very difficult to give any clear analysis
of philosophical contrary-to-fact conditional statements. It *is*
possible to explain what is meant by the statement, "If I were to
drop this pencil at time *t*, it would strike the floor", but it is a different
matter to attempt to deal with such a statement as this: "If all minds
were destroyed, there would be no colors and no sounds".

EXERCISES

1. Prove $[\Diamond[p \mathbin{\&} q] \supset [\Diamond p \mathbin{\&} \Diamond q]]$.
2. Prove $[\Diamond \Box p \supset \Diamond p]$.
3. Prove $[\sim[\Diamond p \mathbin{\&} \Diamond q] \supset [\Box \sim p \mathbin{v} \Box \sim q]]$.
4. Prove $[\sim\Diamond[p \mathbin{v} q] \supset \sim[\Diamond p \mathbin{v} \Diamond q]]$.
5. Prove $[\sim[\Diamond p \mathbin{v} \Diamond q] \mathbin{-\!3} \sim\Diamond[p \mathbin{v} q]]$.
6. Prove $[\Diamond p \equiv [p \mathbin{o} p]]$.
7. Prove $[p \supset [q \supset [p \mathbin{o} q]]]$.
8. Prove $[\Diamond[[p \mathbin{-\!3} q] \mathbin{\&} \Diamond p] \mathbin{-\!3} \Diamond \Diamond q]$.
9. Prove $[[p \mathbin{-\!3} q] \supset \sim\Diamond[p \mathbin{\&} \sim q]]$ on the hypothesis $\Box[p \mathbin{v} \sim p]$.
10. Prove $[\Diamond \Diamond p \supset \Diamond p]$ on the hypothesis $[\Diamond p \mathbin{v} \sim\Diamond p]$.

13. Strict Coimplication

13.1. The concept of **strict coimplication** can be dealt with fairly
briefly. It bears the same sort of relation to coimplication that strict
implication bears to implication. We let a quadruple bar express
strict coimplication and take "$[p \equiv q]$" to be an abbreviation for
"$[[p \mathbin{-\!3} q] \mathbin{\&} [q \mathbin{-\!3} p]]$". We may read "$[p \equiv q]$" as "*p* strictly coimplies *q*" or as "*p* is strictly equivalent to *q*".

13.2. The rule for strict coimplication introduction ("s coimp int")
is exactly like the rule for coimplication introduction (7.4), except
that the two subordinate proofs are strict subordinate proofs, i.e.,
have squares prefixed. This rule is obtainable from the rules already
available, because if *p* and *q* are derivable from each other by strict

subordinate proofs, then $[p \dashv 3\ q]$ and $[q \dashv 3\ p]$ follow from those subordinate proofs by strict implication introduction, and $[p \equiv q]$, which is the same as $[[p \dashv 3\ q]\ \&\ [q \dashv 3\ p]]$, follows by conjunction introduction.

13.3.

1	$p \equiv q$	hyp
2	$p \dashv 3\ q$	1, def, conj elim
3	$q \dashv 3\ p$	1, def, conj elim
4	$\square$ $p \dashv 3\ q$	2, reit
5	$q \dashv 3\ p$	3, reit
6	$p \supset q$	4, def, nec elim
7	$q \supset p$	5, def, nec elim
8	$p \equiv q$	6, 7, conj int, def
9	$\square[p \equiv q]$	4–8, nec int

13.4. In a similar way, $[p \equiv q]$ is derivable from $\square[p \equiv q]$. The fact that $[p \equiv q]$ and $\square[p \equiv q]$ are derivable from each other will be called the **rule relating coimplication to strict coimplication** ("coimp s coimp"). This rule is used in 13.5 below.

13.5.

1	$\square$ $p \equiv q$	hyp
2	$\square[p \equiv q]$	1, coimp s coimp
3	$\square$ $\square[p \equiv q]$	hyp
4	$p \equiv q$	3, coimp s coimp
5	$[p \equiv q] \equiv \square[p \equiv q]$	1–2, 3–4, s coimp int

13.6. If we wish to reiterate $[p \equiv q]$ into a strict subordinate proof, we can first write $\square[p \equiv q]$ by "coimp s coimp", reiterate the latter proposition into the strict subordinate proof, and then write $[p \equiv q]$ by "coimp s coimp". Since this procedure can always be carried out, we will simply short-circuit it and hereafter allow propositions of the form $[p \equiv q]$ to be themselves reiterated into strict subordinate proofs. It was already permissible to reiterate into strict subordinate proofs expressions of the form $\square p$ and those of the form $\sim \lozenge p$.

13.7. The following six forms of **modus ponens for strict coimplication** ("m p s c") are easily established. Details are left to the reader to supply.

$$
\begin{array}{l}
p \\
\underline{p \equiv q} \\
q
\end{array}
\qquad
\begin{array}{l}
p \\
\underline{q \equiv p} \\
q
\end{array}
$$

$$
\begin{array}{l}
\Box p \\
\underline{p \equiv q} \\
\Box q
\end{array}
\qquad
\begin{array}{l}
\Box p \\
\underline{q \equiv p} \\
\Box q
\end{array}
$$

$$
\begin{array}{l}
\Diamond p \\
\underline{p \equiv q} \\
\Diamond q
\end{array}
\qquad
\begin{array}{l}
\Diamond p \\
\underline{q \equiv p} \\
\Diamond q
\end{array}
$$

13.8. Reflexivity of strict coimplication ("refl s coimp").

1	$\Box\ \underline{\ \ }\ p$	hyp
2	$\underline{\ \ }\ p$	1, rep
3	$p \equiv p$	1–2, 1–2, s coimp int

13.9. Symmetry of strict coimplication ("sym s coimp")

1	$p \equiv q$	hyp
2	$q \dashv 3\ p$	1, def, conj elim
3	$p \dashv 3\ q$	1, def, conj elim
4	$q \equiv p$	2, 3, conj int, def

13.10. Transitivity of strict coimplication ("trans s coimp").

1	$p \equiv q$	hyp
2	$q \equiv r$	hyp
3	$p \dashv 3\ q$	1, def, conj elim
4	$q \dashv 3\ p$	1, def, conj elim
5	$q \dashv 3\ r$	2, def, conj elim
6	$r \dashv 3\ q$	2, def, conj elim
7	$p \dashv 3\ r$	3, 5, trans s imp (11.14)
8	$r \dashv 3\ p$	4, 6, trans s imp
9	$p \equiv r$	7, 8, conj int, def

13.11.

1	$p \equiv q$		hyp
2	$\square$	$\square p$	hyp
3		$p \equiv q$	1, reit
4		$\square q$	2, 3, m p s c (13.7)
5	$\square$	$\square q$	hyp
6		$p \equiv q$	1, reit
7		$\square p$	5, 6, m p s c (13.7)
8		$\square p \equiv \square q$	2–4 5–7, s coimp int

EXERCISES

1. Prove $[\Diamond p \equiv \Diamond q]$ on the hypothesis $[p \equiv q]$.
2. Prove $[[p \equiv [p \supset p]] \equiv \square p]$.
3. Prove $[[p \ \& \ q] \equiv [r \ \& \ s]]$ on the hypotheses $[p \equiv r]$ and $[q \equiv s]$.
4. Prove $[[p \lor q] \equiv [r \lor s]]$ on the hypotheses $[p \equiv r]$ and $[q \equiv s]$.
5. Prove $[[p \supset q] \equiv [r \supset s]]$ on the hypotheses $[p \equiv r]$ and $[q \equiv s]$.

Chapter 4

RELATIONAL AND ATTRIBUTIVE CONCEPTS

14. Identity

14.1. Identity is a relation that relates each thing to itself and to nothing else. Here the word "thing" is being used in the most inclusive way possible, so that propositions, classes, relations, physical objects, persons, ideas, and so on are all regarded as "things". We will refer to things by using the letters "a", "b", "c", and "d". Identity will be expressed by the symbol "$=$". Thus $[a = b]$ is the proposition that asserts that a is identical with b.

14.2. There will be three rules for identity. The first rule allows us to write $[a = a]$ as a step in any proof. More specifically, we treat $[a = a]$ as an axiom. This rule will be called the **rule of identity introduction.** It has the effect of asserting that each thing is self-identical.

14.3. The second rule for identity is a substitution rule. Suppose that $(\cdots a \cdots)$ is any proposition mentioning a, and that $(\cdots b \cdots)$ is the result of substituting b for a in one or more places in $(\cdots a \cdots)$. According to this rule, we can then infer $(\cdots b \cdots)$ from $(\cdots a \cdots)$ and $[a = b]$. In other words, $(\cdots b \cdots)$ is a direct consequence of the pair of propositions $(\cdots a \cdots)$ and $[a = b]$. We will call this rule the **rule of identity elimination.** It has the effect of saying that if a is identical with b, then b can replace a anywhere. We can also use a second form of this rule that allows us to infer $(\cdots b \cdots)$ from $[b = a]$ and $(\cdots a \cdots)$. This second form of the rule can actually be derived from the first form, owing to the fact that $[a = b]$ and $[b = a]$ are derivable from each other by the method given in 14.7 below. The total effect of the two forms of this rule is to say that if a is identical with b, then a and b can replace each other anywhere. This is practically the same as the familiar mathematical rule that asserts that "equals may be substituted for equals".

14.4. The third rule for identity allows us to write $[[a = b] \lor \sim[a = b]]$ as a step in any proof. In other words, we treat $[[a = b] \lor \sim[a = b]]$ as an axiom. This is the **rule of excluded middle for identity** ("ex mid id"). It may be regarded as a kind of introduction rule and hence as permissible in intelim proofs (5.10). This rule states in effect that a is identical with b or is not.

14.5. These three rules for identity, including the two forms of the second rule, may be expressed schematically as follows:

1 |	$a = a$	id int
1 |	$a = b$	hyp
2	$(\cdots a \cdots)$	hyp
3	$(\cdots b \cdots)$	id elim (first form)
1 |	$b = a$	hyp
2	$(\cdots a \cdots)$	hyp
3	$(\cdots b \cdots)$	id elim (second form)
1 |	$[a = b] \lor \sim[a = b]$	ex mid id

14.6. In virtue of the rule of excluded middle for identity, it is seen that every identity, that is, every proposition of the form $[a = b]$, is treated as satisfying the principle of excluded middle. Hence every identity is treated as being a definite proposition (2.12, 10.19). The unrestricted form of reductio ad absurdum will hold for identities (10.16).

14.7. Symmetry of identity ("sym id").

1	$a = b$	hyp
2	$a = a$	id int
3	$b = a$	1, 2, id elim (first form)

Notice that in obtaining step 3, we do not replace a by b everywhere throughout step 2. Only the first occurrence of a in step 2 is replaced by b to give step 3.

14.8. Transitivity of identity ("trans id").

1	$a = b$	hyp
2	$c = a$	hyp
3	$c = b$	1, 2, id elim (first form)

Notice that step 3 is obtained by replacing a by b in step 2. In a similar way we could, of course, derive $[a = c]$ from $[a = b]$ and $[b = c]$. In fact we could just as well write the above proof thus:

$$
\begin{array}{lll}
1 & b = c & \text{hyp} \\
2 & a = b & \text{hyp} \\
3 & a = c & \text{1, 2, id elim (first form)}
\end{array}
$$

Here step 3 is obtained by replacing b by c in step 2.

14.9. A proof of the transitivity of identity, using the second form of identity elimination, is as follows:

$$
\begin{array}{lll}
1 & b = a & \text{hyp} \\
2 & a = c & \text{hyp} \\
3 & b = c & \text{1, 2, id elim (second form)}
\end{array}
$$

This could also be written as follows:

$$
\begin{array}{lll}
1 & a = b & \text{hyp} \\
2 & b = c & \text{hyp} \\
3 & a = c & \text{1, 2, id elim (second form)}
\end{array}
$$

14.10.

$$
\begin{array}{lll}
1 & a = b & \text{hyp} \\
2 & (\cdots a \cdots) = (\cdots a \cdots) & \text{id int} \\
3 & (\cdots a \cdots) = (\cdots b \cdots) & \text{1, 2, id elim}
\end{array}
$$

14.11.

$$
\begin{array}{lll}
1 & \sim[(\cdots a \cdots) = (\cdots b \cdots)] & \text{hyp} \\
2 & [a = b] \vee \sim[a = b] & \text{ex mid id} \\
3 & \quad a = b & \text{hyp} \\
4 & \quad (\cdots a \cdots) = (\cdots b \cdots) & \text{3, 14.10} \\
5 & \quad \sim[(\cdots a \cdots) = (\cdots b \cdots)] & \text{1, reit} \\
6 & \sim[a = b] & \text{2, 3–5, res neg int (10.15)}
\end{array}
$$

EXERCISES

1. Prove $[[[a = b] \ \& \ [b = c]] \supset [c = a]]$.
2. Prove $[[a = b] \supset [\sim[a = c] \supset \sim[b = c]]]$.
3. Prove $[[a = b] \supset [\sim[a = c] \equiv \sim[b = c]]]$.

4. Show that the first form of identity elimination is derivable from the second form.

5. Prove $[\sim[a = b] \supset \sim[b = a]]$.

15. Ordered Couples

15.1. Given any two things, a and b, we may form the **ordered couple** (a, b) of those two things.[1] If a is different from b, the ordered couple (a, b) is regarded as different from the ordered couple (b, a). Thus the order of a and b is relevant. If, however, a and b are the same thing, then the ordered couples (a, b) and (b, a) are the same ordered couple and are the same as (a, a). Ordered couples of the form (a, a) are indeed permissible. In other words, we can form ordered couples (a, b) even for the case where a is identical with b. Ordered couples must be distinguished from unordered couples (17.45).

15.2. Ordered couples are of great importance in mathematics and logic. By using ordered couples, we can define fractions in terms of whole numbers. The fraction $\frac{1}{2}$ can be defined as $(1, 2)$, the fraction $\frac{2}{3}$ as $(2, 3)$, and so on. Also, it is possible to treat relations as being classes of ordered couples. More will be said of this later.

15.3. Hereafter we will usually omit the comma in writing ordered couples, except where ambiguity might result from so doing. Thus we will usually write "(ab)" instead of "(a, b)". Also we will often refer to ordered couples simply as "couples".

15.4. We will call a the **left term** of the couple (ab), and we will call b the **right term** of the couple (ab). The couple (aa) has a for its left term and also for its right term.[2]

---

[1] The notion of ordered couple is here being treated as an undefined notion. In some systems of logic it is convenient to define this notion in terms of other notions, but not in the present system. This is because we wish to formulate the system in such a way that ordered coupling can eventually be regarded as the ultimate combining principle of the system. See 28.1 of Appendix A.

[2] It might be better to speak of the "first term" and the "second term" instead of the "left term" and the "right term", because the words "left" and "right" wrongly suggest that couples are oriented in space. Of course the *expressions* we write down to designate couples *are* oriented in space, and we assume the convention that the left-hand component of such an expression designates the first term of the couple, while the right-hand component designates the second term.

15.5. There is an introduction rule for couples (15.6 below) and an elimination rule for them (15.9 below). The introduction rule has three forms and is derivable from rules already available. The elimination rule has two forms. It is not derivable from rules already available.

15.6. Rule of couple introduction ("coup int") in its three forms.

$$
\begin{array}{lll}
1 & a = c & \text{hyp} \\
2 & b = d & \text{hyp} \\
3 & (ab) = (cd) & \text{1, 2, coup int (first form)} \\
\end{array}
$$

$$
\begin{array}{lll}
1 & a = c & \text{hyp} \\
2 & (ab) = (cb) & \text{1, coup int (second form)} \\
\end{array}
$$

$$
\begin{array}{lll}
1 & b = d & \text{hyp} \\
2 & (ab) = (ad) & \text{1, coup int (third form)} \\
\end{array}
$$

15.7. The first form of the rule of couple introduction can be derived as follows from rules previously available. Proof of the second form is provided by steps 1–4. Proof of the third form is left to the reader.

$$
\begin{array}{lll}
1 & a = c & \text{hyp} \\
2 & b = d & \text{hyp} \\
3 & (ab) = (ab) & \text{id int} \\
4 & (ab) = (cb) & \text{1, 3, id elim} \\
5 & (ab) = (cd) & \text{2, 4, id elim} \\
\end{array}
$$

15.8. From 15.7 we see that if the left terms of two couples are identical, and if the right terms are also identical, then the couples themselves are identical. Conversely, it will be guaranteed by 15.9 that if two couples are identical (and hence not really "two"), their left terms must be identical with each other and their right terms must also be identical with each other. Thus two couples are identical with each other if and only if they have identical left terms and identical right terms.

15.9. Rule of couple elimination ("coup elim") in its two forms.

$$
\begin{array}{ll}
1 & (ab) = (cd) \qquad\qquad \text{hyp} \\
2 & a = c \qquad\qquad\qquad \text{1, coup elim (first form)}
\end{array}
$$

$$
\begin{array}{ll}
1 & (ab) = (cd) \qquad\qquad \text{hyp} \\
2 & b = d \qquad\qquad\qquad \text{1, coup elim (second form)}
\end{array}
$$

15.10. The following three coimplications can easily be proved:

$$[(ab) = (cd)] \equiv [[a = c] \;\&\; [b = d]],$$
$$[(ab) = (cb)] \equiv [a = c],$$
$$[(ab) = (ad)] \equiv [b = d].$$

15.11.
$$
\begin{array}{lll}
1 & \sim[(ab) = (cb)] & \text{hyp} \\
2 & [a = c] \lor \sim[a = c] & \text{ex mid id} \\
3 & \quad a = c & \text{hyp} \\
4 & \quad (ab) = (cb) & \text{3, coup int} \\
5 & \quad \sim[(ab) = (cb)] & \text{1, reit} \\
6 & \sim[a = c] & \text{2, 3–5, res neg int (10.15)}
\end{array}
$$

15.12. Similarly, $\sim[b = d]$ follows from $\sim[(ab) = (ad)]$.

15.13.
$$
\begin{array}{lll}
1 & \sim[(ab) = (cd)] & \text{hyp} \\
2 & [b = d] \lor \sim[b = d] & \text{ex mid id} \\
3 & \quad b = d & \text{hyp} \\
4 & \quad \sim[(ab) = (cd)] & \text{1, reit} \\
5 & \quad \sim[(ab) = (cb)] & \text{3, 4, id elim} \\
6 & \quad \sim[a = c] & \text{5, 15.11} \\
7 & \quad \sim[a = c] \lor \sim[b = d] & \text{6, dis int} \\
8 & \quad \sim[b = d] & \text{hyp} \\
9 & \quad \sim[a = c] \lor \sim[b = d] & \text{8, dis int} \\
10 & \sim[a = c] \lor \sim[b = d] & \text{2, 3–7, 8–9, dis elim}
\end{array}
$$

15.14.

1	$\sim[a = c]$	hyp
2	$[(ab) = (cd)] \vee \sim[(ab) = (cd)]$	ex mid id
3	$(ab) = (cd)$	hyp
4	$a = c$	3, coup elim
5	$\sim[a = c]$	1, reit
6	$\sim[(ab) = (cd)]$	2, 3–5, res neg int (10.15)

15.15. Similarly, $\sim[(ab) = (cd)]$ can be derived from $\sim[b = d]$.

15.16. The following three coimplications can easily be proved:

$$\sim[(ab) = (cd)] \equiv [\sim[a = c] \vee \sim[b = d]],$$
$$\sim[(ab) = (cb)] \equiv \sim[a = c],$$
$$\sim[(ab) = (ad)] \equiv \sim[b = d].$$

Compare the above coimplications with those of 15.10.

15.17. A term of a couple may itself be a couple. Thus the right term of $(a(bc))$ is itself the couple (bc). Similarly, the left term of $((ab)c)$ is itself the couple (ab). The left term of $((ef)(ba))$ is (ef), while the right term of $((ef)(ba))$ is (ba). We can construct still more complicated combinations of couples such as $((((ab)c)d)e)$ and $((a((b(cd))e))f)$.

15.18. The following abbreviations will be used:

"(abc)" for "$((ab)c)$",
"$(abcd)$" for "$(((ab)c)d)$",
"$(abcde)$" for "$((((ab)c)d)e)$",

and so on. Also:

15.19. "$[b \; a \; c]$" for "$(a(bc))$".

15.20. Using the above abbreviations, we could abbreviate

$$\text{"}((ab)(cd))\text{" as "}(ab(cd))\text{" or as "}[c \; (ab) \; d]\text{",}$$

and we could abbreviate

$$\text{"}((a(bc))(de))\text{" as "}(a(bc)(de))\text{" or as "}[d \; [b \; a \; c] \; e]\text{".}$$

In the same way "$(((a(bc))((de)f))(gh))$" could be abbreviated as

$$\text{"}(a(bc)(def)(gh))\text{" or as "}[g \; [(de) \; [b \; a \; c] \; f] \; h]\text{".}$$

EXERCISES

1. Write each of the following expressions in abbreviated form:
   a. $((ab)((cd)(ef)))$.
   b. $((((ab)(cd))e)f)$.
   c. $(a(b(c(d(ef)))))$.
   d. $((a((b(cd))e))f)$.

2. Write each of the following expressions in unabbreviated form:
   a. $(a(bc)d)$.
   b. $[(ab) \ c \ (de)]$.
   c. $((ab)(cd)(efg))$.
   d. $[(abc) \ d \ [e \ f \ [g \ h \ i]]]$.

3. Derive $[(abc) = (cde)]$ and $[[a = c] \ \& \ [b = d] \ \& \ [c = e]]$ from each other.

4. Prove $[[[a \ b \ c] = [d \ e \ f]] \supset [b = e]]$.

16. Relations, Attributes, and Classes

16.1. We call $((ab)c)$ a **left triple** and $(a(bc))$ a **right triple**. The left triple $((ab)c)$ may also be written in form (abc) by 15.18. The right triple $(a(bc))$ may also be written in the form $[b \ a \ c]$ by 15.19.

16.2. If R is a (two-termed) relation, then the right triple $(R(ab))$, also written as $[a \ R \ b]$, is to be understood as the proposition that asserts that a bears to b the relation R. Thus since the symbol "$=$" denotes the relation of identity, the right triple $(=(ab))$, or $[a = b]$, is the proposition asserting that a bears to b the relation of identity, in other words, asserting that a is identical with b. The Greek letter "ϵ" is often used to denote the relation of **class membership,** so that if F is a class, then $[a \ \epsilon \ F]$ is the proposition that asserts that a is a member of the class F. We will treat implication, conjunction, disjunction, and coimplication as relations between propositions. Similarly, in modal logic we will treat strict implication and strict coimplication as relations between propositions. Thus $[p \supset q]$ could equally well have been written $(\supset(pq))$ and is to be understood as asserting that p bears to q the relation of implication. Similarly, $[p \ \& \ q]$, otherwise written as $(\&(pq))$, asserts that p bears to q the relation of conjunction. This latter relation may seem to be a relation of a rather strange sort, since it holds from each true proposition to every other true proposition, and indeed from each true proposition to itself; but there is nothing objectionable in this.[3]

16.3. In addition to the purely logical relations mentioned above, there are empirical relations of all sorts. Such words or phrases as "hates", "loves", "is taller than", "is an uncle of", "is located five miles due south of", clearly can be regarded as referring to empirical relations. Thus if a is Mark Anthony, if b is Cleopatra, and if R is the relation "loves", then $[a \ R \ b]$ is the proposition, "Anthony loves Cleopatra", while $[b \ R \ a]$ is the proposition, "Cleopatra loves Anthony", and of course $[a \ R \ a]$ is the proposition, "Anthony loves himself".

16.4. No sharp distinction will be drawn between classes and attributes. It is possible, indeed, to treat classes as being simply attributes of a special kind, "extensional attributes". It is said to be characteristic of extensional attributes (classes) that if two of them apply to (have as members) exactly the same things, then those two extensional attributes or classes are identical with each other.[4] For present purposes, however, we will not distinguish between a given attribute and the corresponding class. For example, we will not distinguish between the attribute "blue" and the class of blue things, nor will we assert that two classes must be identical if they have the same members. If a is the sky and if F is the class of blue things, then $[a \ \epsilon \ F]$ will be understood as the proposition, "The sky is a member of the class of blue things", and it will also be understood as the proposition, "The sky is blue", or "The sky has the attribute blueness". Thus "ϵ" can be read not only as "is a member of the class", but also as "has the attribute".

16.5. It will be permissible to write a proposition of the form $[a \ \epsilon \ F]$ simply as an ordered couple (Fa). Thus (Fa) can be regarded

[3] The notions of "proposition", "attribute", "class", and "relation" are not designated by any of the formal symbols of this system, and there appears to be no genuine need to designate them by formal symbols, though this could perfectly well be done if desired. See 21.9 in this connection. Of course we do have formal expressions that designate particular propositions, attributes (classes), and relations. Thus "$[\& = \&]$" designates the proposition that conjunction is identical with conjunction, and "$\sim$" designates the attribute untruth.

[4] For some further discussion of these ideas, see my article, "Attribute and Class," which appears in *"Philosophic Thought in France and the United States,"* Buffalo, N. Y., 1950, ed. Marvin Farber.

as being the proposition that asserts that a has the attribute F, or that a is a member of the class F. In fact we can assume a **rule of ε-elimination** ("ε-elim"), according to which (Fa) is a direct consequence of $[a \ \epsilon \ F]$, and a **rule of ε-introduction** ("ε-int"), according to which $[a \ \epsilon \ F]$ is a direct consequence of (Fa). Also we can assume a **rule of negative ε-elimination** ("neg ε-elim"), according to which $\sim(Fa)$ is a direct consequence of $\sim[a \ \epsilon \ F]$, and a **rule of negative ε-introduction** ("neg ε-int"), according to which $\sim[a \ \epsilon \ F]$ is a direct consequence of $\sim(Fa)$. These rules will be used little in the main body of this book. In practice we will usually express "a has the attribute F", or "a is a member of the class F", by the notation "$[a \ \epsilon \ F]$" rather than the notation "(Fa)". We can regard $[a \ \epsilon \ F]$ and (Fa) as different but logically equivalent propositions. The proposition $[a \ \epsilon \ F]$ mentions the relation ϵ, while (Fa) does not.

16.6. Negation (falsity) will be regarded as an attribute, somewhat as conjunction, disjunction, implication, and coimplication are regarded as relations. The symbol "$\sim$" may be thought of as denoting the attribute of falsity, so that the proposition, "p is false", can be expressed as $[p \ \epsilon \sim]$ or as $(\sim p)$. In the case of the proposition $(\sim p)$, we ordinarily omit the parentheses and write simply "$\sim p$". Similarly, in modal logic, the symbol "$\Box$" denotes the attribute necessity so that $[p \ \epsilon \ \Box]$ or $(\Box p)$ is the proposition "p is necessary". Omitting the parentheses gives the usual notation "$\Box p$". Similar remarks apply to the attribute of possibility, expressed by the symbol "$\Diamond$".

16.7. Relations may be treated as being classes of couples or attributes of couples. For example, the relation "loves" may be viewed as the class of all those couples (ab) which are such that a loves b. If R is the relation "loves", then $(R(ab))$ asserts that the couple (ab) is a member of R, and when rewritten as $[a \ R \ b]$ it is seen also to mean that a loves b. As another example, identity, denoted by the symbol "$=$", can be viewed as the class of all those couples (ab) which are such that a is identical with b. To assert $(=(ab))$ is then to assert that (ab) is one such couple belonging to this class, and hence to assert that a is identical with b. But $(=(ab))$, when rewritten in familiar form as $[a = b]$ in accordance with 15.19, is already recognized as meaning that a is identical with b. If couples of the form (aa) are called "identical couples", then identity could be said to be the class of all identical couples, or if we wish to speak of identity as an attribute, then identity is the attribute possessed by identical couples and no others. Finally, the relation "greater than" as among positive integers can be regarded as the class of all those couples (ab) of positive integers a and b where a is greater than b. The couple (6, 3) would belong to this class, and also the couple (2, 1), but not the couple (3, 6) or the couple (1, 2). On the other hand, (3, 6) and (1, 2) would belong to the class of couples that constitutes the relation "less than" among positive integers. (Commas are here inserted in writing the couples so it will be clear that we are not speaking of the numbers sixty-three, twenty-one, thirty-six, or twelve.)

16.8. There is an apparent inconsistency in treating "$[p \equiv q]$" as an abbreviation for "$[[p \supset q] \mathbin{\&} [q \supset p]]$" and at the same time treating it as an abbreviation for "$(\equiv(pq))$". We therefore choose to regard it as an abbreviation for the former expression rather than for the latter expression. Thus the symbol "$\equiv$", as used in "$[p \equiv q]$", does not really denote an attribute of couples, but for convenience we can think of it as denoting such an attribute, and later (24.14) it will be shown that our system actually provides an expression that does denote the requisite attribute of couples. Similar remarks apply to the symbol "$\equiv$" of Section 13.

16.9.
1	$a \mathbin{R} b$	hyp
2	$(R(ab))$	1, rep, def (15.19)
3	$(ab) \in R$	2, ϵ-int

16.10.
1	$(ab) \in R$	hyp
2	$(R(ab))$	1, ϵ-elim
3	$a \mathbin{R} b$	2, rep, def (15.9)

16.11.
1	$\sim[a \mathbin{R} b]$	hyp
2	$\sim(R(ab))$	1, rep, def (15.19)
3	$\sim[(ab) \in R]$	2, neg ϵ-int

16.12.
1	$\sim[(ab) \in R]$	hyp
2	$\sim(R(ab))$	1, neg ϵ-elim
3	$\sim[a \mathbin{R} b]$	2, rep, def (15.19)

16.13. The **domain** of a relation R is the class of all those things which bear R to various things. Thus the domain of the relation "husband of" is the class of all husbands.[5]

16.14. The **converse domain** of a relation R is the class of all those things to which the relation R is borne. Thus the converse domain of the relation "husband of" is the class of all wives.

16.15. The **field** of a relation of R is the class of all things that belong to the domain or the converse domain of R. Thus the class of all husbands and wives is the field of the relation "husband of". It is also the field of the relation "wife of" and of the relation "spouse of".

16.16. The **converse** of a relation R is the relation which b bears to a whenever a bears R to b. Thus the relation "is admired by" is the converse of the relation "admires", and the relation "south of" is the converse of the relation "north of". (The notion of converse is formally defined in 25.19.) The domain of the converse of a relation R has the same members as the converse domain of R.

16.17. A relation R is said to be **reflexive** if [a R a] is true for every member a of the field of R. The relation "as tall as" is reflexive.[6]

16.18. A relation R is said to be **symmetrical** if [b R a] is true whenever [a R b] is true. The relation "spouse of" is symmetrical but not reflexive.

16.19. A relation R is said to be **transitive** if [a R c] is true whenever [a R b] and [b R c] are true. The relation "descendant of" is transitive but not symmetrical or reflexive.

16.20. A relation R is said to be **irreflexive** if $\sim$[a R a] is true for every member a of the field of R. The relation "different from" is irreflexive.

16.21. A relation R is said to be **asymmetrical** if $\sim$[b R a] is true whenever [a R b] is true. The relation "parent of" is asymmetrical.

16.22. A relation R is said to be **intransitive** if $\sim$[a R c] is true whenever [a R b] and [b R c] are true. The relation "father of" is intransitive.

---

[5] The notions discussed informally in 16.13–16.15 will be formally defined in 25.39–25.41.

[6] The notions discussed informally in 16.17–16.22 will be formally defined in 26.53–26.56.

16.23. If a relation is not reflexive, we say it is **non-reflexive**; if it is not symmetrical, we say it is **non-symmetrical**; and if it is not transitive, we say it is **non-transitive**. A relation could be non-reflexive without being irreflexive, it could be non-symmetrical without being asymmetrical, and it could be non-transitive without being intransitive. For example, the relation "proud of" is non-reflexive but not irreflexive. The relation "friendly toward" is non-symmetrical but not asymmetrical. The relation "brother of" is non-transitive but not intransitive.

EXERCISES

1. Suppose that the relation "half as large as", among the positive integers (whole positive numbers) one through ten, is treated as a class of couples. Write down all the couples that belong to this class.

2. Suppose that the relation "twice as large as", among positive integers one through ten, is treated as being a class of couples. Write down all the couples that belong to this class.

3. If you have done Exercises 1 and 2, generalize the results of these two exercises as follows: Suppose that the relations R and S are converses of each other, and the couples belonging to R are known. Show how we find the couples belonging to S.

4. Which of the relations *implication, conjunction, disjunction,* and *coimplication* have been shown to be reflexive? Which have been shown to be symmetrical (or commutative)? Which have been shown to be transitive? Prove that conjunction is transitive.

5. Characterize reflexive relations in terms of the couples that belong to them if they are treated as being classes of couples. Do the same for symmetrical relations.

17. Attributes Assigned by Propositions

17.1. The proposition, "Mars contains life", assigns to the planet Mars the attribute of containing life. It assigns this attribute to Mars. Nobody at present (1952) knows whether this proposition is true or not, so nobody knows whether Mars actually has the attribute assigned to it by this proposition. The proposition, "The earth is larger than Mars", also assigns an attribute to Mars but it does so implicitly rather than explicitly. It assigns to Mars the attribute of being smaller than the earth. The assignment would have been explicit if the proposition had read, "Mars has the attribute of being smaller than the earth", or, more simply, "Mars is smaller than the earth". The proposition, "$3 \times 2 = 6$", implicitly assigns to the number 2 the attribute of being such that three times it equals 6, and it implicitly assigns to the number 3 the attribute of being such that when 2 is multiplied by it the result is 6. Also, it implicitly assigns to 6 the attribute of being equaled by 3×2. In general, if a proposition p mentions something a, then p assigns implicitly or explicitly some attribute to a. All attributes thus assigned by true propositions are really possessed by the things to which they are assigned. The attributes thus assigned by false propositions fail to be possessed by the things to which they are assigned. Thus the proposition, "Mars is larger than the sun", assigns to Mars an attribute that Mars does not have.

17.2. Let p be any proposition and let a be something mentioned by the proposition p. Then there is some attribute which p assigns to a. We will designate this attribute by the notation $(a \setminus p)$. Thus, (Mars \ [Mars contains life]) is the attribute assigned to Mars by the proposition "Mars contains life", and so it is the attribute of containing life. Again, (the North Pole \ [Peary discovered the North Pole]) is the attribute of having been discovered by Peary, while (Peary \ [Peary discovered the North Pole]) is the attribute of having discovered the North Pole. This latter attribute is also (falsely) assigned to Caesar by the false proposition, "Caesar discovered the North Pole". Thus (Caesar\[Caesar discovered the North Pole]) is also the attribute of having discovered the North Pole, and the two notations, "(Peary \ [Peary discovered the North Pole])" and "(Caesar \ [Caesar discovered the North Pole])" are two different names for the attribute of having discovered the North Pole.

17.3. If (---c---) is any proposition mentioning c two or more times, then there are at least three different attributes that (---c---) assigns to c. For example, if (---c---) is $[c = c]$, then the attribute assigned to w by $[w = c]$ is assigned to c by $[c = c]$, and the same is true of the attribute assigned to w by $[c = w]$, and of the attribute assigned to w by $[w = w]$. (Here w is assumed to be something different from c.) In other words, $[c = c]$ assigns to c each of the attributes $(w \setminus [w = c])$, $(w \setminus [c = w])$, and $(w \setminus [w = w])$. But only one of the attributes assigned to c by $[c = c]$ is an attribute that does not mention c, and this we call the **principal attribute** assigned to c by $[c = c]$, and we refer to it as $(c \setminus [c = c])$. It is the same attribute as $(w \setminus [w = w])$. In general, if $(\cdots x \cdots)$ is any proposition mentioning x one or more times, or even if it is a proposition not mentioning x at all, we assume that there is a principal attribute $(x \setminus (\cdots x \cdots))$ that $(\cdots x \cdots)$ assigns to x. If z is something not mentioned anywhere in $(\cdots x \cdots)$, and if $(\cdots z \cdots)$ is the result of replacing x by z throughout $(\cdots x \cdots)$, then $(z \setminus (\cdots z \cdots))$ is the same attribute as $(x \setminus (\cdots x \cdots))$. Suppose, now, that $(\cdots a \cdots)$ is the result of replacing x by a throughout $(\cdots x \cdots)$. We are not excluding the possibility that a may be already mentioned in $(\cdots x \cdots)$, nor the possibility that a may be the same thing as x itself. Then $(\cdots a \cdots)$ assigns to a whatever attribute or attributes $(\cdots x \cdots)$ assigns to x. But $(\cdots x \cdots)$ assigns $(x \setminus (\cdots x \cdots))$ to x. Hence $(\cdots a \cdots)$ assigns $(x \setminus (\cdots x \cdots))$ to a, and the two propositions $(\cdots a \cdots)$ and $[a \in (x \setminus (\cdots x \cdots))]$ coimply each other. Thus we are led to assume rules 17.4 and 17.5 below. Notice, however, that $(a \setminus (\cdots a \cdots))$ may not be the same attribute as $(x \setminus (\cdots x \cdots))$, since a may be mentioned in $(\cdots x \cdots)$. For example, if a is different from x and if $(\cdots x \cdots)$ is $[x = a]$, then clearly the attribute $(x \setminus [x = a])$ is different from the attribute $(a \setminus [a = a])$. The former attribute, if a does not mention x, is the attribute of being identical with a, while the latter attribute is the attribute of self-identity. In the situation that x is not mentioned in $(\cdots x \cdots)$, we still assume that there is a principal attribute $(x \setminus (\cdots x \cdots))$ that $(\cdots x \cdots)$ assigns to x. If $(\cdots x \cdots)$ is a true proposition, this principal attribute is taken to be some universal attribute (see 17.30), while if $(\cdots x \cdots)$ is a false proposition, this principal attribute is taken to be some empty attribute (see 17.33).

17.4. Rule of attribute introduction ("att int"). First form: The proposition $[a \in (x \setminus (\cdots x \cdots))]$ is a direct consequence of the proposition $(\cdots a \cdots)$. Second form: The proposition $((x \setminus (\cdots x \cdots))a)$ is a direct consequence of the proposition $(\cdots a \cdots)$. (The first form can be regarded as a derived rule, derived from the second form and the rule of ϵ-introduction, 16.5.) See 17.6 below.

17.5. Rule of attribute elimination ("att elim"). First form: The proposition $(\cdots a \cdots)$ is a direct consequence of the proposition

$[a \, \epsilon \, (x \setminus (\cdots x \cdots))]$. Second form: The proposition $(\cdots a \cdots)$ is a direct consequence of the proposition $((x \setminus (\cdots x \cdots))a)$. (The first form can be regarded as a derived rule, derived from the second form and the rule of ϵ-elimination, 16.5.) See 17.6 below.

17.6. In 17.4, 17.5, and 17.7, we are to assume that $(\cdots x \cdots)$ is any proposition, possibly but not necessarily one that mentions x. We are to assume that $(\cdots a \cdots)$ is the result of replacing x by a everywhere in $(\cdots x \cdots)$ where x is mentioned.[7] If $(\cdots x \cdots)$ does not mention x, then $(\cdots a \cdots)$ is to be the same proposition as $(\cdots x \cdots)$. Equally well we could take $(\cdots a \cdots)$ to be any proposition, possibly but not necessarily one that mentions a; we could choose x as anything not mentioned in $(\cdots a \cdots)$, or mentioned in $(\cdots a \cdots)$ only by being mentioned in a or by being a itself; and we could choose $(\cdots x \cdots)$ as any proposition such that the result of replacing x by a throughout $(\cdots x \cdots)$ gives the proposition $(\cdots a \cdots)$ again. If x does not occur in $(\cdots a \cdots)$ then $(\cdots x \cdots)$ can be chosen as $(\cdots a \cdots)$ itself. There are thus two different but equivalent ways of looking at the notation used in 17.4, 17.5, and 17.7. In the first way, we start with any proposition $(\cdots x \cdots)$ and let $(\cdots a \cdots)$ be the result of replacing x by a in *all* places where $(\cdots x \cdots)$ mentions x, if there are any such places, and if there are no such places, we let $(\cdots a \cdots)$ be $(\cdots x \cdots)$. Thus if $(\cdots x \cdots)$ is chosen to be $[\sim[x = a] \vee \sim[x = b]]$, where x is mentioned only twice as shown, then $(\cdots a \cdots)$ would be $[\sim[a = a] \vee \sim[a = b]]$. In the second way, we start with any proposition $(\cdots a \cdots)$, choose x as something not mentioned in $(\cdots a \cdots)$ or mentioned at most by being mentioned in a or by being a, and we let $(\cdots x \cdots)$ be such that we can obtain $(\cdots a \cdots)$ from it by replacing x everywhere by a. If $(\cdots a \cdots)$ is chosen to be $[\sim[a = a] \vee \sim[a = b]]$, and if x is chosen to be something different from a and not mentioned in a, then $(\cdots x \cdots)$ could be chosen as the proposition that results from replacing a by x at the first and

---

[7] This must be done in such a way that a is mentioned in those places in $(\cdots a \cdots)$ where it replaces x. A similar assumption is always to be understood whenever we speak of replacement. More specifically, suppose that $(\cdots x \cdots)$ is $[(a \setminus [x = a]) = (a \setminus [x = a])]$. We cannot regard $(\cdots a \cdots)$ as being $[(a \setminus [a = a]) = (a \setminus [a = a])]$, because the latter proposition merely asserts that self-identity is identical with self-identity, and it fails to mention a at all. In such a situation the proper procedure is to note that we can treat $(\cdots x \cdots)$ as being $[(b \setminus [x = b]) = (b \setminus [x = b])]$ for suitably chosen b. Then $(\cdots a \cdots)$ is $[(b \setminus [a = b]) = (b \setminus [a = b])]$.

third places in $[\sim[a = a] \vee \sim[a = b]]$ where a is mentioned.   Thus $(\cdots x \cdots)$ would be chosen as the proposition $[\sim[x = a] \vee \sim[x = b]]$. We could also, if we wished, choose $(\cdots x \cdots)$ as being any one of the propositions

$$[\sim[a = a] \vee \sim[a = b]],$$
$$[\sim[a = a] \vee \sim[x = b]],$$
$$[\sim[a = x] \vee \sim[a = b]],$$
$$[\sim[x = a] \vee \sim[a = b]],$$
$$[\sim[a = x] \vee \sim[x = b]],$$
$$[\sim[x = x] \vee \sim[a = b]],$$
$$[\sim[x = x] \vee \sim[x = b]].$$

17.7.

1	$a \in (x \setminus (\cdots x \cdots))$	hyp
2	$(\cdots a \cdots)$	1, att elim
3	$(\cdots a \cdots)$	hyp
4	$a \in (x \setminus (\cdots x \cdots))$	3, att int
5	$[a \in (x \setminus (\cdots x \cdots))] \equiv (\cdots a \cdots)$	1–2, 3–4, coimp int

17.8. An expression of the form "$(x \setminus (\cdots x \cdots))$", where $(\cdots x \cdots)$ is any proposition, will be called an **abstract**. Every abstract is the name of an attribute. Thus "$(x \setminus (\cdots x \cdots))$" is the name of the principal attribute assigned to x by $(\cdots x \cdots)$.[8]

17.9. Although the expression "x" occurs in the expression "$(x \setminus (\cdots x \cdots))$", we are not to think of x itself (the thing denoted or named by the expression "x") as mentioned by the attribute $(x \setminus (\cdots x \cdots))$. For example, the attribute (the North Pole $\setminus$ [Peary discovered the North Pole]) does not mention the North Pole, since it is simply the attribute of having been discovered by Peary. Similarly, the attribute (Peary $\setminus$ [Peary discovered the North Pole]) does not mention Peary. It is the attribute of having discovered the North Pole, and it could equally well be denoted by the abstract, "(Columbus $\setminus$ [Columbus discovered the North Pole])".

17.10. If an expression "a" occurs in another expression "c", there must be one or more places at which "a" occurs in "c". Each instance of the expression "a" in the expression "c" is called an **occurrence** of "a" in "c". There are two occurrences of the expression "water"

---

[8] A different method for dealing with abstracts is presented in Appendix A.

in the abstract "(water \ [water is wet])", but only one occurrence of the expression "is" and only one occurrence of the expression "wet."

17.11. The expression "x" will be called the **initial expression** of the abstract "(x \ ($\cdots x \cdots$))". The expression "water", for example, is the initial expression of the abstract "(water \ [water is wet])".

17.12. Suppose that a certain *occurrence* of an expression "x" is so located in an expression "c" as to be part of an abstract that has the expression "x" as its initial expression. The abstract, let us assume, is either part of c or is c itself. Such an occurrence of the expression "x" will be said to be a **bound occurrence** of "x" in (and relatively to) the expression "c". Suppose, for example, that the expression "x" is "water", and that the expression "c" is "[water ϵ (water \ [water is wet])]". There are three occurrences of "water" in "c". The first of these three occurrences of "water" is the one immediately to the left of "ϵ". This occurrence of "water" fails to be bound in "c" because it is not part of any abstract. The other two occurrences of the expression "water" are bound occurrences of "water" in "c" because they are parts of an abstract that is part of "c" and that has "water" as its initial expression. If we choose the expression "c" as the abstract "(water \ [water is wet])", then both occurrences of "water" in "(water \ [water is wet)]" are bound in "(water \ [water is wet])". If we choose "c" as the sentence "water is wet", then the only occurrence of "water" in "water is wet" fails to be bound in "c". If a certain occurrence of "x" in "c" is not a bound occurrence of "x" in "c", then we say this is a **free occurrence** of "x" in (and relatively to) the expression "c". The only occurrence of "wet" in "(water \ [water is wet])" is a free occurrence.

17.13. If the expression "a" is the name of the thing a, it is possible to *use* the expression "a" without *mentioning* the thing a. For example, in the sentence, "[Peary ϵ (Napoleon \ [Napoleon discovered the North Pole])]", we use the expression "Napoleon" but do not mention the man Napoleon. This is seen from the fact that the meaning of the sentence is the proposition to the effect that Peary has the attribute of having discovered the North Pole. Notice that both occurrences of the expression "Napoleon" in the above sentence are *bound* occurrences. In general, a bound occurrence of an expression does not involve mention of the thing named (denoted) by the expression. The abstract "$(x \setminus (\cdots x \cdots))$" nowhere mentions the thing x, though it uses the expression "x". This is because all the occurrences of "x" in the abstract are bound occurrences. We are assuming, of course, that the expression "x" is the name of x and that we are not using any other name for x. It can also be said that the *attribute* $(x \setminus (\cdots x \cdots))$, denoted by the *abstract* "$(x \setminus (\cdots x \cdots))$", does not mention x. The sense in which an attribute "mentions" is not the same as the sense in which an abstract "mentions", but it is convenient to employ both kinds of mentioning. Similarly, a proposition will be said to mention a or not to mention a in some part of itself if the sentence expressing the proposition mentions a or does not mention a in the corresponding part of itself.

17.14. Notice that $(a \setminus [a = b])$ is the attribute of being identical with b. This is an attribute which b itself possesses but which nothing else possesses. The attribute $(a \setminus \sim[a = b])$ is, on the contrary, an attribute possessed by everything but b. It is the attribute of being different from b. The attribute $(a \setminus [a = a])$ is the attribute of self-identity. Everything has this attribute.

17.15. Sometimes it is convenient to speak of a *class* instead of an *attribute* as the meaning of an abstract, though we make no sharp distinction between class and attribute. Thus we can speak of $(a \setminus (\cdots a \cdots))$ as "the class in which the proposition $(\cdots a \cdots)$ classifies a". For example, (the North Pole $\setminus$ [Peary discovered the North Pole]) could be said to be the class of things discovered by Peary, just as well as it could be said to be the attribute of having been discovered by Peary. The proposition, "Peary discovered the North Pole", implicitly classifies the North Pole in the class of things discovered by Peary. Similarly we could speak of $(a \setminus [a = b])$ as the class of things identical with b. This class has only one member, namely b itself, because b is the only thing identical with b. We could speak of $(a \setminus \sim[a = b])$ as the class of things different from b, or as the class of all things other than b, just as well as we could speak of it as the attribute of being other than b, and we could speak of $(a \setminus [a = a])$ as the class of all self-identical things. This class has the same members as the class of all things whatsoever.

17.16. It is often convenient to read "$(a \setminus (\cdots a \cdots))$" as "the class of those things a such that $(\cdots a \cdots)$" or as "the class of a's such that $(\cdots a \cdots)$". Such a reading is feasible, however, only when

"a" is read as a letter of the alphabet and not when it is read as, or replaced by, such a phrase as "the North Pole".

17.17. In the usual treatment of abstracts, the notation

$$\hat{a}(\cdots a \cdots)$$

is commonly employed and corresponds to the notation

$$(a \setminus (\cdots a \cdots))$$

of the present treatment. Also in the usual treatment, special symbols called "variables of the object language" are used as the initial expressions of the abstracts. The present treatment does not require these variables.[9] Initial expressions of abstracts will usually be referred to by using letters chosen from the end of the alphabet, so that we will write "$(x \setminus (\cdots x \cdots))$" or "$(y \setminus (\cdots y \cdots))$" where previously we might have written "$(a \setminus (\cdots a \cdots))$" or "$(b \setminus (\cdots b \cdots))$".

17.18. Corresponding to every attribute F there is another attribute $(-F)$, called the **complement** of the attribute F, and such that just those things which do not have F do have $(-F)$. The attribute $(-F)$ is, in fact, simply the attribute of not having the attribute F. Thus if F is the attribute of being a resident of New Haven, then $(-F)$ is the attribute of not being a resident of New Haven. We can regard "$(-F)$" as an abbreviation for "$(x \setminus \sim[x \; \epsilon \; F])$". Thus $(-F)$ is the attribute that the proposition $\sim[x \; \epsilon \; F]$ assigns to x. If we are speaking in terms of classes instead of attributes, then we can say that every class F has a complement $(-F)$, and that the members of $(-F)$ are exactly those things which are not members of F. Thus if F is the class of residents of New Haven, then $(-F)$ is the class of non-residents of New Haven.

17.19.

1	$a \; \epsilon \; (-F)$		hyp
2	$a \; \epsilon \; (x \setminus \sim[x \; \epsilon \; F])$		1, rep, def
3	$\sim[a \; \epsilon \; F]$		2, att elim (17.5)

[9] We could, however, mean by a "variable" any expression being used as an initial expression. Thus we could say that an expression is a "variable" in some formal context if it is being used as an initial expression in that context. Similarly in 21.10 the expression "x" in "$(x)(\cdots x \cdots)$" can be called a "variable", and the same applies to the expression "x" in "$(\exists x)\phi x$" in 22.7. Variables even in this sense can be dispensed with. This is done by using the methods set forth in Appendix A.

17.20. 1 | $\sim[a \,\epsilon\, F]$ hyp
2 | $a \,\epsilon\, (x \setminus \sim[x \,\epsilon\, F])$ 1, att int (17.4)
3 | $a \,\epsilon\, (-F)$ 2, rep, def

17.21. From 17.19 and 17.20 we can clearly obtain,

$$[a \,\epsilon\, (-F)] \equiv \sim[a \,\epsilon\, F].$$

This same result can also be obtained by choosing "$(x \setminus (\cdots x \cdots))$" in 17.7 as "$(x \setminus \sim[x \,\epsilon\, F])$".

17.22. Corresponding to every pair of attributes F and G, there is an attribute called the **intersection** or **logical product** of F with G. This attribute, $[F \cap G]$, is the attribute that just those things have which have *both* of the attributes F and G. Thus if F is the attribute of being a resident of New Haven, and if G is the attribute of being a student at Yale, then $[F \cap G]$ is the attribute of being a New Haven resident and Yale student. The notation "$[F \cap G]$" can be treated as an abbreviation for the abstract "$(x \setminus [[x \,\epsilon\, F] \,\&\, [x \,\epsilon\, G]])$". (Here "$x$" is the name of anything not mentioned by F or G.) Thus $[F \cap G]$ is the attribute assigned to x by the proposition $[[x \,\epsilon\, F] \,\&\, [x \,\epsilon\, G]]$. If we are speaking in terms of classes, we can say that for any two classes F and G there is a class $[F \cap G]$ known as the intersection of F with G and having as members just those things which belong to both F and G. In other words, for something to be a member of $[F \cap G]$ it must be a member of both F and G.

17.23. 1 | $a \,\epsilon\, [F \cap G]$ hyp
2 | $a \,\epsilon\, (x \setminus [[x \,\epsilon\, F] \,\&\, [x \,\epsilon\, G]])$ 1, rep, def
3 | $[a \,\epsilon\, F] \,\&\, [a \,\epsilon\, G]$ 2, att elim

17.24. 1 | $[a \,\epsilon\, F] \,\&\, [a \,\epsilon\, G]$ hyp
2 | $a \,\epsilon\, (x \setminus [[x \,\epsilon\, F] \,\&\, [x \,\epsilon\, G]])$ 1, att int
3 | $a \,\epsilon\, [F \cap G]$ 2, rep, def

17.25. From 17.23 and 17.24 we can clearly obtain,

$$[a \,\epsilon\, [F \cap G]] \equiv [[a \,\epsilon\, F] \,\&\, [a \,\epsilon\, G]].$$

This can also be obtained as a special case of 17.7.

17.26. Corresponding to every pair of attributes F and G, there is not only an intersection $[F \cap G]$ but there is also a **join** or **logical**

sum $[F \cup G]$. This latter attribute, $[F \cup G]$, is the attribute that just those things have that have *at least one* of the attributes F and G. If we suppose, as before, that F is the attribute of being a New Haven resident and that G is the attribute of being a Yale student, then $[F \cup G]$ is the attribute of being a New Haven resident or Yale student. It is an attribute that all New Haven residents have and that all Yale students have and that nothing else has. Whatever has the attribute $[F \cap G]$ also has the attribute $[F \cup G]$, but the converse of this does not hold in general. In particular, some people have the attribute of being New Haven residents or Yale students but do not have the attribute of being both New Haven residents and Yale students. The notation "$[F \cup G]$" can be treated as an abbreviation for the abstract "$(x \setminus [[x \in F] \vee [x \in G]])$". Thus $[F \cup G]$ is the attribute assigned to x by the proposition $[[x \in F] \vee [x \in G]]$. If we are speaking in terms of classes, we can say that for any two classes F and G there is a class $[F \cup G]$, known as the join of F with G, and having as members just those things which belong to at least one of the classes F and G. In other words, for something to be a member of $[F \cup G]$ it must be a member of at least one of the classes F and G.

17.27.
1	$a \in [F \cup G]$	hyp
2	$a \in (x \setminus [[x \in F] \vee [x \in G]])$	1, rep, def
3	$[a \in F] \vee [a \in G]$	2, att elim

17.28.
1	$[a \in F] \vee [a \in G]$	hyp
2	$a \in (x \setminus [[x \in F] \vee [x \in G]])$	1, att int
3	$a \in [F \cup G]$	2, rep, def

17.29. From 17.27 and 17.28 we can clearly obtain,

$$[a \in [F \cup G]] \equiv [[a \in F] \vee [a \in G]].$$

This can also be obtained as a special case of 17.7.

17.30. Some attributes are **universal,** that is, they apply to all things. For example, the attribute of being self-identical is universal. It is denoted by the abstract "$(x \setminus [x = x])$". The attribute of self-identity is itself self-identical. Thus the attribute of self-identity has the attribute of self-identity. In other words, the attribute of self-identity has itself as an attribute. A universal attribute will always have itself as an attribute. If we are speaking in terms of classes, we can say that some classes are universal, that is, have all things as members. If we read "$(x \setminus [x = x])$" as denoting a class, it denotes the class of self-identical things. This is a universal class, since there is nothing that is not self-identical. Owing to the fact that the class of all self-identical things is itself self-identical, it has itself as one of its members. Thus we see that some attributes apply to themselves, and that in terms of classes this means that some classes have themselves as members. Although it is true that every universal attribute applies to itself (and that every universal class has itself as a member), it is not true that every attribute that applies to itself is a universal attribute (nor that every class that has itself as a member is universal). More will be said later about universality.

17.31. 1 | $a = a$ id int

2 | $a \in (x \setminus [x = x])$ 1, att int

17.32. 1 | $(x \setminus [x = x]) = (x \setminus [x = x])$ id int

2 | $(x \setminus [x = x]) \in (x \setminus [x = x])$ 1, att int

17.33. Some attributes are **empty,** that is, they do not apply to anything. An example of such an attribute is the attribute of not being self-identical. This attribute is denoted by the abstract "$(x \setminus \sim[x = x])$". Speaking in terms of classes, we can also say that some classes are empty, that is, have no members, and we can regard the abstract "$(x \setminus \sim[x = x])$" as denoting the class of things which are not self-identical, an empty class.

17.34. Just as the rules of attribute introduction and elimination (17.4 and 17.5) enable us to derive $[a \in (x \setminus (\cdots x \cdots))]$ and $(\cdots a \cdots)$ from each other, so also we need rules that will enable us to derive $\sim[a \in (x \setminus (\cdots x \cdots))]$ and $\sim(\cdots a \cdots)$ from each other. These rules are stated in 17.35 and 17.36. We assume that $(\cdots x \cdots)$, $(\cdots a \cdots)$, x, and a are as described in 17.6.

17.35. Rule of negative attribute introduction ("neg att int"). First form: The proposition $\sim[a \in (x \setminus (\cdots x \cdots))]$ is a direct consequence of the proposition $\sim(\cdots a \cdots)$. Second form: The proposition $\sim((x \setminus (\cdots x \cdots))a)$ is a direct consequence of the proposition $\sim(\cdots a \cdots)$. (The first form can be regarded as a derived rule, derived from the second form and the rule of negative $\in$-introduction, 16.5.)

17.36. Rule of negative attribute elimination ("neg att elim"). First form: The proposition $\sim(\cdots a \cdots)$ is a direct consequence of the proposition $\sim[a \; \epsilon \; (x \setminus (\cdots x \cdots))]$. Second form: The proposition $\sim(\cdots a \cdots)$ is a direct consequence of the proposition $\sim((x \setminus (\cdots x \cdots))a)$. (The first form can be regarded as a derived rule, derived from the second form and the rule of negative ϵ-elimination, 16.5.)

17.37. We can of course easily prove,

$$\sim[a \; \epsilon \; (x \setminus (\cdots x \cdots))] \equiv \; \sim(\cdots a \cdots),$$

and also the following coimplications,

$$\sim[a \; \epsilon \; (-F)] \equiv \; \sim\sim[a \; \epsilon \; F],$$
$$\sim[a \; \epsilon \; [F \cap G]] \equiv \; \sim[[a \; \epsilon \; F] \; \& \; [a \; \epsilon \; G]],$$
$$\sim[a \; \epsilon \; [F \cup G]] \equiv \; \sim[[a \; \epsilon \; F] \; \mathsf{v} \; [a \; \epsilon \; G]].$$

17.38.

1	$a = a$	id int
2	$\sim\sim[a = a]$	1, neg$_2$ int
3	$\sim[a \; \epsilon \; (x \setminus \sim[x = x])]$	2, neg att int

17.39. Notice that in using 17.35 to obtain step 3 from step 2 in 17.38 we choose $(\cdots a \cdots)$ of 17.35 as $\sim[a = a]$, so $\sim(\cdots a \cdots)$ is $\sim\sim[a = a]$, while $(x \setminus (\cdots x \cdots))$ is $(x \setminus \sim[x = x])$.

17.40.

1	$(x \setminus \sim[x = x]) = (x \setminus \sim[x = x])$	id int
2	$\sim\sim[(x \setminus \sim[x = x]) = (x \setminus \sim[x = x])]$	1, neg$_2$ int
3	$\sim[(x \setminus \sim[x = x]) \; \epsilon \; (x \setminus \sim[x = x])]$	2, neg att int

17.41. Observe that 17.32 shows that $(x \setminus [x = x])$ is an attribute of itself, while 17.40 shows that $(x \setminus \sim[x = x])$ is not an attribute of itself.

17.42. Corresponding to each thing a there is the attribute $(x \setminus [x = a])$, the attribute of being identical with a. We will let "$\{a\}$" be an abbreviation for "$(x \setminus [x = a])$". Thus $\{a\}$ is an attribute that is had by a and by nothing else. We may call it the **unit attribute** of a. Viewed as a class, $\{a\}$ is a class that has a as its only member, and it may be called the **unit class** of a. It is the class of things identical with a.

17.43. Clearly, we can prove $[a \; \epsilon \; \{a\}]$ and also $[[a = b] \supset [\{a\} = \{b\}]]$.

17.44. We will let "$\{ab\}$" be an abbreviation for "$[\{a\} \cup \{b\}]$", and we will let "$\{abc\}$" be an abbreviation for "$[\{a\} \cup \{b\} \cup \{c\}]$", and we will let "$\{abcd\}$" be an abbreviation for "$[\{a\} \cup \{b\} \cup \{c\} \cup \{d\}]$", and so on. Thus $\{ab\}$ is a class that has a and b as members and nothing else, while $\{abc\}$ is a class that has a, b, and c as its only members. If a is identical with b, then the class $\{ab\}$ has exactly the same member as $\{a\}$, and the class $\{abc\}$ then has exactly the same members as $\{ac\}$.

17.45. We will call $\{ab\}$ the **unordered couple** of a with b, and we will call $\{abc\}$ the **unordered triple** of a with b and c, and we will call $\{abcd\}$ the **unordered quadruple** of a with b, c, and d. The unordered couple $\{ab\}$ is "unordered" only in the sense that $\{ab\}$ and $\{ba\}$ have exactly the same members, and not in the sense of being identical, since in this system of logic we do not assume that $\{ab\}$ and $\{ba\}$ are identical with each other (unless, of course, a is identical with b). Similar remarks apply to unordered triples, quadruples, quintuples, and so on.

17.46. Each proposition of the following pairs of propositions can easily be derived from the other:

$a \; \epsilon \; \{b\}$	$a = b$
$a \; \epsilon \; \{bc\}$	$[a = b] \vee [a = c]$
$a \; \epsilon \; \{bcd\}$	$[a = b] \vee [a = c] \vee [a = d]$
$a \; \epsilon \; \{bcde\}$	$[a = b] \vee [a = c] \vee [a = d] \vee [a = e]$

and so on.

17.47. It will sometimes be convenient to use "U" as an abbreviation for "$(x \setminus [x = x])$". Thus U is the class of self-identical things. From 17.31 we see that U is a universal class, since $[a \; \epsilon \; \mathsf{U}]$ is provable for each thing a. In particular, $[\mathsf{U} \epsilon \mathsf{U}]$ is provable, as in 17.32. Thus everything is a member of U, and in particular U itself.

17.48. By a proof somewhat like 17.38 we can prove $\sim[a \; \epsilon \; (-\mathsf{U})]$ for each thing a. In particular, $\sim[(-\mathsf{U}) \; \epsilon \; (-\mathsf{U})]$ is provable. Thus there is nothing that is a member of $(-\mathsf{U})$. In particular, $(-\mathsf{U})$ itself is not a member of $(-\mathsf{U})$. We call $(-\mathsf{U})$ an empty class or empty attribute.

EXERCISES

1. Interpret as an attribute and as a class each of the following:

    a. (William the Conqueror \ [William the Conqueror conquered England]).

    b. (Caesar \ [Caesar conquered England]).

    c. (England \ [William the Conqueror conquered England]).

    d. (Hitler \ [Hitler hated Hitler]).

    e. $(2 \setminus [2 \times 4 = 8])$.

    f. $(3 \setminus [3 \times 4 = 8])$.

    g. $(2 \setminus [8 < 2])$.

    h. $(a \setminus [[a = b]\ \&\ \sim[a = c]])$.

    i. $(a \setminus [[a \in F]\ \&\ [a \in G]])$.

2. Write an abstract that denotes each of the following attributes or classes, using as far as possible logical or mathematical symbols:

    a. The attribute of being an ambassador to France.

    b. The class of ambassadors to France.

    c. The attribute being a number having a square equal to 3.

    d. The class of fractions having squares less than 2.

    e. The class of things identical with the moon.

    f. The attribute of having both of the attributes F and G.

    g. The attribute of not having the attribute F.

    h. The class of things belonging to class F or to class G.

    i. The class of things not belonging to class F.

3. Prove $[[a \in F] \supset [[a \in G] \supset [a \in [F \cap G]]]]$.

4. Prove $[[a \in (-(-F))] \equiv [a \in F]]$.

5. Prove $[[a \in [(-F) \cup (-G)]] \equiv [a \in (-[F \cap G])]]$.

6. Prove $[[[b \in [G \cup H]] \supset [b \in F]] \supset [b \in (x \setminus [[x \in G] \supset [x \in F]])]]$.

18. Curry's Paradox and Russell's Paradox

18.1. Prior to adding to it the various rules for attributes given in 17.4, 17.5, 17.34, 17.35, the present system was consistent as so far formulated. After the addition to it of these rules, a restriction is required in order to be certain that there is no inconsistency in the system. (See Section 20.) For the benefit of those readers who wish a simpler kind of restriction than the rather complicated one stated later on in 18.6, the following requirement can at once be said to be sufficient to guarantee consistency; and it will be referred to as

the **simple restriction** (in contrast to the "special restriction" of 18.6):
No item of a main proof or of a subordinate proof can have an elimination rule as a reason if some preceding item of that same proof has
an introduction rule as a reason. Negation elimination is excepted
from this stipulation. Reiteration counts as introduction or elimination depending on whether the reiterated item was originally by an
introduction or elimination rule. It is clear that the last step of 18.4
violates the simple restriction. Steps 1–7 do not violate the simple
restriction, but they will be shown to violate the special restriction.
Without a restriction like one of these a contradiction becomes derivable. (In practice we will use the special restriction of 18.6 rather
than the simple restriction. It is likely, however, that proofs that
do not conform to the simple restriction can be dispensed with.)

18.2. The contradiction is obtained as shown in 18.4. We call 18.4
Curry's paradox, since the method of it is due to H. B. Curry.[10] It
provides a general procedure for proving any proposition p. In
particular, we could prove p by this method and then prove $\sim p$ by
the same method. Or we could choose p to be a proposition of the
form [q & $\sim q$], so that the propositions q and $\sim q$ would then follow
from p by conjunction elimination. In proving both p and $\sim p$ (or
both q and $\sim q$), we show the system to be inconsistent if some restriction is not imposed.

18.3. We will let "Y" in 18.4 be an abbreviation for the abstract
"$(x \setminus [[x \, \epsilon \, x] \supset p])$", where p is an arbitrarily chosen proposition
which is to be proved. Thus Y is the attribute that the proposition
$[[x \, \epsilon \, x] \supset p]$ assigns to x, so Y is the attribute that x has, provided
the following proposition is true: "If x has itself as an attribute, then
p is true". It must not be supposed meaningless or impossible for
something to have itself as an attribute. It was shown in 17.32 that
the attribute of self-identity has itself as an attribute.

18.4. Curry's paradox.

1	$Y \, \epsilon \, Y$	hyp
2	$Y \, \epsilon \, (x \setminus [[x \, \epsilon \, x] \supset p])$	1, rep, def (18.3)
3	$[Y \, \epsilon \, Y] \supset p$	2, att elim
4	p	1, 3, m p

[10] H. B. Curry, "The Inconsistency of Certain Formal Logics", *Journal of
Symbolic Logic*, vol. 7 (1942), pp. 115–17.

5	$[Y \in Y] \supset p$	1–4, imp int
6	$Y \in (x \setminus [[x \in x] \supset p])$	5, att int
7	$Y \in Y$	6, rep, def (18.3)
8	p	5, 7, m p

18.5. Before stating the special restriction, it is necessary to define the notion of **resultant**. If a proposition occurs anywhere within a proof as an item of that proof or of a proof subordinate to it, and subsequently elsewhere as a different item of that proof or of a proof subordinate to it, then the second of these two items is a resultant of the first, and vice versa. If a certain item is asserted to be a direct consequence of one or more preceding items by any one of the rules of direct consequence,[11] then such an item is a resultant of each of those preceding items. (One or more of those preceding items might be subordinate proofs.) A subordinate proof will be said to be a resultant of each of its own items and also of each item external to it which is reiterated into it. If one item is a resultant of another item, and if that other item is a resultant of a third item, then the first item is a resultant of the third item. Similarly for four items, five items, and so on for any finite number of items. If one step follows from another by "repetition" (6.22), we regard it as a resultant of that other. Thus in 18.4 the second step is a resultant of the first step, the third step is a resultant of the second step, and the fourth step is a resultant of the first and third steps. Hence the fourth step is a resultant of all the preceding steps. The fifth step is a resultant of the whole preceding subordinate proof, since it is a direct consequence of the subordinate proof by implication introduction. Since the subordinate proof is a resultant of each of its items, and since the fifth step is a resultant of the subordinate proof, it is seen that the fifth step is a resultant of each of the four steps of the subordinate proof. The sixth step is a resultant of the fifth step, and the seventh step of the sixth step. Finally, the eighth step is a resultant of the fifth and seventh steps. Thus each step is a resultant of all the preceding steps, and each of the steps 5 through 8 is a resultant of the subordinate proof. In modal logic the concept of resultant must be further extended in such a way that q is a resultant of r if the identification of $\Diamond p$ and $\Box p$ with p for every p would make q a resultant of r.

---

[11] Actually we can omit the rule of negation elimination in this connection.

18.6. Special restriction. The required restriction that invalidates 18.4 and guarantees the consistency of the system is this: A propositional item p cannot appear in a proof in such a way as to be a resultant of a subordinate proof that (i) has p as an hypothesis and (ii) has some proposition other than p as an item. This restriction is violated by step **7** of 18.4, since the propositional item $[Y \epsilon Y]$ at step 7 is a resultant of the subordinate proof, and since the subordinate proof has $[Y \epsilon Y]$ as hypothesis and has some proposition other than $[Y \epsilon Y]$ as one of its items. Hence we do not regard 18.4 as being a correct proof. In Section 20 we will show that the above restriction guarantees that the system, as so far developed, contains no contradiction. The stipulation that the subordinate proof "has some proposition other than p as an item" makes it possible to treat as valid those proofs that can be expressed by the short-cut method described in 8.21. Such proofs, when written out in full, would otherwise violate the above restriction, since p would be a resultant of a subordinate proof which has no proposition other than p for any of its items. In virtue of this stipulation, we can allow p to be a resultant of such a subordinate proof.

18.7. The notion of resultant is to be understood as relative to the actual assignment of "reasons" to steps in a proof, since in some cases there may be alternative ways of assigning reasons to steps. A proof is regarded as conforming to the restriction stated in 18.6 if the assignment of reasons can be carried out in such a way that no propositional item p is thereby a resultant of a subordinate proof having p as a hypothesis and some other proposition as another item.

18.8. In order to formulate a result known as **Russell's paradox,** let "Z" serve temporarily as an abbreviation for "$(x \setminus \sim[x \epsilon x])$". This makes Z the attribute of not being a self-applicative attribute, where by a "self-applicative attribute" we mean an attribute that applies to itself. Thus Z is the attribute of being a non-self-applicative attribute. The attribute $(x \setminus \sim[x = x])$, for example, has the attribute Z, since in 17.40 we showed that $(x \setminus \sim[x = x])$ does not apply to itself. Now in Russell's paradox we ask the question, Does the attribute Z have the attribute Z? We know that for every attribute F, it is the case that F has the attribute Z if and only if F does not have F itself as an attribute, because Z is the attribute of being non-self-applicative. Hence, in particular, choosing F as Z

itself, we have the result that Z has the attribute Z if and only if Z does not have the attribute Z. In other words, the propositions $[Z \epsilon Z]$ and $\sim[Z \epsilon Z]$ imply each other. This is established formally in 18.7 below. This is not in itself a contradiction. If, however, we assume that $[Z \epsilon Z]$ satisfies the principle of excluded middle, then we can obtain the contradictory result $[[Z \epsilon Z] \& \sim[Z \epsilon Z]]$. In 18.8 we show that this contradiction follows from the hypothesis that $[Z \epsilon Z]$ satisfies excluded middle. Of course, if all propositions were supposed to satisfy excluded middle, then $[Z \epsilon Z]$ would also, and we would have the contradiction $[[Z \epsilon Z] \& \sim[Z \epsilon Z]]$ as a theorem of our system. The system then would really contain Russell's paradox. As it is, we avoid Russell's paradox by failing to assume that every proposition satisfies excluded middle. Moreover, the consistency proof given in Section 20 makes it clear that we avoid not only Russell's paradox and Curry's paradox but all contradictory results.

18.9.

1	$Z \epsilon Z$	hyp
2	$Z \epsilon (x \setminus \sim[x \epsilon x])$	1, rep, def (18.8)
3	$\sim[Z \epsilon Z]$	2, att elim
4	$\sim[Z \epsilon Z]$	hyp
5	$Z \epsilon (x \setminus \sim[x \epsilon x])$	4, att int
6	$Z \epsilon Z$	5, rep, def (18.8)
7	$[Z \epsilon Z] \equiv \sim[Z \epsilon Z]$	1–3, 4–6, coimp int

18.10.

1	$[Z \epsilon Z] \vee \sim[Z \epsilon Z]$	hyp
2	$Z \epsilon Z$	hyp
3	$[Z \epsilon Z] \equiv \sim[Z \epsilon Z]$	18.9
4	$\sim[Z \epsilon Z]$	2, 3, m p c
5	$[Z \epsilon Z] \& \sim[Z \epsilon Z]$	2, 4, conj int
6	$\sim[Z \epsilon Z]$	hyp
7	$[Z \epsilon Z] \equiv \sim[Z \epsilon Z]$	18.9
8	$Z \epsilon Z$	6, 7, m p c
9	$[Z \epsilon Z] \& \sim[Z \epsilon Z]$	6, 8, conj int
10	$[Z \epsilon Z] \& \sim[Z \epsilon Z]$	1, 2–5, 6–9, dis elim

18.11. We may also speak of Z as a class. It can be thought of as the class of those things or classes that are not members of themselves. Thus a class F is a member of Z if and only if F is not a member of F itself. In particular, Z is a member of Z if and only if Z is not a member of Z, choosing F as being Z. As Russell originally stated this paradox, he treated Z as a class. This way of speaking can of course easily be applied to 18.9 and 18.10.

18.12. The way devised by Russell himself for avoiding the Russell paradox was to assume that all propositions satisfy the principle of excluded middle, but to narrow the class of propositions in such a way that he would assert that there is no such proposition as $[Z \; \epsilon \; Z]$ and that the expression "$[Z \; \epsilon \; Z]$" is meaningless. More particularly, he invented a **theory of types** according to which each attribute is of "higher type" than the things to which it applies (and each class is of higher type than its members). Expressions which appear to be assertions to the effect that an attribute applies to itself, or that a class is a member of itself, are treated by Russell as meaningless, since no type, in his sense, can be assigned to such an attribute or such a class. There are two forms of the theory of types. The "branched" or "ramified" form is more restrictive and is known to be consistent, but it must be supplemented by the questionable "axiom of reducibility" to make possible a derivation of foundations for mathematics. The "simple" form is less restrictive but is not known to guarantee consistency. Both forms seem to rule out as "meaningless" all statements that refer to *all* types, though it seems impossible to formulate the theory of types (in either form) in any genuine way without making statements about all types. The theory of types rejects as meaningless all statements involving the application of attributes to themselves, while the present treatment allows the self-application of attributes. The writer believes that many philosophically important arguments make use of the self-application of attributes, and that the theory of types wrongly treats such arguments as meaningless.[12] The attribute of self-identity is an example of a self-applicative attribute. Another example is the attribute of being an object of thought. The present treatment also has the advantages of guaranteeing consistency, and of providing consistent foundations for a major part of mathematics.

[12] For further discussion of this point, see Appendix C.

19. An Alternative Treatment of Identity

19.1. We will now present an alternative method for dealing with identity. This method will provide all the results already obtained in Section 14, but it will also provide at least one further result. This further result is that it will now be possible to prove, for each a and b, one of the two propositions $[a = b]$ and $\sim[a = b]$. By incorporating this method into the present system, the proof of the consistency of the system, as given in Section 20, becomes simpler than it would otherwise be.

19.2. Observe first that it is possible to tell by inspection whether or not two abstracts denote the same attribute. For example, the abstract "(Peary \ [Peary discovered the North Pole])" and the abstract "(Napoleon \ [Napoleon discovered the North Pole])" clearly denote the same attribute. Suppose now that two abstracts, like the two above, are such that neither of them contains another abstract within itself. The necessary and sufficient condition for two such abstracts to denote the same attribute is that the two abstracts should be exactly the same, except that the initial expression of the first abstract occurs in the first abstract in exactly those places in which the initial expression of the second abstract occurs in the second abstract. In other words, the two abstracts differ at most with respect to their initial expressions, and the initial expression of each occurs in the same way and in the same places as the initial expression of the other. If the two abstracts contain other abstracts as parts, similar though more complicated conditions can be formulated for deciding whether or not they denote the same attribute.

19.3. In order to use the alternative method for dealing with identity, it is necessary to assume that the expressions used in our system are so chosen that we never have two different non-abbreviational expressions denoting the same thing. The only case so far where, on the contrary, two non-abbreviational expressions are regarded as denoting the same thing is the case where several abstracts denote the same attribute, as discussed in 19.2. This case can be eliminated by arbitrarily choosing some one of the abstracts to serve as *the* abstract denoting the attribute in question.[13] The rejected abstracts

---

[13] This case does not arise at all if we employ the theory of abstracts presented in Appendix A. By a "non-abbreviational expression" is meant any expression which is not being used as an abbreviation for some other expression.

can then be treated as mere abbreviations for the one that is retained. We then have arranged matters in such a way that no two non-abbreviational expressions, in this system, denote the same thing. (It is, incidentally, desirable to choose the retained abstracts in such a way that no two of them have the same initial expressions. This avoids certain complications which arise when one abstract is part of another.) If abstracts are thought of as denoting classes rather than attributes, then it can be said that we regard two classes as different if they are denoted by different abstracts, regardless of whether or not they have the same members. This is because we are not for present purposes making any sharp distinction between attributes and classes, and because two attributes can be regarded as different, even though they apply to the same things.

19.4. The following two rules may now be asserted. They are the only rules for identity required in the alternative treatment of identity. The first of them is the same as the already familiar rule of identity introduction (14.2).

19.5. Rule of identity introduction ("id int"). The proposition $[a = a]$ is an axiom and hence can appear as a step in any proof.

19.6. Rule of negative identity introduction ("neg id int"). If the expressions "a" and "b", written in unabbreviated form, are different from each other, then the proposition $\sim[a = b]$ is an axiom and hence can appear as a step in any proof. (Here it is assumed that the expressions referred to are such as are used in the system to denote various things. If desired, a systematic definition of this class of expressions could be given. It would be necessary to include an infinity of symbols as names of various empirical entities such as persons, places, and physical objects, as well as names of logical relations and attributes, and names of empirical relations and attributes.)

19.7. We now see that for any a and b at least one of the two propositions, $[a = b]$ and $\sim[a = b]$, is not only provable but is an axiom. If "a" and "b" are the same expression, then $[a = b]$ is an axiom because $[a = a]$ is an axiom by identity introduction. If "a" and "b" are different expressions, then $\sim[a = b]$ is an axiom by negative identity introduction. In either case we can obtain $[[a = b] \lor \sim[a = b]]$ by disjunction introduction (from $[a = b]$ or from $\sim[a = b]$, as the case may be). Hence, for all things a and b, we have $[[a = b] \lor$

$\sim[a = b]]$ as a theorem of the system. This shows that the effect of the rule of excluded middle for identity (14.4) is obtainable within this alternative treatment of identity.

19.8. The effect of the rule of identity elimination (14.3) is also obtainable within this alternative treatment of identity. If we wish to prove $(\cdots b \cdots)$ under the hypotheses $[a = b]$ and $(\cdots a \cdots)$, we have two cases to consider. The first case is that in which "a" and "b" are the same expression. This case is trivial, since "$(\cdots a \cdots)$" and "$(\cdots b \cdots)$" are here the same expression, so $(\cdots b \cdots)$ is the same proposition as $(\cdots a \cdots)$ and follows from it by mere repetition. Thus we have in this case:

$$
\begin{array}{r|ll}
1 & a = b & \text{hyp} \\
2 & (\cdots a \cdots) & \text{hyp} \\
3 & (\cdots b \cdots) & \text{2, rep}
\end{array}
$$

The second case is that in which "a" and "b" are different expressions. In this case we derive $(\cdots b \cdots)$ from $[a = b]$ and $(\cdots a \cdots)$ by the following method:

$$
\begin{array}{r|ll}
1 & a = b & \text{hyp} \\
2 & (\cdots a \cdots) & \text{hyp} \\
3 & \sim[a = b] & \text{neg id int} \\
4 & (\cdots b \cdots) & \text{1, 3, neg elim}
\end{array}
$$

The same procedure can be used in each case if the hypothesis $[b = a]$ takes the place of the hypothesis $[a = b]$, as in the second form of the rule of identity elimination. Thus we see that identity elimination in both its forms is a derived rule within this alternative treatment of identity. Hence all the previous theorems concerning identity are also derivable, and results established in Section 14 can continue to be referred to and used in subsequent proofs.

19.9. We can show also that the rule of couple introduction (15.6) and the rule of couple elimination (15.9) are derivable in the present treatment of identity. It was shown in 15.7 that the rule of couple introduction is derivable from the theory of identity of Section 14, and so it is clearly also derivable in the alternative treatment. In order to derive the first form of the rule of couple elimination, we have two cases to consider. In the first case "*a*" and "*c*" are the same expression, and we proceed as follows:

$$
\begin{array}{ll}
1 \big| \quad (ab) = (cd) & \text{hyp} \\
2 \big|^{-} \; a = c & \text{id int}
\end{array}
$$

In the second case, "*a*" and "*c*" are different expressions, so "(*ab*)" and "(*cd*)" are also different expressions. We proceed as follows:

$$
\begin{array}{ll}
1 \big| \quad (ab) = (cd) & \text{hyp} \\
2 \big|^{-} \; {\sim}[(ab) = (cd)] & \text{neg id int} \\
3 \big| \quad a = c & \text{1, 2, neg elim}
\end{array}
$$

The second form of the rule of couple elimination is derived in a similar way.

20. The Consistency of the System

[This section is of a more advanced nature than most of the other sections. It can be omitted if the book is being used as a textbook or if the reader does not feel prepared to study some of the more difficult phases of symbolic logic.]

20.1. We now turn to the task of showing that the system as so far developed is free from contradiction. We begin by summarizing the underived introduction and elimination rules which must be assumed in formulating the system. We use the treatment of identity given in Section 19. Notice also that we state a second form of implication introduction in R6 under 20.2. According to this second form, the proposition $[p \supset q]$ is a direct consequence of q. This could really be regarded as the derived rule called the principle of added condition (5.28), but the demonstration of consistency can be presented more easily if this rule is treated as one of the fundamental underived rules of the system. Except where otherwise noted, we will assume the special restriction stated in 18.6 rather than the simple restriction stated in 18.1. If the simple restriction is used, then every categorical proof can be shown to be "normal" in the sense of 20.6, and consistency can be established as in 20.45 and 20.46.

20.2. Summary of underived introduction and elimination rules:

R1. Identity introduction (19.5). If "*a*" and "*b*" are the same expression, then $[a = b]$ is an axiom. (This way of stating the rule is slightly different from that given previously.)

R2. Negative identity introduction (19.6). If "a" and "b" are different expressions when written in unabbreviated form, then $\sim[a = b]$ is an axiom.

R3. Negation elimination (10.4). q is a d.c. (direct consequence) of p and $\sim p$.

R4. Double negation introduction (10.5). $\sim\sim p$ is a d.c. of p.

R5. Double negation elimination (10.6). p is a d.c. of $\sim\sim p$.

R6. Implication introduction (5.6, 20.1). $[p \supset q]$ is a d.c. of a subproof (subordinate proof) having hypothesis p and conclusion q. Also, $[p \supset q]$ is a d.c. of q.

R7. Implication elimination or modus ponens (3.6). q is a d.c. of p and $[p \supset q]$.

R8. Conjunction introduction (6.6). $[p \,\&\, q]$ is a d.c. of p and q.

R9. Conjunction elimination (6.3). p is a d.c. of $[p \,\&\, q]$, and q also is a d.c. of $[p \,\&\, q]$.

R10. Negative conjunction introduction (10.25). $\sim[p \,\&\, q]$ is a d.c. of $[\sim p \,\mathsf{v}\, \sim q]$.

R11. Negative conjunction elimination (10.26). $[\sim p \,\mathsf{v}\, \sim q]$ is a d.c. of $\sim[p \,\&\, q]$.

R12. Disjunction introduction (8.4). $[p \,\mathsf{v}\, q]$ is a d.c. of p, and it is also a d.c. of q.

R13. Disjunction elimination (8.7). r is a d.c. of $[p \,\mathsf{v}\, q]$ and two subproofs, one having hypothesis p and conclusion r, and the other having hypothesis q and conclusion r.

R14. Negative disjunction introduction (10.27). $\sim[p \,\mathsf{v}\, q]$ is a d.c. of $[\sim p \,\&\, \sim q]$.

R15. Negative disjunction elimination (10.28). $[\sim p \,\&\, \sim q]$ is a d.c. of $\sim[p \,\mathsf{v}\, q]$.

R16. ϵ-introduction (16.5). $[a \,\epsilon\, F]$ is a d.c. of (Fa).

R17. ϵ-elimination (16.5). (Fa) is a d.c. of $[a \,\epsilon\, F]$.

R18. Negative ϵ-introduction (16.5). $\sim[a \,\epsilon\, F]$ is a d.c. of $\sim(Fa)$.

R19. Negative ϵ-elimination (16.5). $\sim(Fa)$ is a d.c. of $\sim[a \,\epsilon\, F]$.

R20. Attribute introduction (17.4). $((x \setminus (\cdots x \cdots))a)$ is a d.c. of $(\cdots a \cdots)$.

R21. Attribute elimination (17.5). $(\cdots a \cdots)$ is a d.c. of $((x \setminus (\cdots x \cdots))a)$.

R22. Negative attribute introduction (17.35). $\sim((x \setminus (\cdots x \cdots))a)$ is a d.c. of $\sim(\cdots a \cdots)$.

R23. Negative attribute elimination (17.36). $\sim(\cdots a \cdots)$ is a d.c. of $\sim((x \setminus (\cdots x \cdots))a)$.

R24. Necessity introduction (11.3). $\square p$ is a d.c. of a categorical strict subproof having p as conclusion.

R25. Necessity elimination (11.2). p is a d.c. of $\square p$.

R26. Negative necessity introduction (12.5). $\sim\square p$ is a d.c. of $\Diamond \sim p$.

R27. Negative necessity elimination (12.6). $\Diamond \sim p$ is a d.c. of $\sim\square p$.

R28. Possibility introduction (12.2). $\Diamond p$ is a d.c. of p.

R29. Possibility elimination (12.3). $\Diamond q$ is a d.c. of $\Diamond p$ and a strict subproof having hypothesis p and conclusion q.

R30. Negative possibility introduction (12.7). $\sim\Diamond p$ is a d.c. of $\square \sim p$.

R31. Negative possibility elimination (12.8). $\square \sim p$ is a d.c. of $\sim\Diamond p$.

20.3. We will assume that all proofs are written out in full and that the only introduction and elimination rules used are those listed in 20.2. The rules of identity elimination and couple elimination are regarded as derived rules as in Section 19, and so are not included among the rules of 20.2.

20.4. In order to show that the system is consistent, it will suffice to show that the system without the modal rules R24–R31 is consistent. This is because if there were an inconsistency in the total system, then this inconsistency could be reduplicated in the narrower system (lacking R24–R31) by identifying $\square p$ and $\Diamond p$ each with p itself. Accordingly we disregard R24–R31 in the rest of this section.

20.5. By the **length** of a proof we mean the number of propositional items belonging to it or to proofs subordinate to it. A proposition occurring more than once as an item is counted as many times as it occurs as an item. Thus the length of a proof (written out in full) is the same as the last number written to the left of the proof in the process of numbering the steps in the customary way.

20.6. A categorical proof will be said to be **normal** if every propositional item of the categorical proof can have an introduction rule assigned to it as its reason. Proofs subordinate to a normal categorical proof may use elimination rules.

20.7. If $\mathfrak{I}$ is a categorical proof that has p and

$$
\begin{array}{|l}
\;\; p \\
\overline{} \\
\;\; q_1 \\
\;\; \circ \\
\;\; \bullet \\
\;\; \bullet \\
\;\; q_n
\end{array}
$$

as items, if

at least one of $q_1, \cdots, q_n$ is different from p, and if $\mathfrak{I}'$ is a categorical proof obtainable from $\mathfrak{I}$ by the process about to be described, we will say that $\mathfrak{I}'$ is a **direct reduction** of $\mathfrak{I}$. The process is as follows: First place the above-mentioned subordinate proof so that it is located *after* the item p if this is not already the case. This can always be done by a slight rearrangement of the proof $\mathfrak{I}$, since by 18.6 we know that p cannot be a resultant of this subordinate proof. Furthermore, the proof in this rearranged form will continue to conform to 18.6. Next, the item which is this same subordinate proof is to be replaced by the sequence $q_1, \cdots, q_n$, which are the steps of the subordinate proof except for the hypothesis p. More accurately, we should say that a list of all items of the subordinate proof, except for the hypothesis itself, takes the place of the subordinate proof. These items now become items of the main categorical proof itself. Some of these items may themselves be subordinate proofs. Again, if the proof previously did not violate 18.6, it still will not do so. The proof thus obtained is the proof referred to above as $\mathfrak{I}'$, and is said to be a direct reduction of $\mathfrak{I}$.

20.8. If a proof $\mathfrak{I}_1$ is a direct reduction of $\mathfrak{I}_2$, and if $\mathfrak{I}_2$ is a direct reduction of $\mathfrak{I}_3$, and $\mathfrak{I}_3$ of $\mathfrak{I}_4$, and so on down to $\mathfrak{I}_n$, then we will say that $\mathfrak{I}_1$ is a **reduction** of $\mathfrak{I}_n$. Also we will say that each categorical proof is (in a trivial sense) a reduction of itself, though of course not a direct reduction. Thus a categorical proof $\mathfrak{S}$ is a reduction of a categorical proof $\mathfrak{I}$ if $\mathfrak{S}$ is identical with $\mathfrak{I}$ or if it is possible to pass from $\mathfrak{I}$ to $\mathfrak{S}$ by a finite series of direct reductions. In particular, if $\mathfrak{S}$ is a direct reduction of $\mathfrak{I}$, then $\mathfrak{S}$ is a reduction of $\mathfrak{I}$. It turns out that a reduction of a proof is never of greater length than the proof itself. This is because a direct reduction of a proof is always shorter than the proof itself by one unit. A reduction of a proof has as an item every proposition that the original proof has. If it fails to have as an item some subordinate proof that the original proof has as an item, then at least it has as an item each proposition that is an item of that subordinate proof. If a proof conforms to 18.6, so will any reduction of it.

20.9. A categorical proof will be said to be **consistent** if there is no proposition p such that p and $\sim p$ are both items of it; otherwise it will be said to be **inconsistent.**

20.10. The fundamental theorem concerning categorical proofs is stated in 20.11 below for categorical proofs of some specific length n. This is because the plan is first to establish the theorem for the case where $n = 1$, and next to show that the theorem holds for the case $n = m + 1$ if it holds for the case $n = m$. The theorem can then be seen to hold not only for $n = 1$ but also successively for $n = 2$, $n = 3$, $n = 4$, and so on, and hence for every choice of n as a positive integer.

20.11. Fundamental theorem concerning categorical proofs of length n. Every categorical proof of length n or less is consistent and has at least one reduction which is consistent, normal, and no longer than it.

20.12. Demonstration of the fundamental theorem for the case $n = 1$. Let $\mathfrak{I}$ be a categorical proof of length 1. Then $\mathfrak{I}$ can have only one item, and this item must be either a propositional item or else a subordinate proof which is itself of length 1. If this single item is a propositional item, then its reason must be either identity introduction or negative identity introduction, so in this case $\mathfrak{I}$ is normal and is its own normal reduction. If the single item is a subordinate proof of length 1, then the categorical proof $\mathfrak{I}$ is normal in the trivial sense of having no propositional item, so again $\mathfrak{I}$ is a normal reduction of itself. $\mathfrak{I}$ is clearly consistent because every inconsistent proof must have at least two items, p and $\sim p$.

20.13. Demonstration of the fundamental theorem for the case $n = m + 1$, assuming it true for the case $n = m$. (Here m is any fixed positive integer.) We let $\mathfrak{I}$ be a categorical proof of length $m + 1$ or less. We are to show that $\mathfrak{I}$ is consistent and has at least one normal reduction. If $\mathfrak{I}$ has only one item, we can argue as in 20.12. If $\mathfrak{I}$ has more than one item, we let $\mathfrak{S}$ be the shorter proof that results if the last item of $\mathfrak{I}$ is dropped. Since we are assuming that the fundamental theorem holds for $n = m$, and since the length of $\mathfrak{S}$ is $\leq m$, we can conclude that $\mathfrak{S}$ is consistent and has a consistent normal reduction which we will call $\mathfrak{S}'$. Every proposition that is an item of $\mathfrak{S}$ is also an item of S′, and every propositional item of S′ has an introduction rule as its reason. There are now various cases to consider, depending on the nature of the last item of ℑ:

20.14. CASE 1: The last item of ℑ is a subordinate proof. Here ℑ is consistent because S is consistent. A consistent normal reduction of ℑ is obtainable by adding to S′ the last item of ℑ.

20.15. CASE 2: The last item of ℑ has identity introduction as its reason. Let this last item be $[a = a]$. Let ℑ′ be the proof that results from adding $[a = a]$ to S′. If ℑ′ were inconsistent, it would have to have an item $\sim[a = a]$ by an introduction rule, since all the propositional items of ℑ′ have introduction rules as their reasons and since S′ is consistent. But no introduction rule can give $\sim[a = a]$, as an inspection of the various available introduction rules clearly shows. Hence ℑ′ is consistent and therefore also ℑ, since every proposition that is an item of ℑ is also an item of ℑ′. Furthermore, ℑ′ is easily seen to be a consistent normal reduction of ℑ.

20.16. CASE 3: The last item of ℑ has negative identity introduction as its reason. Let this last item be $\sim[a = b]$, where "a" is a different expression from "b". Let ℑ′ be the proof that results from adding $\sim[a = b]$ to S′. If ℑ′ were inconsistent, it would have to have the item $[a = b]$ by an introduction rule or the item $\sim\sim[a = b]$ by an introduction rule, since all the propositional items of ℑ′ have introduction rules as their reasons and since S′ is consistent. The latter alternative implies the former, because if ℑ′ has $\sim\sim[a = b]$ by an introduction rule, the introduction rule would have to be double negation introduction, and $\sim\sim[a = b]$ would have to be preceded in ℑ′ by $[a = b]$, so in any case $[a = b]$ would have to be an item of ℑ′ by an introduction rule. But no introduction rule gives $[a = b]$ where "a" is a different expression from "b". Hence ℑ′ is consistent and therefore also ℑ. Furthermore, ℑ′ is a consistent normal reduction of ℑ. (In the above argument we suppose "a" and "b" to be written in unabbreviated form.)

20.17. CASE 4: The last item of ℑ has negation elimination as its reason. This case cannot arise, because S would have to be inconsistent, and we know that S is not inconsistent.

20.18. CASE 5: The last item of ℑ has double negation introduction as its reason. Let this last item be $\sim\sim p$. Let ℑ′ be the proof that results from adding $\sim\sim p$ to S'. If $\mathfrak{I}'$ were inconsistent, it would have to have the item $\sim p$ by an introduction rule or the item $\sim\sim\sim p$ by an introduction rule. The latter alternative implies the former, as in 20.16, so in any case $\mathfrak{I}'$ would have to have the item $\sim p$ by an introduction rule, and so would S'. Also p must be an item of S and of S' if $\sim\sim p$ is an item of $\mathfrak{I}$ by double negation introduction. But then S' would be inconsistent, and we know that S' is consistent. Hence $\mathfrak{I}'$ and $\mathfrak{I}$ are consistent, and $\mathfrak{I}'$ is a consistent normal reduction of $\mathfrak{I}$.

20.19. CASE 6: The last item of $\mathfrak{I}$ has double negation elimination as its reason. Let this last item be p. Then $\sim\sim p$ must be an item of S and therefore an item of S'. But since all the propositional items of S' are by introduction rules, the reason for $\sim\sim p$ in S' must be double negation introduction, and p must be an item of S'. Now S' is already known to be consistent, and every propositional item of $\mathfrak{I}$ is an item of S'. Hence, adding p to S' as a redundant item gives a consistent normal reduction of $\mathfrak{I}$, and $\mathfrak{I}$ itself must be consistent.

20.20. CASE 7: The last item of $\mathfrak{I}$ has implication introduction as its reason. Let this last item be $[p \supset q]$. Let $\mathfrak{I}'$ be the proof that results from adding $[p \supset q]$ to S'. If $\mathfrak{I}'$ were inconsistent, then $\sim[p \supset q]$ would be an item of $\mathfrak{I}'$ and also of S'. But this is impossible because every propositional item of S' has an introduction rule as its reason, and there is no introduction rule that can serve as a reason for $\sim[p \supset q]$. Hence $\mathfrak{I}'$ and $\mathfrak{I}$ are consistent, and $\mathfrak{I}'$ is a consistent normal reduction of $\mathfrak{I}$.

20.21. CASE 8: The last item of $\mathfrak{I}$ has implication elimination (modus ponens) as its reason. Let this last item be q. Then there must be a proposition p such that p and $[p \supset q]$ are items of S, and hence also items of S'. But since all propositional items of S' are by introduction rules, the reason for $[p \supset q]$ in S' must be implication introduction, and S' must have as an item either q or a subordinate proof with hypothesis p and conclusion q. If q is an item of S', we simply add q to S' as a redundant item to give a consistent normal reduction of $\mathfrak{I}$. This would be the case, in particular, if p and q are the same proposition. On the other hand, if a subordinate proof with hypothesis p and conclusion q is an item of S', and if q is different from p, we form a direct reduction $\mathfrak{R}$ of S' in such a way that the subordinate proof is replaced by a sequence of all its items except its hypothesis, as explained in 20.7. (The process of forming the direct reduction actually gives a valid categorical proof because no elimination rules are used in S', so that the removal of the subordinate proof would not produce the deficiency that we would have if one of the subordinate proofs required for a use of disjunction elimination were removed. The removal of a subordinate proof used in connection with implication introduction causes no difficulty, since the required implication can still follow from what was originally the last item of the subordinate proof. This is why two forms of implication introduction are given under R6 of 20.2.) Since $\mathfrak{R}$ is a direct reduction of the consistent proof S' we know that $\mathfrak{R}$ must be a reduction of the proof S. Also, since $\mathfrak{R}$ is of length not greater than m, we know that $\mathfrak{R}$ has a consistent normal reduction, which we shall call $\mathfrak{R}'$. It is clear that $\mathfrak{R}'$ is a consistent normal reduction of S as well as of $\mathfrak{R}$. Since q is an item of $\mathfrak{R}$, it is also an item of $\mathfrak{R}'$. Every propositional item of $\mathfrak{I}$ is an item of $\mathfrak{R}'$, so that the consistency of $\mathfrak{R}'$ guarantees that of $\mathfrak{I}$. The result of adding q to $\mathfrak{R}'$ as a redundant item gives a consistent normal reduction of $\mathfrak{I}$.

20.22. Case 9: The last item of $\mathfrak{I}$ has conjunction introduction as its reason. Let this last item be $[p \ \& \ q]$. Let $\mathfrak{I}'$ be the proof that results from adding $[p \ \& \ q]$ to S'. If $\mathfrak{I}'$ were inconsistent, it would have to have the item $\sim[p \ \& \ q]$ by an introduction rule, specifically by the rule of negative conjunction introduction, and so it would have to have the item $[\sim p \ \mathsf{v} \sim q]$ by an introduction rule, specifically by the rule of disjunction introduction, and so it would have to have $\sim p$ as an item or $\sim q$ as an item, and so would S'. But since the reason for $[p \ \& \ q]$ in $\mathfrak{I}$ is conjunction introduction, the propositions p and q must be items of $\mathfrak{I}$ and hence also of $\mathfrak{I}'$ and S'. Thus if $\mathfrak{I}'$ is inconsistent, S' must also be inconsistent since S' must have as items both $\sim p$ and p, or else both $\sim q$ and q. But we know that S' is consistent. Hence $\mathfrak{I}'$ is consistent too and is clearly a consistent normal reduction of $\mathfrak{I}$, and $\mathfrak{I}$ itself is consistent.

20.23. Case 10: The last item of $\mathfrak{I}$ has conjunction elimination as its reason. Let this last item be p. Then there must be a proposition q such that $[p \ \& \ q]$ or $[q \ \& \ p]$ is an item of S and therefore of S' too. But since all the propositional items of S' are by introduction rules, the reason for $[p \ \& \ q]$ or for $[q \ \& \ p]$ in S' must be conjunction introduction, and p must be an item of S'. Hence, adding p to S' as a redundant item gives a consistent normal reduction of ℑ, and ℑ itself is consistent.

20.24. Case 11: The last item of ℑ has negative conjunction introduction as its reason. Let this last item be $\sim[p$ **&** $q]$. Let ℑ′ be the proof that results from adding $\sim[p$ **&** $q]$ to S′. It can be shown that $[\sim p$ **v** $\sim q]$ must be an item of S′ and hence that at least one of the two propositions $\sim p$ and $\sim q$ must be an item of S′ since all the propositional items of S′ are by introduction rules. If ℑ′ were inconsistent, then S′ would have to have $[p$ **&** $q]$ or $\sim\sim[p$ **&** $q]$ as an item by an introduction rule, and hence it would have to have $[p$ **&** $q]$, p, and q as items, and so would be inconsistent. But we know that S′ is not inconsistent. Hence ℑ′ is consistent and is a normal consistent reduction of ℑ, and ℑ itself is consistent.

20.25. Case 12: The last item of ℑ has negative conjunction elimination as its reason. Let this last item be $[\sim p$ **v** $\sim q]$. Then $\sim[p$ **&** $q]$ must be an item of S and hence of S′. The reason for $\sim[p$ **&** $q]$ in S′ must be an introduction rule and so must be negative conjunction introduction. Hence $[\sim p$ **v** $\sim q]$ is an item of S′. Adding $[\sim p$ **v** $\sim q]$ to S′ as a redundant item gives a consistent normal reduction of ℑ, and ℑ itself is consistent.

20.26. Case 13: The last item of ℑ has disjunction introduction as its reason. Let this last item be $[p$ **v** $q]$. Let ℑ′ be the proof that results from adding $[p$ **v** $q]$ to S′. Since S must have at least one of the two propositions, p and q, as an item, S′ must also have at least one of them as an item. If ℑ′ were inconsistent, then S′ would have to have $\sim[p$ **v** $q]$ as an item by negative disjunction introduction, and so would also have to have $[\sim p$ **&** $\sim q]$ and $\sim p$ and $\sim q$ as items, since all the propositional items of S′ are by introduction rules. But then S′ would be inconsistent, and we know it is not. Hence ℑ′ must be consistent and indeed a consistent normal reduction of ℑ, and ℑ itself is consistent.

20.27. Case 14: The last item of ℑ has disjunction elimination as its reason. Let this last item be r. Then there must be propositions p and q such that $[p$ **v** $q]$ is an item of S, such that a subordinate proof with p as hypothesis and r as conclusion is an item of S, and such that a subordinate proof with q as hypothesis and r as conclusion is an item of S. These two subordinate proofs must be items of S′, or else all the items of one or both of them must be items of S′. In the latter case, we know that r itself is an item of S′, so that adding r to S′ as a redundant item gives a consistent normal reduction of ℑ, and ℑ itself is consistent. Suppose, however, that the two subordinate proofs are items of S′. Since $[p \lor q]$ is an item of S′ and since all the propositional items of S′ are by introduction rules, we know that at least one of the two propositions p and q is an item of S′. Suppose that p is an item of S′ and that r is different from p. We then form a direct reduction of S′ in such a way that the subordinate proof having hypothesis p and conclusion r is replaced by the sequence of all its items (except for its hypothesis p, which is already an item of S′). This direct reduction of S′ must have a reduction ℜ which is a consistent normal reduction of S and which has r as an item. If r is added to this proof as a redundant item, we have a consistent normal reduction of ℑ, and ℑ itself is consistent. The case where r and p are the same proposition is trivial, since r is then already an item of S′. If q rather than p is an item of S′, we proceed in a similar way.

20.28. Case 15: The last item of ℑ has negative disjunction introduction as its reason. Let this last item be $\sim[p \lor q]$. Let ℑ′ be the proof that results from adding $\sim[p \lor q]$ to S′. The proposition $[\sim p \ \& \sim q]$ must be an item of S and so it must be an item of S′ by conjunction introduction. Hence $\sim p$ and $\sim q$ must be items of S′. If ℑ′ were inconsistent, $[p \lor q]$ or $\sim\sim[p \lor q]$ would be items of S′ by introduction rules, and hence $[p \lor q]$ and at least one of the two propositions p and q would be items of S′. But then S′ would be inconsistent, and we know it is not. Hence ℑ′ is consistent and is a consistent normal reduction of ℑ, and ℑ itself is consistent.

20.29. Case 16: The last item of ℑ has negative disjunction elimination as its reason. Let this last item be $[\sim p \ \& \sim q]$. Then $\sim[p \lor q]$ must be an item of S and hence of S′. The reason for $\sim[p \lor q]$ in S′ must be an introduction rule and so must be negative disjunction introduction. Hence $[\sim p \ \& \sim q]$ is an item of S′. Adding $[\sim p \ \& \sim q]$ to S′ as a redundant item gives a consistent normal reduction of ℑ, and ℑ itself is consistent.

20.30. Case 17: The last item of ℑ is by ϵ-introduction. Let this last item be $[a \ \epsilon \ F]$. Let ℑ′ be the proof that results from adding $[a \ \epsilon \ F]$ to S′. The proposition (Fa) must be an item of S and so also of S′. If ℑ′ were inconsistent, it would have to have $\sim[a \ \epsilon \ F]$ by an introduction rule, specifically by the rule of negative ϵ-introduction, so that $\sim(Fa)$ would have to be an item of $\mathfrak{I}'$ and of $\mathfrak{s}'$. But then $\mathfrak{s}'$ would be inconsistent, and we know it is not. Hence $\mathfrak{I}'$ and $\mathfrak{I}$ are consistent and $\mathfrak{I}'$ is a consistent normal reduction of $\mathfrak{I}$.

20.31. CASE 18: The last item of $\mathfrak{I}$ is by ϵ-elimination. Let this last item be (Fa). Then $[a \; \epsilon \; F]$ must be an item of $\mathfrak{s}$ and of $\mathfrak{s}'$. Since all the propositional items of $\mathfrak{s}'$ are by introduction rules, the reason for $[a \; \epsilon \; F]$ in $\mathfrak{s}'$ must be ϵ-introduction, and (Fa) must be an item of $\mathfrak{s}'$. Hence, adding (Fa) to $\mathfrak{s}'$ as a redundant item gives a consistent normal reduction of $\mathfrak{I}$, and $\mathfrak{I}$ itself is consistent.

20.32. CASE 19: The last item of $\mathfrak{I}$ is by negative ϵ-introduction. Similar to Case 17.

20.33. CASE 20: The last item of $\mathfrak{I}$ is by negative ϵ-elimination. Similar to Case 18.

20.34. CASE 21: The last item of $\mathfrak{I}$ is by attribute introduction. Similar to Case 17.

20.35. CASE 22: The last item of $\mathfrak{I}$ is by attribute elimination. Similar to Case 18.

20.36. CASE 23: The last item of $\mathfrak{I}$ is by negative attribute introduction. Similar to Case 17.

20.37. CASE 24: The last item of $\mathfrak{I}$ is by negative attribute elimination. Similar to Case 18.

20.38. The demonstration begun in 20.13 is now completed. We did not need to consider rules R24–R31 of 20.2 for reasons given in 20.4. By the method outlined in 20.10, it can be shown for each n that the fundamental theorem 20.11 is valid, so we conclude:

20.39. THEOREM. Every categorical proof is consistent and has at least one consistent normal reduction.

20.40. By similar methods the following important theorem can also be established:

20.41. THEOREM. There is no proposition p such that p is an item of one categorical proof and $\sim p$ is an item of another categorical proof.

20.42. It might be supposed that 20.41 follows fairly directly from 20.39 by means of the following sort of argument: If there were a categorical proof with p as an item and another with $\sim p$ as an item, these two proofs could be placed end to end to give an inconsistent proof, contrary to 20.39; so there cannot be two such categorical proofs. The fallacy in this argument is that we cannot be sure that the result of placing two categorical proofs end to end is again a categorical proof, since each of the original proofs might conform to 18.6, but the sequence of items resulting from placing them end to end might not satisfy 18.6 and so might not be a categorical proof.

20.43. The correct way to establish 20.41 is to state the following theorem, show that it holds for the case $n = 1$, and then show that if it holds for the case $n = m$, it also holds for the case $n = m + 1$:

20.44. Theorem. There is no proposition p such that p is an item of some categorical proof of length n or less, while $\sim p$ is an item of some other categorical proof of length n or less.

20.45. The case for $n = 1$ can be handled analogously to 20.14–20.16, since if each of the two categorical proofs has only one propositional item, each such item must have identity introduction or identity elimination as its reason, while if one or more of the two categorical proofs has a subordinate proof as an item, such a proof does not have a propositional item at all, being of length 1.

20.46. The case for $n = m + 1$, where the case for $n = m$ is assumed established, may be handled as follows: We let $\mathfrak{I}_1$ be a categorical proof of length $m + 1$ or less having p as an item, and we let $\mathfrak{I}_2$ be a categorical proof of length $m + 1$ or less and having $\sim p$ as an item, and then we show that this is an impossible situation, as follows: Let $\mathfrak{I}_1'$ be normal reduction of $\mathfrak{I}_1$ and let $\mathfrak{I}_2'$ be a normal reduction of $\mathfrak{I}_2$. (We know by 20.39 that there are such normal reductions, given $\mathfrak{I}_1$ and $\mathfrak{I}_2$.) Now p must be an item of $\mathfrak{I}_1'$ by an introduction rule, and $\sim p$ must be an item of $\mathfrak{I}_2'$ by an introduction rule. If p is of the form $[a = b]$, we know that a and b cannot be so chosen that $[a = b]$ and $\sim[a = b]$ can both have introduction rules as reasons, since the former can have identity introduction as its reason only if "a" and "b" are the same expression, while $\sim[a = b]$ can have negative identity introduction as its reason only if "a" and "b" are different expressions. So p cannot be of the form $[a = b]$. If p is of the form $[r \supset s]$, then some introduction rule would have to give $\sim[r \supset s]$. But none does, so p is not of the form $[r \supset s]$. If p is of the form $[r \, \& \, s]$, then r and s would have to be items of $\mathfrak{I}_1'$ preceding the item $[r \, \& \, s]$, while $[\sim r \vee \sim s]$ would have to be an item of $\mathfrak{I}_2'$ preceding the item $\sim[r \, \& \, s]$, and hence the latter item would also have to be preceded by either $\sim r$ or $\sim s$ as an item of $\mathfrak{J}_2{}'$. Suppose it is preceded by $\sim r$. Then by omitting the last item of $\mathfrak{J}_1{}'$ we get a categorical proof having r as an item and of length not greater than m, and by omitting the last item of $\mathfrak{J}_2{}'$ we get a categorical proof having $\sim r$ as an item and of length not greater than m. But this is impossible, since we are assuming 20.44 for the case $n = m$. Similarly, if $\sim s$ rather than $\sim r$ is an item of $\mathfrak{J}_2{}'$ preceding $\sim[r \; \& \; s]$. Hence p is not of the form $[r \; \& \; s]$. By similar methods we can show that p is not of the form $[r \lor s]$, nor of the form $[a \; \epsilon \; F]$, nor of the form $((x \setminus (\cdots x \cdots))a$. Finally, suppose that p is of one of the forms $\sim q$ or $\sim\sim q$, or $\sim\sim\sim q$, or $\sim\sim\sim\sim q$, and so on, where q is of one of the forms $[a = b]$, $[r \supset s]$, $[r \; \& \; s]$, $[r \lor s]$, $[a \; \epsilon \; F]$, or $((x \setminus (\cdots x \cdots))a$. Then q must be an item of one of the two proofs $\mathfrak{J}_1{}'$ and $\mathfrak{J}_2{}'$, while $\sim q$ must be an item of the other, as we see by considering what uses must have been made of double negation introduction in $\mathfrak{J}_1{}'$ and $\mathfrak{J}_2{}'$. But then q cannot be of any of the above six forms after all, for the same reason that p itself cannot be of any of those six forms. We have now considered all the forms that p might conceivably take in this system of logic and have shown them all to be impossible. Hence there cannot be two proofs $\mathfrak{J}_1$ and $\mathfrak{J}_2$ of the kind described, and 20.44 is established for the case $n = m + 1$ on the assumption that it is true for the case $n = m$.

20.47. From 20.43–20.46 we see that 20.41 has been established. This completes the proof of the consistency of as much of the present system of logic as has so far been presented.

20.48. Suppose that the present system were extended by adding to it two rules: a rule of negative implication introduction according to which $\sim[p \supset q]$ would be treated as a direct consequence of the pair of propositions p and $\sim q$, and a rule of negative implication elimination according to which p and $\sim q$ would each be treated as a direct consequence of $\sim[p \supset q]$. We would then still be able to establish 20.39, but it is known that 20.41 cannot be established for such a system.[14] Fortunately these negative implication rules are not required for our purposes, and we shall not use them or assume them.

[14] More specifically, it is possible to give a proof of $[[(YY) \supset p] \supset p]$ and also possible to give a proof of the denial of this same proposition in such a system, provided that Y is defined as in 18.3, and that p is any proposition such that $\sim p$ can be proved. I am indebted to Mr. H. P. Galliher and Dr. J. R. Myhill for this information. They discovered this result independently of each other.

Chapter 5

UNIVERSALITY AND EXISTENCE

21. Universality and the Universal Quantifier

21.1. It has been pointed out in 17.29 that some attributes are universal and others are not. An attribute is said to be universal if it applies to all things whatsoever. The attribute of self-identity, denoted by "$(x \setminus [x = x])$", is a universal attribute. It applies to everything, even to propositions and to itself and other attributes. Now the attribute of "being a universal attribute" is itself a perfectly good attribute. Some attributes have it and others do not. This attribute of being a universal attribute will be referred to as "universality". It is not itself universal, since it applies only to attributes that are universal and hence not to all things whatsoever.

21.2. The capital letter "A" will be used to denote the attribute universality. Thus $[F \; \epsilon \; A]$ is the proposition that F has the attribute A, in other words, that F is a universal attribute. More specifically, if F is the attribute $(x \setminus [x = x])$, then $[F \; \epsilon \; A]$ is the true proposition to the effect that self-identity is universal, while if F is the attribute "blue", then $[F \; \epsilon \; A]$ is the false proposition to the effect that blue is universal. We could also speak in terms of classes instead of attributes. Then we would say that some classes are universal classes and others are not, and that A is the class of all universal classes. The proposition $[F \; \epsilon \; A]$ would then be read as asserting that the class F is a member of the class of universal classes. We would say that if F is the class $(x \setminus [x = x])$ of all self-identical things, then $[F \; \epsilon \; A]$ is the true proposition to the effect that the class of all self-identical things is a member of the class of universal classes, while if F is the class of blue things, then $[F \; \epsilon \; A]$ is the false proposition to the effect that the class of blue things is a member of the class of universal classes.

128

21.3. The rule of **universality elimination** ("univ elim") asserts that $[a \; \epsilon \; F]$ is a direct consequence of $[F \; \epsilon \; \mathsf{A}]$. The rule may be expressed schematically thus:

$$
\begin{array}{ll}
1 & F \; \epsilon \; \mathsf{A} \qquad\qquad\qquad\qquad\qquad\qquad\text{hyp} \\
2 & a \; \epsilon \; F \qquad\qquad\qquad\qquad\qquad\quad\;\; \text{1, univ elim}
\end{array}
$$

Step 1 asserts that F is universal (that everything has F). Step 2 follows from step 1 by universality elimination and asserts that (in particular) a has F. We next present a proof using this rule. Notice that in applying universality elimination in the following proof, F is chosen as $(x \setminus [[c \; \epsilon \; x] \supset [d \; \epsilon \; x]])$, and a is chosen as $(y \setminus [c = y])$.

21.4.

1	$(x \setminus [[c \; \epsilon \; x] \supset [d \; \epsilon \; x]]) \; \epsilon \; \mathsf{A}$	hyp
2	$(y \setminus [c = y]) \; \epsilon \; (x \setminus [[c \; \epsilon \; x] \supset [d \; \epsilon \; x]])$	1, univ elim
3	$[c \; \epsilon \; (y \setminus [c = y])] \supset [d \; \epsilon \; (y \setminus [c = y])]$	2, att elim
4	$c = c$	id int
5	$c \; \epsilon \; (y \setminus [c = y])$	4, att int
6	$d \; \epsilon \; (y \setminus [c = y])$	3, 5, m p
7	$c = d$	6, att elim
8	$[(x \setminus [[c \; \epsilon \; x] \supset [d \; \epsilon \; x]]) \; \epsilon \; \mathsf{A}] \supset [c = d]$	1–7, imp int

The converse of the above theorem will later be proved, so that it will be seen that c is identical with d if and only if the attribute $(x \setminus [[c \; \epsilon \; x] \supset [d \; \epsilon \; x]])$ is universal. To say that the attribute $(x \setminus [[c \; \epsilon \; x] \supset [d \; \epsilon \; x]])$ is universal amounts to saying that d has every attribute that c has. This is because if $(x \setminus [[c \; \epsilon \; x] \supset [d \; \epsilon \; x]])$ is universal, then the proposition $[F \; \epsilon \; (x \setminus [[c \; \epsilon \; x] \supset [d \; \epsilon \; x]])]$ is true for *every* attribute F, and so by attribute elimination the proposition $[[c \; \epsilon \; F] \supset [d \; \epsilon \; F]]$ is also true for every attribute F.

21.5. The rule of universality introduction, stated in 21.6 below, will require a special kind of subordinate proof which we will call a **general** subordinate proof. Suppose that some subordinate proof has as an item a proposition mentioning something a, and suppose that the subordinate proof would be equally valid if a were everywhere replaced throughout the subordinate proof by any other thing b. Then we say that the subordinate proof is general with respect to a, and to indicate this fact we write "a" to the left of and near the top of the vertical line associated with that subordinate proof. We will use this device, to begin with, only in connection with *categorical* subordinate proofs (those having no hypothesis). Here is an example of a proof having a categorical subordinate proof that is general with respect to a:

1	q		hyp
2	a	$a = a$	id int
3		$p \vee [a = a]$	2, dis int
4	$q \vee r$		1, dis int

Of course the subordinate proof in this example does not contribute anything to the rest of the proof, but such a subordinate proof *would* be able to make a contribution to the rest of the proof after the rule of universality introduction becomes available. The above subordinate proof is general with respect to a because it would be equally valid if a were everywhere replaced by b throughout it. Such a replacement is always to be understood as restricted to the subordinate proof in question and as not referring to items outside that subordinate proof. For example, the subordinate proof in the following proof is not general with respect to a, because if we replace a by anything else b throughout the subordinate proof, leaving the rest of the proof unchanged, the first step of the subordinate proof would no longer be valid, since it would become $[b = d]$, while the second step of the main proof would remain $[a = d]$.

1	q		hyp
2	$a = d$		hyp
3		$a = d$	2, reit
4		$[a = d] \vee p$	3, dis int
5	$q \vee r$		1, dis int

If a subordinate proof is general with respect to a, we must be able to replace a by anything else whatsoever without destroying the validity of that subordinate proof. If this cannot be done, the subordinate proof is not to be regarded as general with respect to a. Ordinarily, if a subordinate proof is general with respect to a, we cannot reiterate into that subordinate proof a proposition that mentions a. The reason is that the reiteration becomes invalid when a is replaced by something else b in the subordinate proof, but not replaced in the main proof from which the reiteration is made.

21.6. The rule of **universality introduction** ("univ int") may now be stated as follows: The proposition $[F \epsilon A]$ is a direct consequence of a categorical subordinate proof that is general with respect to x and that has $[x \epsilon F]$ as one of its items (in practice usually as its last item). Schematically, the rule of universality introduction can be represented thus:

$$
\begin{array}{c|c|l}
\cdot & \cdot & \\
\cdot & \cdot & \\
\cdot & \cdot & \\
i & x\ \ \cdot & \\
 & \ \ \ \cdot & \\
 & \ \ \ \cdot & \\
 & \ \ \ \cdot & \\
j & \ \ x \epsilon F & \\
k & F \epsilon A & i\text{--}j, \text{ univ int}
\end{array}
$$

Notice the expression "x" attached to the upper left corner of the subordinate proof i--j. This is to indicate that the subordinate proof i--j is general with respect to x. We are to assume, incidentally, that x is not mentioned by F. It will be our practice that letters from the latter part of the alphabet are used to refer to things that are mentioned only where there is explicit indication of such mention or of the possibility of such mention. Since there is no indication that F might mention x, we assume it does not do so.

21.7. Here is an example of a proof using universality introduction:

$$
\begin{array}{r|l|l}
1 & G \epsilon A & \text{hyp} \\
2 & x\ \ G \epsilon A & 1, \text{ reit} \\
3 & \ \ x \epsilon G & 2, \text{ univ elim} \\
4 & \ \ [x \epsilon G] \vee [x \epsilon H] & 3, \text{ dis int} \\
5 & \ \ x \epsilon [G \cup H] & 4, 17.28 \\
6 & [G \cup H] \epsilon A & 2\text{--}5, \text{ univ int}
\end{array}
$$

21.8. Here is a proof of the converse of 21.4:

1		$c = d$	hyp
2	y	$c = d$	1, reit
3		$[c \in y] \supset [c \in y]$	refl imp
4		$[c \in y] \supset [d \in y]$	2, 3, id elim
5		$y \in (x \setminus [[c \in x] \supset [d \in x]])$	4, att int
6		$(x \setminus [[c \in x] \supset [d \in x]]) \in A$	2–5, univ int
7	$[c = d] \supset [(x \setminus [[c \in x] \supset [d \in x]]) \in A]$		1–6, imp int

Notice that the reiteration of step 1 into the subordinate proof is compatible with the fact that the subordinate proof is general with respect to y. This is because y is not mentioned by step 1.

21.9. It might be argued that the subordinate proof 2–5 of 21.8 is not really general with respect to y on the ground that y cannot be replaced by anything at all, but only by some attribute, and must itself be an attribute. This argument would be valid if we refused to regard $[a \in b]$ as being a proposition in case b is not an attribute. However, we consider $[a \in b]$ as being a proposition regardless of what sort of things a and b may be. Furthermore, we regard $[a \supset b]$ as being a proposition regardless of what a and b may be, and we regard $[a \supset a]$ as being a true proposition regardless of what a may be. Wherever the rules of this system are stated in such a way as to appear to apply only to propositions, they can be understood in a more general sense as applying to things of all sorts, so that we could use implication introduction to prove $[a \supset a]$, where a is not a proposition, just as well as we can use implication introduction to prove $[p \supset p]$, where p is a proposition. Similarly, where we have rules using such letters as "F", "G", "H" to refer to attributes, the rules can be understood in a wider sense using "a", "b", "c" in place of "F", "G", "H", and referring to things in general rather than merely to attributes.

21.10. Hereafter we will let "$(x)(\cdots x \cdots)$" serve as an abbreviation for "$[(x \setminus (\cdots x \cdots)) \in A]$". Thus in order to write in symbols the proposition, "Everything is self-identical", we can write merely

"$(x)[x = x]$" instead of the more complicated expression "$[(x \setminus [x = x]) \in A]$". The usual way of reading "$(x)[x = x]$" is "For every ex, ex is identical with ex", or "For all ex, ex is identical with ex". The expression "(x)" is read "for every ex" or "for all ex", and the expression "(y)" is read "for every wye" or "for all wye", and the expression "(z)" is read "for every zee" or "for all zee", and similarly for other letters. This same sort of notation provides a simple way of saying in symbols that one attribute is included in another (in the sense that the latter attribute applies to everything the former attribute applies to). Suppose we wish to say that all humans are mortal, in other words, that the attribute "human" is included in the attribute "mortal". If H is the attribute "human" and M is the attribute "mortal", then the required proposition can be expressed as $(x)[[x \in H] \supset [x \in M]]$. This may be read as "For all ex, if ex is human then ex is mortal", or more colloquially as "All men are mortal". Similarly, the proposition, "No men are mortal", could be expressed as $(x)[[x \in H] \supset \sim[x \in M]]$. Such expressions as "$(x)$", "$(y)$", and "$(z)$" are called **universal quantifiers.**

21.11. Two derived rules will now be stated in schematic form and their derivation from other rules will be indicated.

21.12. Rule of universal quantifier elimination ("u q elim"):

$$
\begin{array}{ll}
1 \ \big| \ \ (x)(\cdots x \cdots) & \text{hyp} \\
2 \ \big| \ \ (\cdots a \cdots) & \text{1, u q elim}
\end{array}
$$

In the above rule $(\cdots x \cdots)$, $(\cdots a \cdots)$, x, and a are to be chosen as in 17.6. It is to be understood that $(\cdots a \cdots)$ is the proposition obtained by replacing x by a throughout $(\cdots x \cdots)$ wherever x is mentioned in $(\cdots x \cdots)$. We are to suppose that a may mention x or even may be x, though the symbolism, strictly speaking, does not indicate this fact. This rule is derived as follows:

$$
\begin{array}{lll}
1 \ \big| \ \ (x)(\cdots x \cdots) & & \text{hyp} \\
2 \ \big| \ \ (x \setminus (\cdots x \cdots)) \in A & & \text{1, rep, def (21.10)} \\
3 \ \big| \ \ a \in (x \setminus (\cdots x \cdots)) & & \text{2, univ elim} \\
4 \ \big| \ \ (\cdots a \cdots) & & \text{3, att elim}
\end{array}
$$

21.13. Rule of universal quantifier introduction ("u q int"):

$$
\begin{array}{ll}
& \vdots \quad \Big|\ \vdots \\
& \vdots \quad \Big|\ \vdots \\
i\ & x\Big|\ \cdot \\
& \vdots \quad \Big|\ \vdots \\
j\ & \quad\ (\cdots x \cdots) \\
k\ & (x)(\cdots x \cdots) \qquad\qquad\qquad i\text{--}j,\ \text{u q int}
\end{array}
$$

According to this rule, we treat $(x)(\cdots x \cdots)$ as a consequence of a categorical subordinate proof that is general with respect to x and has $(\cdots x \cdots)$ as an item.[1] This rule is derived as follows:

$$
\begin{array}{ll}
& \vdots \quad \Big|\ \vdots \\
i\ & x\Big|\ \cdot \\
& \vdots \quad \Big|\ \vdots \\
j\ & \quad (\cdots x \cdots) \\
m\ & \quad x \,\epsilon\, (x \setminus (\cdots x \cdots)) \qquad\quad j,\ \text{att int} \\
n\ & (x \setminus (\cdots x \cdots)) \,\epsilon\, \mathsf{A} \qquad\quad i\text{--}m,\ \text{univ int} \\
k\ & (x)(\cdots x \cdots) \qquad\qquad\qquad n,\ \text{rep, def (21.10)}
\end{array}
$$

The above is a derivation of the rule of universal quantifier introduction in the sense that if the requisite subordinate proof i–j can be constructed, then an additional step m can be added to such a subordinate proof and the result $(x)(\cdots x \cdots)$ can be obtained by universality introduction. The rule of universal quantifier introduction therefore is derivable from the rule of universality introduction. Notice that x is not really mentioned by $(x \setminus (\cdots x \cdots))$ and that

---

[1] Equally well we could say that we treat $(y)(\cdots y \cdots)$ as a consequence of a categorical subordinate proof that is general with respect to x and has $(\cdots x \cdots)$ as an item, where $(\cdots y \cdots)$ is a proposition exactly like $(\cdots x \cdots)$ except that $(\cdots y \cdots)$ mentions y in those places and only those places where $(\cdots x \cdots)$ mentions x. This is sometimes a more convenient form of the rule. The propositions $(x)(\cdots x \cdots)$ and $(y)(\cdots y \cdots)$ are really the same proposition anyway in virtue of 21.10 and 17.3.

every occurrence of "x" in "$(x \setminus (\cdots x \cdots))$" is therefore a bound occurrence of "x". (See 17.9–17.13.) Hence we may choose $(x \setminus (\cdots x \cdots))$ as the F of 21.6 without violating the requirement that x must not be mentioned by F. Since x is not even mentioned by $(x \setminus (\cdots x \cdots))$, there would be no need to replace x by anything else in $(x \setminus (\cdots x \cdots))$ in the process of testing the subordinate proofs i–j and i–m for generality.

21.14. The proofs 21.4 and 21.8 will now be given in a more concise form that uses the abbreviation stated in 21.10 and the quantifier rules stated in 21.12 and 21.13. The greater economy gained should be evident. The rules for the universal quantifier will be used frequently hereafter, but the rules for universality will be seldom or never used.

21.15.

1	$(x)[[c \; \epsilon \; x] \supset [d \; \epsilon \; x]]$	hyp
2	$[c \; \epsilon \; (y \setminus [c = y])] \supset [d \; \epsilon \; (y \setminus [c = y])]$	1, u q elim
3	$c = c$	id int
4	$c \; \epsilon \; (y \setminus [c = y])$	3, att int
5	$d \; \epsilon \; (y \setminus [c = y])$	2, 4, m p
6	$c = d$	5, att elim
7	$(x)[[c \; \epsilon \; x] \supset [d \; \epsilon \; x]] \supset [c = d]$	1–6, imp int

21.16.

1	$c = d$	hyp
2	x $c = d$	1, reit
3	$[c \; \epsilon \; x] \supset [c \; \epsilon \; x]$	refl imp
4	$[c \; \epsilon \; x] \supset [d \; \epsilon \; x]$	2, 3, id elim
5	$(x)[[c \; \epsilon \; x] \supset [d \; \epsilon \; x]]$	2–4, u q int
6	$[c = d] \supset (x)[[c \; \epsilon \; x] \supset [d \; \epsilon \; x]]$	1–5, imp int

21.17. Notice that the conclusion of 21.15 is to be read, "If it is the case that, for every ex, if c has ex then d has ex, then c is identical with d", but should *not* be read, "For every ex, if it is the case that if c has ex then d has ex, then c is identical with d". This is because the universal quantifier "(x)" does not operate on the whole of the expression for step 7, but just on the part preceding the second horseshoe symbol. We now present other proofs using the rules for the universal quantifier.

21.18.

1	$(x)[[x \; \epsilon \; F] \supset [x \; \epsilon \; G]]$	hyp
2	$a \; \epsilon \; F$	hyp
3	$[a \; \epsilon \; F] \supset [a \; \epsilon \; G]$	1, u q elim
4	$a \; \epsilon \; G$	2, 3, m p

The above proof may be thought of as illustrated by the well-known syllogism of classical logic: "If all men are mortal and if Socrates is a man, then Socrates is mortal".

21.19.

1	$(x)[[x \; \epsilon \; F] \supset [x \; \epsilon \; G]]$	hyp
2	$(x)[[x \; \epsilon \; G] \supset [x \; \epsilon \; H]]$	hyp
3	x $(x)[[x \; \epsilon \; F] \supset [x \; \epsilon \; G]]$	1, reit
4	$(x)[[x \; \epsilon \; G] \supset [x \; \epsilon \; H]]$	2, reit
5	$[x \; \epsilon \; F] \supset [x \; \epsilon \; G]$	3, u q elim
6	$[x \; \epsilon \; G] \supset [x \; \epsilon \; H]$	4, u q elim
7	$[x \; \epsilon \; F] \supset [x \; \epsilon \; H]$	5, 6, trans imp
8	$(x)[[x \; \epsilon \; F] \supset [x \; \epsilon \; H]]$	3–7, u q int

The above proof may be thought of as illustrated by such a syllogism as: "If all men are living creatures, and if all living creatures are mortal, then all men are mortal". Notice that the two reiterations in the above proof are permissible because x is not mentioned by $(x \setminus [[x \; \epsilon \; F] \supset [x \; \epsilon \; G]])$ or by $(x \setminus [[x \; \epsilon \; G] \supset [x \; \epsilon \; H]])$, as was pointed out in 17.9 and 17.13, and so is not mentioned in $(x)[[x \; \epsilon \; F] \supset [x \; \epsilon \; G]]$ or in $(x)[[x \; \epsilon \; G] \supset [x \; \epsilon \; H]]$. Recall that "$(x)[[x \; \epsilon \; F] \supset [x \; \epsilon \; G]]$" is an abbreviation for "$[(x \setminus [[x \; \epsilon \; F] \supset [x \; \epsilon \; G]]) \; \epsilon \; A]$". In fact, x is never mentioned in a proposition of the form $(x)(\cdots x \cdots)$, though the usual way of reading the universal quantifier "(x)" as "for all ex" wrongly suggests that x is mentioned in $(x)(\cdots x \cdots)$. Just as every occurrence of "x" in "$(x \setminus (\cdots x \cdots))$" is a bound occurrence of "x" relatively to "$(x \setminus (\cdots x \cdots))$", as was pointed out in 17.12, so also every occurrence of "x" in "$(x)(\cdots x \cdots)$" is a bound occurrence of "x" relatively to "$(x)(\cdots x \cdots)$".

21.20. In the following proof we are to think of $(\cdots x \cdots)$ as some proposition which may or may not mention x, and we are to think of $(---x---)$ as some other proposition which may or may not mention x. In case x is not mentioned by $(\cdots x \cdots)$, we can still assume that there is an attribute $(x \setminus (\cdots x \cdots))$ assigned to x by $(\cdots x \cdots)$, and so we can regard $[(x \setminus (\cdots x \cdots)) \, \epsilon \, \mathsf{A}]$, that is, $(x)(\cdots x \cdots)$ as being a proposition. (If x is not mentioned by $(\cdots x \cdots)$, the attribute $(x \setminus (\cdots x \cdots))$ can be taken to be any universal attribute if $(\cdots x \cdots)$ is a true proposition, and any empty attribute if $(\cdots x \cdots)$ is a false proposition.)

1	$(x)[(\cdots x \cdots) \supset (---x---)]$	hyp
2	$(x)(\cdots x \cdots)$	hyp
3	x $(x)(\cdots x \cdots)$	2, reit
4	$(x)[(\cdots x \cdots) \supset (---x---)]$	1, reit
5	$(\cdots x \cdots)$	3, u q elim
6	$(\cdots x \cdots) \supset (---x---)$	4, u q elim
7	$(---x---)$	5, 6, m p
8	$(x)(---x---)$	3–7, u q int
9	$(x)(\cdots x \cdots) \supset (x)(---x---)$	2–8, imp int
10	$(x)[(\cdots x \cdots) \supset (---x---)] \supset [(x)(\cdots x \cdots) \supset (x)(---x---)]$	1–9, imp int

21.21. From now on it will often be convenient to use the non-capital Greek letters phi, psi, and theta to indicate arbitrary contexts instead of using triple dots or triple dashes as has been done heretofore. Thus the notation "ϕx" can replace the notation "$(\cdots x \cdots)$", and the notation "ψx" can replace the notation "$(---x---)$", and the notation "ϕxy" can replace the notation "$(\cdots x \cdots y \cdots)$", and so on. For example, step 10 of 21.20 can be written:

$$(x)[\phi x \supset \psi x] \supset [(x)\phi x \supset (x)\psi x].$$

21.22.	1	$(x)[\phi x \, \& \, \psi x]$	hyp
	2	x $(x)[\phi x \, \& \, \psi x]$	1, reit
	3	$\phi x \, \& \, \psi x$	2, u q elim
	4	ϕx	2, conj elim
	5	$(x)\phi x$	2–4, u q int
	6	x $(x)[\phi x \, \& \, \psi x]$	1, reit
	7	$\phi x \, \& \, \psi x$	6, u q elim

8	$\mid \psi x$	7, conj elim
9	$(x)\psi x$	6–8, u q int
10	$(x)\phi x$ & $(x)\psi x$	5, 9, conj int

21.23. The above proof will now be presented in a shortened form. Steps 2 and 3 will be combined into a single step, and a single subordinate proof will be made to serve the purpose originally served by the two subordinate proofs. The combining of steps 2 and 3 into a single step is merely a shorthand procedure and is valid only as a kind of abbreviation for the longer process. The use of a single subordinate proof in place of two does not, however, need to be regarded here as an abbreviational device, since 21.13 requires that $(\cdots x \cdots)$ must be an item of the subordinate proof without requiring that $(\cdots x \cdots)$ has to be the last item of the subordinate proof, so that in 21.24 we can regard both steps 5 and 6 as direct consequences of the subordinate proof 2–4.

21.24.

1	$(x)[\phi x$ & $\psi x]$	hyp
2	$x\mid$ ϕx & ψx	1, reit, u q elim
3	ϕx	2, conj elim
4	ψx	2, conj elim
5	$(x)\phi x$	2–4, u q int
6	$(x)\psi x$	2–4, u q int
7	$(x)\phi x$ & $(x)\psi x$	5, 6, conj int

21.25. The converse of 21.24 can be proved thus:

1	$(x)\phi x$ & $(x)\psi x$	hyp
2	$x\mid$ $(x)\phi x$ & $(x)\psi x$	1, reit
3	$(x)\phi x$	2, conj elim
4	$(x)\psi x$	2, conj elim
5	ϕx	3, u q elim
6	ψx	4, u q elim
7	ϕx & ψx	5, 6, conj int
8	$(x)[\phi x$ & $\psi x]$	2–7, u q int

21.26. Notice that the reiterations employed in 21.22, 21.24, and 21.25 are all valid, because in each case x is not really mentioned by the reiterated proposition. (See 21.19.) On the other hand, we assume that x is possibly mentioned by ϕx and ψx. Hence these latter propositions could not be reiterated into a subordinate proof which is general with respect to x. In particular, the following method of deriving $(x)[\phi x \ \& \ \psi x]$ from $[(x)\phi x \ \& \ (x)\psi x]$ is *incorrect:*

1	$(x)\phi x \ \& \ (x)\psi x$	hyp
2	$(x)\phi x$	1, conj elim
3	$(x)\psi x$	1, conj elim
4	ϕx	2, u q elim
5	ψx	3, u q elim
6	x | ϕx	4, reit (*invalid*)
7	ψx	5, reit (*invalid*)
8	$\phi x \ \& \ \psi x$	6, 7, conj int
9	$(x)[\phi x \ \& \ \psi x]$	6–8, u q int

The following form of the proof, however, would be just as correct as 21.25:

1	$(x)\phi x \ \& \ (x)\psi x$	hyp
2	$(x)\phi x$	1, conj elim
3	$(x)\psi x$	1, conj elim
4	x | ϕx	2, reit, u q elim
5	ψx	3, reit, u q elim
6	$\phi x \ \& \ \psi x$	4, 5, conj int
7	$(x)[\phi x \ \& \ \psi x]$	4–6, u q int

In the above proof, x is not mentioned in the reiterated propositions $(x)\phi x$ and $(x)\psi x$, so the reiterations are valid and are compatible with the fact that the subordinate proof 4–6 is general with respect to x.

21.27. Another point to notice in connection with 21.25 is that there is no way to apply the universal quantifier elimination rule directly to step 2. This rule cannot be applied to *part* of a propositional item. Since we wish to apply it to part of step 2, we must first separate step 2 into parts to which it can be applied. This separation is accomplished by conjunction elimination, giving steps 3 and 4 of 21.25. We then apply the rule of universal quantifier elimination to the separate parts to get steps 5 and 6. It would also be wrong to suppose that step 7 of 21.25 could be treated as following from step 2 by universal quantifier elimination. The quantifier eliminated by the use of this rule must always have the appearance of being prefixed to the whole expression for the step to which the rule is applied, and not merely to the left part of it. In the simplest form of the use of the rule of universal quantifier elimination, we simply drop the universal quantifier (provided, as we have just said, that it is prefixed to the *whole* expression and not just to part of it). This is the form of the rule used in 21.19, 21.20, 21.22, 21.24, 21.25. It is the special case where a of 21.12 is chosen as being simply x itself. However, in step 2 of 21.15 we not only drop the universal quantifier, but we also replace x by $(y \setminus [c = y])$. Here $(y \setminus [c = y])$ corresponds to a of 21.12 and is clearly different from x. Another example of a use of universal quantifier elimination that involves more than mere dropping of the universal quantifier is to be found in step 3 of 21.18. Here the quantifier is dropped and x is replaced by a. Thus the rule of universal quantifier elimination in any case involves the dropping of a universal quantifier (prefixed to the *whole* of an expression), and it may or may not also involve a replacement of x by something else such as a or $(y \setminus [c = y])$ in all those places where x is mentioned in the proposition to which the universal quantifier was prefixed.

21.28. From 21.24, 21.25, and the rule of coimplication introduction, we can get the result:

$$(x)[\phi x \ \& \ \psi x] \equiv [(x)\phi x \ \& \ (x)\psi x].$$

We will call this the distributive law of universal quantification into conjunction.

21.29.

1		$p \ \mathsf{v} \ (x)\phi x$	hyp
2	x	$p \ \mathsf{v} \ (x)\phi x$	1, reit
3		p	hyp
4		$p \ \mathsf{v} \ \phi x$	3, dis int

5	$\underline{\quad (x)\phi x}$	hyp
6	ϕx	5, u q elim
7	$p \vee \phi x$	6, dis int
8	$p \vee \phi x$	2, 3–4, 5–7, dis elim
9	$(x)[p \vee \phi x]$	2–8, u q int

Notice that we presume that x is not mentioned in p, since no indication is given that it may be mentioned there. (See the last two sentences of paragraph 21.6.) Hence, since x is not mentioned in $(x)\phi x$ either, it is not mentioned in step 1 above, so the reiteration from step 1 to step 2 is valid.

21.30. It is apparently not possible to derive $[p \vee (x)\phi x]$ from $(x)[p \vee \phi x]$ by use of rules so far available, but the implication of $[p \vee (x)\phi x]$ by $(x)[p \vee \phi x]$ is ordinarily treated as a valid principle of universal quantification. We are able to assume a further rule that guarantees this implication and still permits a consistency proof of the system. The rule is as follows:

21.31. Elimination rule relating universal quantification and disjunction ("u q dis"): $[p \vee (x)\phi x]$ is a direct consequence of $(x)[p \vee \phi x]$. Schematically,

| 1 | $\underline{\quad (x)[p \vee \phi x]}$ | hyp |
| 2 | $p \vee (x)\phi x$ | 1, u q dis |

In this rule, as in 21.29, it is assumed that x is not mentioned by p.

21.32. The following result is closely analogous to the rule stated in 21.31, follows from it, and can be referred to by the same name:

1	$\underline{\quad (x)[\phi x \vee p]}$	hyp
2	$x \mid \phi x \vee p$	1, reit, u q elim
3	$p \vee \phi x$	2, comm dis (8.10)
4	$(x)[p \vee \phi x]$	2–3, u q int
5	$p \vee (x)\phi x$	4, u q dis
6	$(x)\phi x \vee p$	5, comm dis (8.10)

21.33. Following the method used in 21.29, it is clearly possible to derive $(x)[\phi x \vee p]$ from $[(x)\phi x \vee p]$, in other words, to establish the converse of 21.32. Gathering these results together and using the rule of coimplication introduction, we see that we can prove

$$[p \lor (x)\phi x] \equiv (x)[p \lor \phi x],$$
$$[(x)\phi x \lor p] \equiv (x)[\phi x \lor p].$$

These next two coimplications can also be proved without difficulty:

$$[p \,\&\, (x)\phi x] \equiv (x)[p \,\&\, \phi x],$$
$$[(x)\phi x \,\&\, p] \equiv (x)[p \,\&\, \phi x].$$

Also this coimplication:

$$p \equiv (x)p.$$

In the above coimplications it is understood that x is not mentioned in p.

21.34.

1	$(x)[p \supset \phi x]$		hyp
2	p		hyp
3	x	p	2, reit
4		$p \supset \phi x$	1, reit, u q elim
5		ϕx	3, 4, m p
6	$(x)\phi x$		3–5, u q int
7	$p \supset (x)\phi x$		2–6, imp int

Here and elsewhere it is assumed that x is not mentioned in p. See end of 21.6.

21.35.

1	$p \supset (x)\phi x$		hyp
2	x	p	hyp
3		$p \supset (x)\phi x$	1, reit
4		$(x)\phi x$	2, 3, m p
5		ϕx	4, u q elim
6	$p \supset \phi x$		2–5, imp int
7	$(x)[p \supset \phi x]$		2–6, u q int

21.36. From 21.34 and 21.35 we can obtain the coimplication,

$$[p \supset (x)\phi x] \equiv (x)[p \supset \phi x].$$

Using the method of 21.20 it is also possible to prove,

$$(x)[\phi x \supset p] \supset [(x)\phi x \supset p],$$

but the converse of this implication is not logically valid.

21.37. Suppose that some proposition ψx is such that we can give a categorical proof of it that is general with respect to x. Then it is possible to give a categorical proof of $(x)\psi x$. This is done as follows:

$$
\begin{array}{ll}
\quad x \quad \cdot & \\
\qquad \cdot & \\
\qquad \cdot & \\
\quad \psi x & \\
\quad (x)\psi x & \text{u q int}
\end{array}
$$

The original proof of ψx, in other words, is simply rewritten as a subordinate proof that is general with respect to x, and the required result is then obtained by universal quantifier introduction. For example, we can give a categorical proof of $[[\phi y \,\&\, \theta y] \supset \theta y]$ that is general with respect to y as follows:

$$
\begin{array}{lll}
1 & \phi y \,\&\, \theta y & \text{hyp} \\
2 & \theta y & \text{1, conj elim} \\
3 & [\phi y \,\&\, \theta y] \supset \theta y & \text{1–2, imp int}
\end{array}
$$

Hence we can give a categorical proof of $(y)[[\phi y \,\&\, \theta y] \supset \theta y]$ thus:

$$
\begin{array}{llll}
1 & y & \phi y \,\&\, \theta y & \text{hyp} \\
2 & & \theta y & \text{1, conj elim} \\
3 & & [\phi y \,\&\, \theta y] \supset \theta y & \text{1–2, imp int} \\
4 & & (y)[[\phi y \,\&\, \theta y] \supset \theta y] & \text{1–3, u q int}
\end{array}
$$

21.38. The interchangeability of two immediately adjacent universal quantifiers is shown by the following proof:

$$
\begin{array}{lllll}
1 & & & (x)(y)\phi xy & \text{hyp} \\
2 & y & x & (x)(y)\phi xy & \text{1, reit} \\
3 & & & (y)\phi xy & \text{2, u q elim} \\
4 & & & \phi xy & \text{3, u q elim} \\
5 & & (x)\phi xy & & \text{2–4, u q int} \\
6 & & (y)(x)\phi xy & & \text{2–5, u q int}
\end{array}
$$

Here ϕxy is any proposition that may mention x or y or both of them or neither of them. The essential method of the above proof is seen to be to remove the quantifiers successively and then put them

back on again in the order we desire. In a similar way it is possible
to derive $(x)(z)(y)\psi xyz$, $(z)(y)(x)\psi xyz$, and $(y)(z)(x)\psi xyz$ from

$$(x)(y)(z)\psi xyz.$$

(This general method has close affinity with that used in 6.10, 6.11,
8.10, and 8.11.)

21.39. Observe that the reiteration at step 2 of 21.38 is a reiteration
into two general subordinate proofs, an outer one general with respect
to y and an inner one general with respect to x, so the reiterated proposition can mention neither x nor y. Clearly $(x)(y)\phi xy$ satisfies this
requirement. It does not mention x because no proposition of the
form $(x)(\cdots x \cdots)$ mentions x, and it does not mention y because, for
a similar reason, the part of it $(y)\phi xy$ does not mention y. Notice
that $(y)\phi xy$ may mention x even though $(x)(y)\phi xy$ does not do so.
Similarly, $(\cdots x \cdots)$ may mention x even though $(x)(\cdots x \cdots)$ does
not do so.

21.40. Since $(x)(y)\phi xy$ can be derived from $(y)(x)\phi xy$ by the same
general method as is used in 21.38, we can establish the coimplication,

$$(x)(y)\phi xy \equiv (y)(x)\phi xy.$$

We could also establish such a coimplication as the following:

$$(x)(y)(z)\psi xyz \equiv (z)(y)(x)\psi xyz.$$

It is also possible to derive $(x)(y)\phi xy$ and $(x)(y)\phi yx$ from each other.
This can be done since $(x)(y)\phi xy$ and $(x)(z)\phi zx$ are easily derivable
from each other and since $(x)(z)\phi zx$ and $(x)(y)\phi yx$ are easily derivable from each other. By going back to the theory of abstracts it
can also be argued that $(x)(y)\phi yx$ and $(y)(x)\phi xy$ are really the same
proposition. Using this fact we can then derive $(x)(y)\phi xy$ and
$(x)(y)\phi yx$ from each other by the method of **21.38**.

EXERCISES

Prove:

1. $[[F \cap G] \epsilon A] \supset [G \epsilon A]$.
2. $[(-(-F)) \epsilon A] \supset [F \epsilon A]$.
3. $[[F \cap (-F)] \epsilon A] \supset p$.
4. $p \equiv (x)p$. (Here p does not mention x. See end of 21.6.)

5. $[p \;\&\; (x)\phi x] \equiv (x)[p \;\&\; \phi x]$.   (Here p does not mention x.)

6. $(x)(z)(y)\phi xyz \supset (z)(y)(x)\phi xyz$.

7. $(y)[[\phi y \lor (x)\psi xy] \supset (x)[\phi y \lor \psi xy]]$.   (Here ϕy does not mention x.)

8. $[(x)[[\phi x \lor \psi x] \supset \theta x] \;\&\; (z)\phi z] \supset (z)\theta z$.

9. $(x)[(y)\phi xy \;\&\; (z)\psi z] \supset (z)(y)(x)[\phi xy \;\&\; \psi z]$.

10. $(y)[(x)[[x = y] \supset \theta xy] \equiv \theta yy]$.

11. $[F \,\epsilon\, A] \equiv (y)[y \,\epsilon\, F]$.

12. $(z)[[[z \cup (-z)] \,\epsilon\, A] \equiv (x)[[x \,\epsilon\, z] \lor \sim[x \,\epsilon\, z]]]$.

13. $(x)\psi x \equiv (y)\psi y$.

14. $(y)(x)(y)\phi xy \equiv (y)(x)\phi yx$.

15. $(z)(x)(y)(w)\theta yxw \equiv (x)(y)(w)\theta wxy$.   (Here θyxw does not mention z.)

22. Existence and the Existence Quantifier

22.1. An attribute is said to be **non-empty** or **existent** if something has the attribute. Thus non-emptiness is an attribute of attributes. It applies to just those attributes which themselves apply to something. An attribute is empty if its complement is universal. It is non-empty if its complement is not universal.

22.2. The capital letter "E" will be used to denote the attribute of non-emptiness. Thus $[F \,\epsilon\, E]$ is the proposition that F has the attribute E, in other words, that F is non-empty (existent). Thus if F is the attribute A (universality), then $[A \,\epsilon\, E]$ is the true proposition to the effect that universality is non-empty, in other words to the effect that universality applies to something. The proposition $[E \,\epsilon\, A]$, incidentally, is false, because non-emptiness is not a universal attribute. We could also speak in terms of classes instead of attributes. Then we would say that some classes are existent (non-empty) and others are non-existent (empty), and that E is the class of all existent classes. The proposition $[F \,\epsilon\, E]$ would then be read as asserting that the class F is a member of the class of existent (non-empty) classes. If F is the class of blue things, then $[F \,\epsilon\, E]$ would be the true proposition to the effect that the class of blue things is a non-empty class, in other words, to the effect that something is blue. In terms of attributes we would say that F is the attribute "blue" (instead of the class of blue things) and that $[F \; \epsilon \; \mathsf{E}]$ is the proposition to the effect that the attribute "blue" is existent, and hence, as before, to the effect that something is blue. It is important to emphasize that the words "existent" and "existence" here mean respectively "non-empty" and "non-emptiness". For example, $[(x \setminus [x = x]) \; \epsilon \; \mathsf{E}]$ does *not* assert that the attribute $(x \setminus [x = x])$ "exists" in the sense that "there is such an attribute as $(x \setminus [x = x])$", but rather it does assert that the attribute of self-identity $(x \setminus [x = x])$ is existent in the sense of being a non-empty attribute. The fact that we are using the expression "$(x \setminus [x = x])$" as the name of the attribute of self-identity indicates that we take it for granted that there is such an attribute as self-identity. It is a further question, however, as to whether self-identity is an empty or a non-empty attribute. It happens to be possible to show that self-identity is non-empty and even that it is universal. The attribute of emptiness can be regarded as being the complement of E, that is, as $(-\mathsf{E})$. An example of an empty attribute is the attribute of non-self-identity, $(x \setminus \sim[x = x])$. The following is therefore a true proposition: $[(x \setminus \sim[x = x]) \; \epsilon \; (-\mathsf{E})]$. This proposition asserts that non-self-identity is empty, in other words, that there is nothing that is non-self-identical. We are not denying that there is an attribute of non-self-identity, but we are denying that non-self-identity applies to anything.

22.3. The rule of **existence introduction** ("exist int") or non-emptiness introduction asserts that $[F \; \epsilon \; \mathsf{E}]$ is a direct consequence of $[a \; \epsilon \; F]$. This rule may be expressed schematically thus:

$$
\begin{array}{ll}
1 \;\Big|\; a \; \epsilon \; F & \text{hyp} \\
2 \;\;\;\; F \; \epsilon \; \mathsf{E} & \text{1, exist int}
\end{array}
$$

Step 1 asserts that a has the attribute F. Step 2 follows from step 1 by existence introduction and asserts that F is non-empty, in other words, that F applies to something.

22.4. The rule of **existence elimination** ("exist elim") or non-emptiness elimination asserts that p is a direct consequence of $[F \; \epsilon \; \mathsf{E}]$ and a subordinate proof which is general with respect to x, which has $[x \; \epsilon \; F]$ as its only hypothesis, and which has p as one of its items.

It is assumed that p does not mention x.   (See end of paragraph 21.6.)
The rule can be expressed schematically thus:

$$
\begin{array}{c|c}
\vdots & \vdots \\
i & F \,\epsilon\, \mathbf{E} \\
j & x\big|\ \ x \,\epsilon\, F \qquad\qquad\qquad\text{hyp} \\
\vdots & \vdots \\
k & \big|\ \ p \\
m & p \qquad\qquad\qquad\qquad\qquad i,\ j\text{–}k,\ \text{exist elim}
\end{array}
$$

Notice that the reason given for step m involves a reference to the
step $[F \,\epsilon\, \mathbf{E}]$ as well as to the subordinate proof j–k.   This rule is like
universality introduction in requiring a subordinate proof that is
general with respect to some entity x, but it is unlike universality
introduction in the fact that the general subordinate proof must have
a hypothesis, and in the fact that reference must be made to a step
outside the subordinate proof and of the form $[F \,\epsilon\, \mathbf{E}]$.   The hypothesis
of the subordinate proof must be $[x \,\epsilon\, F]$, where x is the entity with
respect to which the subordinate proof is general.   It is assumed that
x is not mentioned by the last step p of the subordinate proof, as we
infer from the fact that there is no indication x may be mentioned
by p.   The proposition p may be written outside the subordinate
proof and considered as following from it and the proposition $[F \,\epsilon\, \mathbf{E}]$.
It is essential for the validity of this rule that p does not mention x.
Actually, p does not have to be the last item of the subordinate proof.
It could be any propositional item of the subordinate proof, provided
that it does not mention x.   We now present some proofs using the
two existence rules.

22.5.

1	$[G \cap H] \,\epsilon\, \mathbf{E}$	hyp
2	$x\big|\ \ x \,\epsilon\, [G \cap H]$	hyp
3	$[x \,\epsilon\, G]\ \&\ [x \,\epsilon\, H]$	2, 17.23
4	$x \,\epsilon\, G$	3, conj elim
5	$G \,\epsilon\, \mathbf{E}$	4, exist int
6	$G \,\epsilon\, \mathbf{E}$	1, 2–5, exist elim

Notice that, as required, x is not mentioned by $[G \in E]$. In applying the rule of existence elimination in order to obtain step 6, we choose F of 22.4 as $[G \cap H]$ and we choose p as $[G \in E]$. In a similar way, we can derive $[H \in E]$ from $[[G \cap H] \in E]$. Hence we can prove,

$$[[G \cap H] \in E] \supset [[G \in E] \And [H \in E]].$$

This means that if the intersection of two attributes is non-empty, so are the attributes themselves.

22.6.

1	$(x \setminus [[x = y] \And \phi x]) \in E$	hyp
2	$z \in (x \setminus [[x = y] \And \phi x]$	hyp
3	$[z = y] \And \phi z$	2, att elim
4	$z = y$	3, conj elim
5	ϕz	3, conj elim
6	ϕy	4, 5, id elim
7	ϕy	1, 2–6, exist elim
8	ϕy	hyp
9	$y = y$	id int
10	$[y = y] \And \phi y$	8, 9, conj int
11	$y \in (x \setminus [[x = y] \And \phi x])$	10, att int
12	$(x \setminus [[x = y] \And \phi x]) \in E$	11, exist int
13	$\phi y \equiv [(x \setminus [[x = y] \And \phi x]) \in E]$	2–7, 8–12, coimp int

Notice that, as required, z is not mentioned by step 6. It is also interesting to observe that in the first subordinate proof only elimination rules are used, while in the second subordinate proof only introduction rules are used.

22.7. Just as we let "$(x)\phi x$" serve as an abbreviation for "$[(x \setminus \phi x) \in A]$", so also we let "$(\exists x)\phi x$" serve as an abbreviation for "$[(x \setminus \phi x) \in E]$". In order to write in symbols the proposition, "Something is self-identical", we can then write merely "$(\exists x)[x = x]$" instead of the more complicated expression "$[(x \setminus [x = x]) \in E]$". The usual way of reading "$(\exists x)[x = x]$" is "There is an ex such that ex is identical with ex", or "For some ex, ex is identical with ex". We may read "$(\exists x)$" as "for some ex" or as "there is an ex such that", and we may read "$(\exists y)$" as "for some wye" or as "there is a wye such that", and similarly for "$(\exists z)$", "$(\exists w)$", and so on.   This same notation provides a simple way of saying in symbols that one attribute overlaps another in the sense that there is at least one thing to which both attributes apply.   Suppose that we wish to express in symbols the proposition that some house is made of metal, in other words, the proposition asserting that the attribute of being a house overlaps the attribute of being made of metal.   If H is the former attribute and M is the latter attribute, then the required proposition can be expressed as $(\exists x)[[x \ \epsilon \ H] \ \& \ [x \ \epsilon \ M]]$.   This may be read as, "For some ex, ex is a house and ex is made of metal", or it may be read in the more colloquial way as, "Some house is made of metal".   Similarly the proposition, "Some house is not made of metal", could be expressed as $(\exists x)[[x \ \epsilon \ H] \ \& \ \sim[x \ \epsilon \ M]]$, or equally well as $(\exists x)[[x \ \epsilon \ H] \ \& \ [x \ \epsilon \ (-M)]]$.   Such expressions as "$(\exists x)$", "$(\exists y)$", and "$(\exists z)$" will be called **existential quantifiers** or **existence quantifiers.** Just as x is not really mentioned in $(x)\phi x$, so also x is not really mentioned in $(\exists x)\phi x$.   This is because $(\exists x)\phi x$ is the same proposition as $[(x \setminus \phi x) \ \epsilon \ \mathsf{E}]$, and x is not mentioned in $(x \setminus \phi x)$.   Every occurrence of the expression "x" in the expression "$(\exists x)\phi x$" is therefore a bound occurrence.   Two derived rules will now be stated and their derivation indicated.

22.8. Rule of existence quantifier introduction ("e q int").   The proposition $(\exists x)\phi x$ is a consequence of ϕa.   Schematically,

$$
\begin{array}{ll}
1 \ \Big|_{-} \ \phi a & \text{hyp} \\
2 \ \Big| \ \ (\exists x)\phi x & \text{1, e q int}
\end{array}
$$

In the above rule we are to understand ϕa as being any proposition that may or may not mention a but that does not mention x except insofar as a itself may mention x or may be x.   As in 21.12, we are to suppose that a may mention x or even be x, though the symbolism, strictly speaking, does not indicate this fact.   We are to understand ϕx to be such that ϕa is the result of replacing x by a everywhere in ϕx where x is mentioned.   For example, if ϕa is $[a = a]$, we could regard ϕx as being $[x = x]$, or we could regard ϕx as being $[x = a]$, or we could regard it as being $[a = x]$, or even as $[a = a]$ itself.   This is the same as the situation described in 17.6, but with ϕa corresponding to $(\cdots a \cdots)$ and with ϕx corresponding to $(\cdots x \cdots)$.   We are here using the "second way" of 17.6.   The derivation of the rule of existence quantifier introduction from the rule of existence introduction is shown as follows:

$$
\begin{array}{ll}
1 & \phi a & \text{hyp} \\
2 & a \in (x \setminus \phi x) & \text{1, att int} \\
3 & (x \setminus \phi x) \in \mathsf{E} & \text{2, exist int} \\
4 & (\exists x)\phi x & \text{3, rep, def (22.7)}
\end{array}
$$

22.9. Rule of existence quantifier elimination ("e q elim"). The proposition p is a consequence of $(\exists x)\phi x$ and a subordinate proof that is general with respect to x, that has ϕx as its only hypothesis, and that has p as one of its items (ordinarily as its last item).[2] It is assumed, as in 22.4, that p does not mention x. The rule can be expressed schematically in this way:

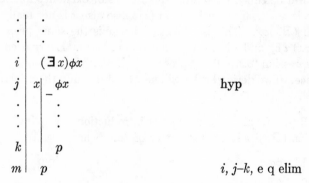

The following scheme indicates how the above rule is derivable from the rule of existence elimination, since if a subordinate proof can be constructed having ϕx as hypothesis and p as an item, so can a subordinate proof having $[x \in (x \setminus \phi x)]$ and p as an item. Of course this is a derivation only in the sense that it shows that if the rule of existence quantifier elimination is added to the system, no proposition p becomes provable that was not already provable by use of existence elimination. The scheme is as follows:

[2] In the statement of this rule we could equally well have written "$(\exists y)\phi y$" instead of "$(\exists x)\phi x$", provided that ϕy is a proposition exactly like ϕx except ϕy mentions y in those and only those places where ϕx mentions x. The propositions $(\exists x)\phi x$ and $(\exists y)\phi y$ are really the same proposition in virtue of 22.7 and 17.3.

$$
\begin{array}{ll}
\;\vdots \quad \Big| \quad \vdots & \\
i \quad (\exists x)\phi x & \\
i' \quad (x \setminus \phi x) \in \mathbf{E} & i, \text{ rep, def (22.7)} \\
j \quad \Big| x \Big| \; x \in (x \setminus \phi x) & \text{hyp} \\
j' \quad \Big| \;\; \phi x & j, \text{ att elim} \\
\;\vdots \quad \Big| \quad \vdots & \\
k \quad \Big| \;\; p & \\
m \quad p & i', j\text{–}k, \text{ exist elim}
\end{array}
$$

22.10. We now give 22.6 in a form that makes use of the new rules and abbreviation.

$$
\begin{array}{lll}
1 & (\exists x)[[x = y] \;\&\; \phi x] & \text{hyp} \\
2 & \quad x \;\; [x = y] \;\&\; \phi x & \text{hyp} \\
3 & \quad\quad x = y & 2, \text{ conj elim} \\
4 & \quad\quad \phi x & 2, \text{ conj elim} \\
5 & \quad\quad \phi y & 3, 4, \text{ id elim} \\
6 & \quad \phi y & 1, 2\text{–}5, \text{ e q elim} \\
7 & \quad \phi y & \text{hyp} \\
8 & \quad y = y & \text{id int} \\
9 & \quad [y = y] \;\&\; \phi y & 7, 8, \text{ conj int} \\
10 & \quad (\exists x)[[x = y] \;\&\; \phi x] & 9, \text{ e q int} \\
11 & \phi y \equiv (\exists x)[[x = y] \;\&\; \phi x] & 1\text{–}6, 7\text{–}10, \text{ coimp int}
\end{array}
$$

22.11. Some further proofs using the existence quantifier rules will now be given.

$$
\begin{array}{lll}
\textbf{22.12.} \quad 1 & (\exists x)\phi x & \text{hyp} \\
2 & \quad x \;\; \phi x & \text{hyp} \\
3 & \quad\quad \phi x \lor \psi x & 2, \text{ dis int} \\
4 & \quad\quad (\exists x)[\phi x \lor \psi x] & 3, \text{ e q int} \\
5 & \quad (\exists x)[\phi x \lor \psi x] & 1, 2\text{–}4, \text{ e q elim}
\end{array}
$$

22.13.

1	$(\exists x)\phi x \vee (\exists x)\psi x$		hyp
2		$(\exists x)\phi x$	hyp
3		$(\exists x)[\phi x \vee \psi x]$	2, 22.12
4		$(\exists x)\psi x$	hyp
5		$(\exists x)[\phi x \vee \psi x]$	4, similarly to 22.12
6	$(\exists x)[\phi x \vee \psi x]$		1, 2–3, 4–5, dis elim

22.14. The converse of 22.13 will now be proved:

1	$(\exists x)[\phi x \vee \psi x]$		hyp
2	x	$\phi x \vee \psi x$	hyp
3		ϕx	hyp
4		$(\exists x)\phi x$	3, e q int
5		$(\exists x)\phi x \vee (\exists x)\psi x$	4, dis int
6		ψx	hyp
7		$(\exists x)\psi x$	6, e q int
8		$(\exists x)\phi x \vee (\exists x)\psi x$	7, dis int
9		$(\exists x)\phi x \vee (\exists x)\psi x$	2, 3–5, 6–8, dis elim
10	$(\exists x)\phi x \vee (\exists x)\psi x$		1, 2–9, e q elim

22.15. From 22.13 and 22.14 we can get the distributive law of existence quantification into disjunction (compare with 21.28):

$$(\exists x)[\phi x \vee \psi x] \equiv [(\exists x)\phi x \vee (\exists x)\psi x]$$

22.16.

1	$(\exists x)[p \And \phi x]$		hyp
2	x	$p \And \phi x$	hyp
3		p	2, conj elim
4		ϕx	2, conj elim
5		$(\exists x)\phi x$	4, e q int
6		$p \And (\exists x)\phi x$	3, 5, conj int
7	$p \And (\exists x)\phi x$		1, 2–6, e q elim

22.17.

1	$p \And (\exists x)\phi x$	hyp
2	p	1, conj elim
3	$(\exists x)\phi x$	1, conj elim

4	x	ϕx	hyp
5		p	2, reit
6		$p \ \& \ \phi x$	4, 5, conj int
7		$(\exists x)[p \ \& \ \phi x]$	6, e q int
8	$(\exists x)[p \ \& \ \phi x]$		3, 4–7, e q elim

Notice that step 5 above is a valid reiteration because p is assumed not to mention x. Step 8 is valid because x is not really mentioned in $(\exists x)[p \ \& \ \phi x]$.

22.18. From 22.16 and 22.17 we get the coimplication,

$$(\exists x)[p \ \& \ \phi x] \equiv [p \ \& \ (\exists x)\phi x].$$

By similar methods we can also obtain the coimplication,

$$(\exists x)[\phi x \ \& \ p] \equiv [(\exists x)\phi x \ \& \ p].$$

The following two coimplications can be obtained by methods similar to those used for obtaining 22.15:

$$(\exists x)[p \lor \phi x] \equiv [p \lor (\exists x)\phi x],$$

$$(\exists x)[\phi x \lor p] \equiv [(\exists x)\phi x \lor p].$$

The following implication is seen to hold in virtue of 22.19 below:

$$(\exists x)[p \supset \phi x] \supset [p \supset (\exists x)\phi x],$$

but it is not possible to derive $(\exists x)[p \supset \phi x]$ from $[p \supset (\exists x)\phi x]$. Just because p implies that something has an attribute F, it does not follow, in this system of logic, that there is some particular thing a such that p implies that a has F. The fact that $(\exists x)[p \supset \phi x]$ does not follow from $[p \supset (\exists x)\phi x]$ is analogous to the fact that $[[p \supset q] \lor [p \supset r]]$ does not follow, in this system of logic, from $[p \supset [q \lor r]]$. The analogy can be seen more clearly by looking upon $(\exists x)[p \supset \phi x]$ as if it were a sort of infinite disjunction,

$$[p \supset \phi a_1] \lor [p \supset \phi a_2] \lor [p \supset \phi a_3] \lor \cdots,$$

and similarly, by regarding $(\exists x)\phi x$ as if it were the infinite disjunction,

$$\phi a_1 \lor \phi a_2 \lor \phi a_3 \lor \cdots.$$

Then we are saying that

$$[p \supset \phi a_1] \vee [p \supset \phi a_2] \vee [p \supset \phi a_3] \vee \cdots$$

does not follow from

$$p \supset [\phi a_1 \vee \phi a_2 \vee \phi a_3 \vee \cdots].$$

In addition to looking at $(\exists x)\phi x$ as if it were an infinite disjunction

$$\phi a_1 \vee \phi a_2 \vee \phi a_3 \vee \cdots,$$

it is often convenient to view $(x)\phi x$ as an infinite conjunction

$$\phi a_1 \ \& \ \phi a_2 \ \& \ \phi a_3 \ \& \ \cdots.$$

22.19.

1	$(\exists x)[p \supset \phi x]$	hyp
2	p	hyp
3	$(\exists x)[p \supset \phi x]$	1, reit
4	$x \mid p \supset \phi x$	hyp
5	p	2, reit
6	ϕx	4, 5, m p
7	$(\exists x)\phi x$	6, e q int
8	$(\exists x)\phi x$	3, 4–7, e q elim
9	$p \supset (\exists x)\phi x$	2–8, imp int

22.20. The interchangeability of two immediately adjacent existence quantifiers is shown by the following proof:

1	$(\exists x)(\exists y)\phi xy$	hyp
2	$x \mid (\exists y)\phi xy$	hyp
3	$y \mid \phi xy$	hyp
4	$(\exists x)\phi xy$	3, e q int
5	$(\exists y)(\exists x)\phi xy$	4, e q int
6	$(\exists y)(\exists x)\phi xy$	2, 3–5, e q elim
7	$(\exists y)(\exists x)\phi xy$	1, 2–6, e q elim

In a similar way we could, for example, derive $(\exists z)(\exists y)(\exists x)\phi xyz$ from $(\exists x)(\exists y)(\exists z)\phi xyz$.

22.21. Since $(\exists x)(\exists y)\phi xy$ can be derived from $(\exists y)(\exists x)\phi xy$ by the same general method as is used in 22.20, we can establish the coimplication,

$$(\exists x)(\exists y)\phi xy \equiv (\exists y)(\exists x)\phi xy.$$

We could also establish such a coimplication as the following:

$$(\exists x)(\exists y)(\exists z)\psi xyz \equiv (\exists z)(\exists y)(\exists x)\psi xyz.$$

22.22.

1	$(\exists x)(y)\phi xy$	hyp
2	y $(\exists x)(y)\phi xy$	1, reit
3	x $(y)\phi xy$	hyp
4	ϕxy	3, u q elim
5	$(\exists x)\phi xy$	4, e q int
6	$(\exists x)\phi xy$	2, 3–5, e q elim
7	$(y)(\exists x)\phi xy$	2–6, u q int

22.23. From 22.22 we can obtain the implication,

$$(\exists x)(y)\phi xy \supset (y)(\exists x)\phi xy.$$

If ϕxy is the proposition, "x is a cause of y", then the proposition $(\exists x)(y)\phi xy$ would be the proposition, "There is an ex such that, for every wye, ex is a cause of wye", or in ordinary language, "There is something which is a cause of all things". The proposition $(y)(\exists x)\phi xy$ would be, "For every wye, there is an ex such that ex is a cause of wye", or in ordinary language, "Each thing has a cause". Now we can see that if it is true that "There is something which is a cause of all things", then it must be true that "Each thing has a cause". But from the fact that each thing has a cause it does not follow that there is a cause of all things. Hence it is not possible, in general, to derive $(\exists x)(y)\phi xy$ from $(y)(\exists x)\phi xy$. The derivation can be carried out, however, in case ϕxy is of the form $[\psi x \,\&\, \theta y]$ or of the form $[\psi x \lor \theta y]$. We now carry out this derivation for the first of these two cases. That is, we derive $(\exists x)(y)[\psi x \,\&\, \theta y]$ from $(y)(\exists x)[\psi x \,\&\, \theta y]$.

22.24.

1	$(y)(\exists x)[\psi x \,\&\, \theta y]$	hyp
2	$(\exists x)[\psi x \,\&\, \theta y]$	1, u q elim
3	x $\psi x \,\&\, \theta y$	hyp
4	ψx	3, conj elim

5	y	$(y)(\exists x)[\psi x \mathbin{\&} \theta y]$	1, reit
6		$(\exists x)[\psi x \mathbin{\&} \theta y]$	5, u q elim
7	x	$\psi x \mathbin{\&} \theta y$	hyp
8		θy	7, conj elim
9		θy	6, 7–8, e q elim
10		ψx	4, reit
11		$\psi x \mathbin{\&} \theta y$	9, 10, conj int
12		$(y)[\psi x \mathbin{\&} \theta y]$	5–11, u q int
13		$(\exists x)(y)[\psi x \mathbin{\&} \theta y]$	12, e q int
14		$(\exists x)(y)[\psi x \mathbin{\&} \theta y]$	2, 3–13, e q elim

Notice that it is assumed in the above proof that y is not mentioned in ψx, since otherwise we would have written "ψxy" instead of "ψx". Notice, similarly, that we assume that x is not mentioned in θy, since otherwise we would have written "θxy" instead of "θy". The reiteration at step 5 is valid because neither x nor y is really mentioned in step 1, and the only occurrences of "x" and "y" in "$(y)(\exists x)[\psi x \mathbin{\&} \theta y]$" are bound occurrences. Step 9 is valid because x is not mentioned in θy. The reiteration at step 10 is valid because y is not mentioned in ψx. Step 9 could not have been obtained from step 3 in the same way that step 10 was, because y may be mentioned in θy, so that it would not be permissible to reiterate θy into a subordinate proof that is general with respect to y. For a similar reason, step 6 could not be treated as a reiteration of step 2.

22.25. The following proofs are given mainly to illustrate more completely the use of the quantifier rules, but they also provide a demonstration of the second case mentioned at the end of 22.23.

22.26.	1	$(\exists x)[\psi x \vee \phi y]$	hyp
	2	x	$\psi x \vee \phi y$	hyp
	3		ψx	hyp
	4		$(\exists x)\psi x$	3, e q int
	5		$(\exists x)\psi x \vee \phi y$	4, dis int
	6		ϕy	hyp
	7		$(\exists x)\psi x \vee \phi y$	6, dis int

8		$\mid$	$(\exists x)\psi x \vee \phi y$	2, 3–5, 6–7, dis elim
9		$(\exists x)\psi x \vee \phi y$		1, 2–8, e q elim

22.27.

1	$(y)(\exists x)[\psi x \vee \phi y]$	hyp
2	$(y)(\exists x)[\psi x \vee \phi y]$	1, reit
3	$(\exists x)[\psi x \vee \phi y]$	2, u q elim
4	$(\exists x)\psi x \vee \phi y$	3, 22.26
5	$(y)[(\exists x)\psi x \vee \phi y]$	2–4, u q int
6	$(\exists x)\psi x \vee (y)\phi y$	5, u q dis (21.31)
7	$(\exists x)\psi x$	hyp
8	ψx	hyp
9	ψx	8, reit
10	$\psi x \vee \phi y$	9, dis int
11	$(y)[\psi x \vee \phi y]$	9–10, u q int
12	$(\exists x)(y)[\psi x \vee \phi y]$	11, e q int
13	$(\exists x)(y)[\psi x \vee \phi y]$	7, 8–12, e q elim
14	$(y)\phi y$	hyp
15	$(y)\phi y$	14, reit
16	ϕy	15, u q elim
17	$\psi x \vee \phi y$	16, dis int
18	$(y)[\psi x \vee \phi y]$	15–17, u q int
19	$(\exists x)(y)[\psi x \vee \phi y]$	18, e q int
20	$(\exists x)(y)[\psi x \vee \phi y]$	6, 7–13, 14–19, dis elim

22.28. From 22.24 we obtain the implication,

$$(y)(\exists x)[\psi x \,\&\, \theta y] \supset (\exists x)(y)[\psi x \,\&\, \theta y],$$

and from 22.27, using "θy" instead of "ϕy", we obtain the implication,

$$(y)(\exists x)[\psi x \vee \theta y] \supset (\exists x)(y)[\psi x \vee \theta y].$$

Hence we can establish

$$(y)(\exists x)\phi xy \supset (\exists x)(y)\phi xy$$

for the special cases where ϕxy is $[\psi x \,\&\, \theta y]$ or $[\psi x \vee \theta y]$, though not in general. (See 22.23.)

22.29. Some rules for negative universality (or non-universality) and for negative existence (or non-existence) will now be stated. These rules bear some affinity to the rules for negative conjunction and negative disjunction. They are not very important in themselves, but important quantifier rules are derivable from them.

22.30. Rule of negative universality introduction ("neg univ int"). $\sim[F \epsilon \mathsf{A}]$ is a direct consequence of $[(-F) \epsilon \mathsf{E}]$.

22.31. Rule of negative universality elimination ("neg univ elim"). $[(-F) \epsilon \mathsf{E}]$ is a direct consequence of $\sim[F \epsilon \mathsf{A}]$.

22.32. Rule of negative existence introduction ("neg exist int"). $\sim[F \epsilon \mathsf{E}]$ is a direct consequence of $[(-F) \epsilon \mathsf{A}]$.

22.33. Rule of negative existence elimination ("neg exist elim"). $[(-F) \epsilon \mathsf{A}]$ is a direct consequence of $\sim[F \epsilon \mathsf{E}]$.

22.34. The first two of the above four rules say in effect that the necessary and sufficient condition for an attribute not to be universal is that its complement should be existent (non-empty). The second two rules say in effect that the necessary and sufficient condition for an attribute not to be existent (and hence for it to be empty) is that its complement should be universal.

22.35. The following four quantifier rules can be easily obtained from the above four rules.

22.36. Rule of negative universal quantifier introduction ("neg u q int"). $\sim(x)\phi x$ is derivable from $(\exists x)\sim\phi x$.

22.37. Rule of negative universal quantifier elimination ("neg u q elim"). $(\exists x)\sim\phi x$ is derivable from $\sim(x)\phi x$.

22.38. Rule of negative existence quantifier introduction ("neg e q int"). $\sim(\exists x)\phi x$ is derivable from $(x)\sim\phi x$.

22.39. Rule of negative existence quantifier elimination ("neg e q elim"). $(x)\sim\phi x$ is derivable from $\sim(\exists x)\phi x$.

22.40.

1	$(x)\phi x$	hyp
2	x ϕx	1, reit, u q elim
3	$\sim\sim\phi x$	2, $\mathrm{neg_2}$ int
4	$(x)\sim\sim\phi x$	2–3, u q int
5	$\sim(\exists x)\sim\phi x$	4, neg e q int

22.41.

1	$\sim(\exists x)\sim\phi x$	hyp
2	$(x)\sim\sim\phi x$	1, neg e q elim
3	x $\sim\sim\phi x$	2, reit, u q elim
4	ϕx	3, neg_2 elim
5	$(x)\phi x$	3–4, u q int

22.42.

1	$(\exists x)\phi x$	hyp
2	x ϕx	hyp
3	$\sim\sim\phi x$	2, neg_2 int
4	$(\exists x)\sim\sim\phi x$	3, e q int
5	$(\exists x)\sim\sim\phi x$	1, 2–4, e q elim
6	$\sim(x)\sim\phi x$	5, neg u q int

22.43.

1	$\sim(x)\sim\phi x$	hyp
2	$(\exists x)\sim\sim\phi x$	1, neg u q elim
3	x $\sim\sim\phi x$	hyp
4	ϕx	3, neg_2 elim
5	$(\exists x)\phi x$	4, e q int
6	$(\exists x)\phi x$	3–5, e q elim

22.44. By 22.36–22.43 we have the result that each proposition in the left-hand column below implies and is implied by the corresponding proposition in the right-hand column.

$$(x)\phi x \qquad\qquad \sim(\exists x)\sim\phi x$$
$$\sim(x)\phi x \qquad\qquad (\exists x)\sim\phi x$$
$$(x)\sim\phi x \qquad\qquad \sim(\exists x)\phi x$$
$$\sim(x)\sim\phi x \qquad\qquad (\exists x)\phi x$$

22.45. The equivalences listed above can be referred to jointly under the name **De Morgan's theorem for quantifiers** ("d m q"), and 22.36–22.43 can be referred to in the same way.

22.46. The equivalence of the meaning of $(x)\phi x$ with that of $\sim(\exists x)\sim\phi x$ can be seen from reading the former as, "For every ex, phi ex is true", and the latter as, "It is false that, for some ex, phi ex is false". In a similar way, the members of each of the other pairs of 22.44 will be seen to have equivalent meanings.

22.47. If we regard $(x)\phi x$ as an infinite conjunction and $(\exists x)\phi x$ as an infinite disjunction in the way indicated in 22.18, then in saying that $(x)\phi x$ and $\sim(\exists x)\sim\phi x$ coimply each other, we are saying that the two propositions,

$$\phi a_1 \;\&\; \phi a_2 \;\&\; \phi a_3 \;\&\; \cdots$$

and

$$\sim[\sim\phi a_1 \vee \sim\phi a_2 \vee \sim\phi a_3 \vee \cdots]$$

coimply each other. This shows more clearly the analogy between the quantifier form of De Morgan's theorem and the ordinary form (10.34). Use of the quantifier form of De Morgan's theorem is illustrated in 22.48 and 22.49.

22.48.

1	$\sim(\exists x)[\phi x \;\&\; \psi x]$	hyp
2	$(\exists x)\phi x$	hyp
3	x ϕx	hyp
4	$\sim(\exists x)[\phi x \;\&\; \psi x]$	1, reit
5	$(x)\sim[\phi x \;\&\; \psi x]$	4, d m q (neg e q elim)
6	$\sim[\phi x \;\&\; \psi x]$	5, u q elim
7	$\sim\phi x \vee \sim\psi x$	6, d m (neg conj elim)
8	$\sim\sim\phi x$	3, neg$_2$ int
9	$\sim\psi x$	7, 8, m t p (10.11)
10	$(\exists x)\sim\psi x$	9, e q int
11	$(\exists x)\sim\psi x$	2, 3–10, e q elim

22.49.

1	$\sim(x)[\sim\phi x \vee \psi x]$	hyp
2	$(\exists x)\sim[\sim\phi x \vee \psi x]$	1, d m q (neg u q elim)
3	x $\sim[\sim\phi x \vee \psi x]$	hyp
4	$\phi x \;\&\; \sim\psi x$	3, d m
5	$(\exists x)[\phi x \;\&\; \sim\psi x]$	4, e q int
6	$(\exists x)[\phi x \;\&\; \sim\psi x]$	2, 3–5, e q elim

22.50. The Heyting intuitionistic logic (10.17) can be extended by adding to it the introduction and elimination rules for the universal and existence quantifiers, but not rules 22.36–22.39. In the resulting **quantified Heyting logic** there is still no rule of double negation elimination, no rules of attribute introduction or attribute elimination, no rules for identity, and no rules for "ϵ" or for couples; and the De Morgan rules fail to hold in complete generality, both the ordinary De Morgan rules and those for quantifiers. But the Heyting system does have the rule of reductio ad absurdum (negation introduction) in its unrestricted form.

22.51. In the quantified Heyting logic [3] we can obtain the following results:

(1) $(x)\phi x \supset \sim\sim(x)\phi x$

(2) $\sim\sim(x)\phi x \supset (x)\sim\sim\phi x$

(3) $(x)\sim\sim\phi x \equiv \sim\sim(x)\sim\sim\phi x$

(4) $\sim\sim(x)\sim\sim\phi x \equiv \sim(\exists x)\sim\phi x$

(5) $(\exists x)\phi x \supset (\exists x)\sim\sim\phi x$

(6) $(\exists x)\sim\sim\phi x \supset \sim\sim(\exists x)\phi x$

(7) $\sim\sim(\exists x)\phi x \equiv \sim\sim(\exists x)\sim\sim\phi x$

(8) $\sim\sim(\exists x)\sim\sim\phi x \equiv \sim(x)\sim\phi x$

(9) $(\exists x)\sim\phi x \supset \sim\sim(\exists x)\sim\phi x$

(10) $\sim\sim(\exists x)\sim\phi x \equiv \sim(x)\sim\sim\phi x$

(11) $\sim(x)\sim\sim\phi x \supset \sim(x)\phi x$

(12) $(x)\sim\phi x \equiv \sim\sim(x)\sim\phi x$

(13) $\sim\sim(x)\sim\phi x \equiv \sim(\exists x)\sim\sim\phi x$

(14) $\sim(\exists x)\sim\sim\phi x \equiv \sim(\exists x)\phi x$

(15) $\sim\sim[\sim\sim(x)\phi x \supset (x)\phi x]$

(16) $\sim\sim[(\exists x)\sim\sim\phi x \supset (\exists x)\phi x]$

(17) $\sim\sim[\sim\sim(\exists x)\phi x \supset (\exists x)\sim\sim\phi x]$

22.52. In the quantified Heyting logic the following results cannot be obtained, but they are obtainable in the system of logic of this book.

(1) $\sim\sim(x)\phi x \supset (x)\phi x$

(2) $(x)\sim\sim\phi x \supset \sim\sim(x)\phi x$

(3) $(\exists x)\sim\sim\phi x \supset (\exists x)\phi x$

(4) $\sim\sim(\exists x)\phi x \supset (\exists x)\sim\sim\phi x$

(5) $\sim\sim(\exists x)\sim\phi x \supset (\exists x)\sim\phi x$

(6) $\sim(x)\phi x \supset \sim(x)\sim\sim\phi x$

(7) $\sim\sim[(x)\sim\sim\phi x \supset \sim\sim(x)\phi x]$

[3] The following results are discussed in detail in Heyting's paper, "On Weakened Quantification", *Journal of Symbolic Logic*, vol. 11 (1946), pp. 119–21. See also the references in footnote 13 of the Foreword. For a system that combines quantified Heyting logic with modal logic, see my paper, "Intuitionistic Modal Logic with Quantifiers", *Portugaliae Mathematica*, vol. 7 (1948), pp. 113–18.

22.53. From 22.51 and 22.52 we can see that $(\exists x)\phi x$ is not derivable from $\sim(x)\sim\phi x$ in the quantified Heyting logic, because by (5)–(8) of 22.51 it would then be the case that $(\exists x)\phi x$ would be derivable from $(\exists x)\sim\sim\phi x$, contrary to the fact that (3) of 22.52 is not a provable implication in that system. It can also be seen from 22.51 and 22.52 that $(x)\phi x$ is not derivable from $\sim(\exists x)\sim\phi x$ in the quantified Heyting logic. In this case we note (1)–(4) of 22.51 and (1) of 22.52.

22.54. Derivation of $\sim(\exists x)\sim\phi x$ from $(x)\phi x$ in the quantified Heyting logic:

1	$(x)\phi x$	hyp
2	$(\exists x)\sim\phi x$	hyp
3	$x\ \sim\phi x$	hyp
4	$(x)\phi x$	1, reit
5	ϕx	4, u q elim
6	$\sim(\exists x)\sim\phi x$	3, 5, neg elim
7	$\sim(\exists x)\sim\phi x$	2, 3–6, e q elim
8	$\sim(\exists x)\sim\phi x$	2–7, neg int (See 10.16–10.18.)

The contradictory items of the subordinate proof 2–7 are steps 2 and 7. Step 8 is the denial of the hypothesis of this subordinate proof and follows from this subordinate proof by negation introduction, a rule not valid in our system.

22.55. Derivation of $\sim(x)\sim\phi x$ from $(\exists x)\phi x$ in the quantified Heyting logic:

1	$(\exists x)\phi x$	hyp
2	$(x)\sim\phi x$	hyp
3	$(\exists x)\phi x$	1, reit
4	$x\ \phi x$	hyp
5	$(x)\sim\phi x$	2, reit
6	$\sim\phi x$	5, u q elim
7	$\sim(\exists x)\phi x$	4, 6, neg elim
8	$\sim(\exists x)\phi x$	3, 4–7, e q elim
9	$\sim(x)\sim\phi x$	2–8, neg int (See 10.16–10.18.)

The contradictory items of the subordinate proof 2–8 are steps 3 and 8. Step 9 is the denial of the hypothesis of this subordinate proof and follows from this subordinate proof by negation introduction, a rule not valid in our system.

22.56. It will be recalled from 10.20 that the two-valued propositional calculus is obtainable by admitting all the introduction and elimination rules for implication, conjunction, disjunction, and negation, including the unrestricted rule of reductio ad absurdum as a rule of negation introduction. Of course the rules for identity are not included, nor are those for modal concepts, for couples, for attributes, for "ϵ", for universality, for existence, or for quantifiers. If the two-valued propositional calculus is extended by adding to it the introduction and elimination rules for quantifiers, the resulting system is known as the **lower functional calculus.** The theory of quantifiers of the present book differs from that of the lower functional calculus in not possessing the unrestricted reductio ad absurdum and in not possessing some other principles implied by the latter, such as the principle of excluded middle.

22.57. In order that our system can still be shown to be free from contradiction, the special restriction stated in 18.6 must be extended to apply as follows to any general subordinate proof: If such a subordinate proof has ϕx as its hypothesis and is general with respect to x, then ϕa cannot be an item which is a resultant of that subordinate proof.

22.58. The notion of resultant (18.5) must also be further extended so that if a subordinate proof $\mathfrak{I}$ is treated as general with respect to x, and if a is anything different from x, then each item of the subordinate proof $\mathfrak{I}$ must be assumed to have as a resultant and to be a resultant of each other item (of the main proof or of a proof subordinate to the main proof) that is exactly like the given item of $\mathfrak{I}$, except that it mentions a wherever the given item mentions x. This extension of the notion of resultant actually guarantees that 22.57 will be satisfied if the original form of the special restriction (18.6) is satisfied. A further important extension of the notion of resultant is this: We must regard $(\mathbf{A}F)$ as a resultant of (Fa). In examining a proof to see whether it satisfies the special restriction, the proof should first be rewritten in such a way that R32–R40 in 27.4 are used in place of the rules stated in this and the previous section.

EXERCISES

Prove:

1. $[F \; \epsilon \; \mathsf{E}] \supset [[F \cup G] \; \epsilon \; E]$.
2. $[(-(-F)) \; \epsilon \; \mathsf{E}] \supset [F \; \epsilon \; \mathsf{E}]$.
3. $[[F \cap (-F)] \; \epsilon \; \mathsf{E}] \supset p$.
4. $p \equiv (\exists x)p$.
5. $[p \vee (\exists x)\phi x] \equiv (\exists x)[p \vee \phi x]$.
6. $(y)[[(\exists z)\phi yz \supset \psi y] \supset [\phi yx \supset \psi y]]$.
7. $(\exists x)(\exists y)(\exists z)\theta xyz \supset (\exists z)(\exists x)(\exists y)\theta xyz$.
8. $(\exists x)\psi x \equiv (\exists y)\psi y$.
9. $(\exists x)\phi xx \equiv (\exists y)(\exists z)[[y = z] \mathbin{\&} \phi yz]$.
10. $(\exists x)[\phi x \supset p] \supset [(x)\phi x \supset p]$.
11. $(x)[\phi x \supset p] \equiv [(\exists x)\phi x \supset p]$.
12. $(\exists y)(\exists x)(\exists y)\phi xy \equiv (\exists y)(\exists x)\phi yx$.
13. (1)–(17) of 22.51, using the rules of the present system.
14. (1)–(17) of 22.51, using the rules of the Heyting system.
15. (1)–(7) of 22.52, using the rules of the present system.

23. Identity and Quantifiers in Modal Logic

23.1. We now present a few proofs concerned with identity in modal logic and quantifiers in modal logic.

23.2. 1 $\quad\square\quad a = a$ id int

        2 $\quad\square[a = a]$ 1–1, nec int (11.3)

23.3. 1 $\quad\square\quad [a = b] \vee \sim[a = b]$ ex mid id (14.4)

        2 $\quad\square[[a = b] \vee \sim[a = b]]$ 1–1, nec int

23.4. 1 $\quad a = b$ hyp

        2 $\quad\square[a = a]$ 23.2

        3 $\quad\square[a = b]$ 1, 2, id elim

23.5. 1 $\quad\square[a = b]$ hyp

        2 $\quad a = b$ 1, nec elim

23.6. From 23.4 and 23.5 we get the coimplication,

$$[a = b] \equiv \square[a = b].$$

This indicates that a is not contingently identical with b. If a is identical with b, then it is *necessarily* identical with b, and conversely, if a is necessarily identical with b, then a is identical with b.

23.7.

1	$\Box(x)\phi x$	hyp
2	x $\Box$ $\Box(x)\phi x$	1, reit
3	$(x)\phi x$	2, nec elim
4	ϕx	3, u q elim
5	$\Box\phi x$	2–4, nec int
6	$(x)\Box\phi x$	2–5, u q int

23.8. It is not possible to derive $\Box(x)\phi x$ from $(x)\Box\phi x$ unless a special rule to that effect is assumed. Such a rule would not violate the consistency of the system, and it would seem to be a valid principle.

23.9.

1	$(\exists x)\Diamond\phi x$	hyp
2	x $\Diamond\phi x$	hyp
3	$\Box$ ϕx	hyp
4	$(\exists x)\phi x$	3, e q int
5	$\Diamond(\exists x)\phi x$	2, 3–4, pos elim
6	$\Diamond(\exists x)\phi x$	1, 2–5, e q elim

23.10. It is not possible to derive $(\exists x)\Diamond\phi x$ from $\Diamond(\exists x)\phi x$ unless a special rule to this effect is assumed. Such a rule would not violate the consistency of the system, but it seems less clearly valid than does the rule suggested in 23.8. The derivation of $\Box(\exists x)\phi x$ from $(\exists x)\Box\phi x$ can be performed, but $(\exists x)\Box\phi x$ cannot be derived from $\Box(\exists x)\phi x$.

23.11.

1	$\Box(x)[\phi x \supset \psi x]$	hyp
2	$(\exists x)\Diamond\phi x$	hyp
3	x $\Diamond\phi x$	hyp
4	$\Box$ ϕx	hyp
5	$\Box(x)[\phi x \supset \psi x]$	1, reit
6	$(x)[\phi x \supset \psi x]$	5, nec elim
7	$\phi x \supset \psi x$	6, u q elim
8	ψx	4, 7, m p

$$
\begin{array}{ll}
9 \quad\quad \Diamond\psi x & \text{3, 4--8, pos elim} \\
10 \quad\quad (\exists x)\Diamond\psi x & \text{9, e q int} \\
11 \quad (\exists x)\Diamond\psi x & \text{2, 3--10, e q elim}
\end{array}
$$

23.12. Modal concepts will not be used in the system of logic developed in subsequent portions of this book. This omission is largely in the interest of simplicity and economy. Undoubtedly modal concepts are relevant to this subsequent material in many important ways, but space forbids further elaborations in this direction.

EXERCISES
Prove:

1. $\Diamond(\exists x)[\phi x \lor \psi x] \equiv \Diamond[(\exists x)\phi x \lor (\exists x)\psi x]$.
2. $\Box(x)[\phi x \mathbin{\&} \psi x] \equiv [\Box(x)\phi x \mathbin{\&} \Box(x)\psi x]$.
3. $\Box(x)[\phi x \supset \psi x] \supset [\Box(x)\phi x \supset \Box(x)\psi x]$.
4. $\Box(x)[\phi x \supset \psi x] \supset [\Diamond(\exists x)\phi x \supset \Diamond(\exists x)\psi x]$.
5. $\Box(x)[\phi x \supset \psi x] \supset [\Box(\exists x)\phi x \supset \Box(\exists x)\psi x]$.
6. $\Box(x)[\phi x \supset \psi x] \supset [\Diamond(x)\phi x \supset \Diamond(x)\psi x]$.
7. $\Box(x)[\phi x \supset \psi x] \supset [(x)\Box\phi x \supset (x)\Box\psi x]$.
8. $\Box(x)[\phi x \supset \psi x] \supset [(\exists x)\Diamond\phi x \supset (\exists x)\Diamond\psi x]$.
9. $\Box(x)[\phi x \supset \psi x] \supset [(\exists x)\Box\phi x \supset (\exists x)\Box\psi x]$.
10. $\Box(x)[\phi x \supset \psi x] \supset [(x)\Diamond\phi x \supset (x)\Diamond\psi x]$.
11. $\Box(y)[\phi y \supset \psi y] \supset [(\exists x)\Diamond[\phi x \mathbin{\&} \theta x] \supset \Diamond(\exists z)\psi z]$.

Chapter 6

FURTHER PROPERTIES OF RELATIONS AND ATTRIBUTES

24. Relations Assigned by Propositions

24.1. Just as a proposition ϕa assigns to a the attribute $(x \setminus \phi x)$, so a proposition ψab assigns to the couple (ab) an attribute which we will refer to as "$(xy \setminus \psi xy)$" or "the relation of ex to wye such that psi ex wye". We may speak of it as a relation because we regard relations as attributes of couples. For example, the proposition $\sim[a = b]$ assigns an attribute or relation to the couple (ab). The relation it assigns is the relation of non-identity. Thus non-identity is the relation $(xy \setminus \sim[x = y])$, and we may treat "$\neq$" as an abbreviation for "$(xy \setminus \sim[x = y])$". It will later be possible to prove the coimplication,

$$[a \neq b] \equiv \sim[a = b].$$

More generally, we will be able to prove the coimplication,

$$[a \, (xy \setminus \psi xy) \, b] \equiv \psi ab.$$

In order to derive the latter coimplication, it will be convenient to treat "$(xy \setminus \psi xy)$" as an abbreviation as follows:

24.2. "$(xy \setminus \psi xy)$" is an abbreviation for "$(z \setminus (\exists x)(\exists y)[[z = (xy)]$ & $\psi xy])$.

24.3. Rule of relation introduction ("rel int").

1	ψab	hyp
2	$(ab) = (ab)$	id int
3	$[(ab) = (ab)]$ & ψab	1, 2, conj int
4	$(\exists y)[[(ab) = (ay)]$ & $\psi ay]$	3, e q int
5	$(\exists x)(\exists y)[[(ab) = (xy)]$ & $\psi xy]$	4, e q int
6	$((z \setminus (\exists x)(\exists y)[[z = (xy)]$ & $\psi xy])(ab))$	5, att int (17.4)
7	$((xy \setminus \psi xy)(ab))$	6, rep, def (24.2)
8	$a \, (xy \setminus \psi xy) \, b$	7, rep, def (15.19)

167

24.4. Rule of relation elimination ("rel elim").

1	$a \, (xy \setminus \psi xy) \, b$	hyp
2	$((xy \setminus \psi xy)(ab))$	1, rep, def (15.19)
3	$((z \setminus (\exists x)(\exists y)[[z = (xy)] \,\&\, \psi xy])(ab))$	2, rep, def (24.2)
4	$(\exists x)(\exists y)[[(ab) = (xy)] \,\&\, \psi xy]$	3, att elim (17.5)
5	$x \quad (\exists y)[[(ab) = (xy)] \,\&\, \psi xy]$	hyp
6	$y \quad [(ab) = (xy)] \,\&\, \psi xy$	hyp
7	$(ab) = (xy)$	6, conj elim
8	ψxy	6, conj elim
9	$a = x$	7, coup elim (15.9)
10	$b = y$	7, coup elim
11	ψay	8, 9, id elim
12	ψab	10, 11, id elim
13	ψab	5, 6–12, e q elim
14	ψab	4, 5–13, e q elim

24.5. In 24.3 and 24.4 we are to assume that ψxy is any proposition, possibly but not necessarily one that mentions x or y or both of them. It is assumed that x and y do not mention each other and are different from each other in virtue of the stipulation of the next-to-last sentence of paragraph 21.6. The proposition ψab is to be thought of as the result of simultaneous replacement of x by a and of y by b everywhere in ψxy where x or y may be mentioned. The proofs 24.3 and 24.4 would not be valid as given if x or y were assumed to be mentioned in or to be a or b. However, it *is* possible by 24.3 and 24.4 to derive $[a \, (uv \setminus \psi uv) \, b]$ and ψab from each other when x and y are mentioned in or identical with a or b, provided that u and v are not mentioned in ψab, and provided that ψuv and ψxy are exactly alike except that ψuv mentions u in those places and only those places where ψxy mentions x, and similarly for v and y. But since $(uv \setminus \psi uv)$ is the same relation as $(xy \setminus \psi xy)$, we see that $[a \, (xy \setminus \psi xy) \, b]$ and ψab are even in this case derivable from each other by the method of 24.3 and 24.4, though in 24.4 it becomes necessary to use subordinate proofs that are general with respect to some such things as u and v in order that the reiteration into them of propositions mentioning x and y would be allowable. This change of the thing with respect to which a proof is general is to be regarded as a relatively minor or trivial change in a proof. Suppose that a subordinate proof S is general with respect to z (i.e., still holds no matter what z is replaced by) except that for some replacements of z a subordinate proof $\mathfrak{I}$, which is subordinate to S and which is general with respect to w_1, has to be rewritten as general with respect to w_2 instead of w_1. We do not regard this sort of exception as destroying the generality of S with respect to z. Thus we can regard 24.3 and 24.4 as general with respect to a and b. Similar remarks apply to 24.7 and 24.8.

24.6. From 24.3 and 24.4 we get the coimplication,

$$[a \ (xy \setminus \psi xy) \ b] \equiv \psi ab.$$

24.7. Rule of negative relation introduction ("neg rel int").

1	$\sim\psi ab$	hyp
2	x y $[(ab) = (xy)] \vee \sim[(ab) = (xy)]$	ex mid id
3	$(ab) = (xy)$	hyp
4	$\sim\psi ab$	1, reit
5	$a = x$	3, coup elim
6	$b = y$	3, coup elim
7	$\sim\psi xb$	4, 5, id elim
8	$\sim\psi xy$	6, 7, id elim
9	$\sim[(ab) = (xy)] \vee \sim\psi xy$	8, dis int
10	$\sim[(ab) = (xy)]$	hyp
11	$\sim[(ab) = (xy)] \vee \sim\psi xy$	10, dis int
12	$\sim[(ab) = (xy)] \vee \sim\psi xy$	2, 3–9, 10–11, dis elim
13	$\sim[[(ab) = (xy)] \ \& \ \psi xy]$	12, d m
14	$(y)\sim[[(ab) = (xy)] \ \& \ \psi xy]$	2–13, u q int
15	$\sim(\exists y)[[(ab) = (xy)] \ \& \ \psi xy]$	14, d m q
16	$(x)\sim(\exists y)[[(ab) = (xy)] \ \& \ \psi xy]$	2–15, u q int
17	$\sim(\exists x)(\exists y)[[(ab) = (xy)] \ \& \ \psi xy]$	16, d m q
18	$\sim((z \setminus (\exists x)(\exists y)[[z = (xy)] \ \& \ \psi xy])(ab))$	17, neg att int
19	$\sim((xy \setminus \psi xy)(ab))$	18, rep, def (24.2)
20	$\sim[a \ (xy \setminus (\psi xy) \ b]$	19, rep, def (15.19)

24.8. Rule of negative relation elimination ("neg rel elim").

1	$\sim[a\ (xy \setminus \psi xy)\ b]$	hyp
2	$\sim((xy \setminus \psi xy)(ab))$	1, rep, def (15.19)
3	$\sim((z \setminus (\exists x)(\exists y)[[z = (xy)]\ \&\ \psi xy])(ab))$	2, rep, def (24.2)
4	$\sim(\exists x)(\exists y)[[(ab) = (xy)]\ \&\ \psi xy]$	3, neg att elim
5	$(x)\sim(\exists y)[[(ab) = (xy)]\ \&\ \psi xy]$	4, d m q
6	$\sim(\exists y)[[(ab) = (ay)]\ \&\ \psi ay]$	5, u q elim
7	$(y)\sim[[(ab) = (ay)]\ \&\ \psi ay]$	6, d m q
8	$\sim[[(ab) = (ab)]\ \&\ \psi ab]$	7, u q elim
9	$\sim[(ab) = (ab)]\ \mathbf{v}\ \sim\psi ab$	8, d m
10	$(ab) = (ab)$	id int
11	$\sim\psi ab$	9, 10, m t p (10.11)

24.9. From 24.7 and 24.8 we get the coimplication,

$$\sim[a\ (xy \setminus \psi xy)\ b] \equiv \sim\psi ab.$$

24.10. "$\neq$" is an abbreviation for "$(xy \setminus \sim[x = y])$".

24.11. From 24.6 and 24.10 we get the coimplication,

$$[a \neq b] \equiv \sim[a = b],$$

and from 24.9 and 24.10 we get the coimplication,

$$\sim[a \neq b] \equiv \sim\sim[a = b].$$

From the latter coimplication we can of course easily get

$$\sim[a \neq b] \equiv [a = b].$$

24.12. All occurrences of the expressions "x" and "y" in the expression "$(xy \setminus \psi xy)$" are bound occurrences relatively to "$(xy \setminus \psi xy)$", since this is true for the expression for which the latter is an abbreviation by 24.2. See 17.12. The expression "$(xy \setminus \psi xy)$" may be called a **double abstract** or a **relational abstract**.

24.13. Neither x nor y is really mentioned in the relation $(xy \setminus \psi xy)$, just as x is not really mentioned in the attribute $(x \setminus \phi x)$.

24.14. If we wished, we could now define "$\equiv$" as an abbreviation for "$(xy \setminus [[x \supset y]\ \&\ [y \supset x]])$". This would enable us to treat coimplication explicitly as a relation, that is, as an attribute of couples. Similarly, "$\equiv$" could be treated as an abbreviation for "$(xy \setminus [[x \dashv 3\ y]\ \&\ [y \dashv 3\ x]])$". See 16.8, 7.1, and 13.1.

24.15.

1	w		$w\ \epsilon\ (xy \setminus \psi xy)$	hyp
2			$w\ \epsilon\ (z \setminus (\exists x)(\exists y)[[z = (xy)]\ \&\ \psi xy])$	1, rep, def
3			$(\exists x)(\exists y)[[w = (xy)]\ \&\ \psi xy]$	2, att elim
4		x	$(\exists y)[[w = (xy)]\ \&\ \psi xy]$	hyp
5			y $[w = (xy)]\ \&\ \psi xy$	hyp
6			$w = (xy)$	5, conj elim
7			$(\exists u)(\exists v)[w = (uv)]$	6, e q int (twice)
8			$(\exists u)(\exists v)[w = (uv)]$	4, 5–7, e q elim
9			$(\exists u)(\exists v)[w = (uv)]$	3, 4–8, e q elim
10			$[w\ \epsilon\ (xy \setminus \psi xy)] \supset (\exists u)(\exists v)[w = (uv)]$	1–9, imp int
11			$(w)[[w\ \epsilon\ (xy \setminus \psi xy)] \supset (\exists u)(\exists v)[w = (uv)]]$	1–10, u q int

25. Operations on Attributes and Relations

25.1. The notions of complement, intersection, and join, as operations on attributes, have already been discussed in 17.18–17.29 and in 17.37. These notions can also be used as operations on relations, since relations are here taken to be attributes of couples.

25.2. The complement of a given relation R is the relation $(-R)$ such that $[a\ (-R)\ b]$ coimplies $\sim[a\ R\ b]$. Thus if R is the relation "less than", then $(-R)$ is the relation "not less than", or if R is the relation "brother of", then $(-R)$ is the relation "not brother of". Here "$(-R)$" is an abbreviation for "$(x \setminus \sim[x\ \epsilon\ R])$", just as in 17.18 "$(-F)$" is an abbreviation for "$(x \setminus \sim[x\ \epsilon\ F])$". We could have defined "$\neq$" as an abbreviation for "$(- =)$" instead of defining it as an abbreviation for "$(xy \setminus \sim[x = y])$".

25.3. The intersection of two relations R and S is the relation $[R \cap S]$ such that $[a\ [R \cap S]\ b]$ coimplies $[[a\ R\ b]\ \&\ [a\ S\ b]]$. Thus if R is the relation "cousin of" and S is the relation "friend of", then $[R \cap S]$ is the relation "cousin and friend of". Here "$[R \cap S]$" is an abbreviation for "$(x \setminus [[x\ \epsilon\ R]\ \&\ [x\ \epsilon\ S]])$", just as in 17.22 "$[F \cap G]$" is an abbreviation for "$(x \setminus [[x\ \epsilon\ F]\ \&\ [x\ \epsilon\ G]])$".

25.4. The join of two relations R and S is the relation $[R \cup S]$ such that $[a [R \cup S] b]$ coimplies $[[a R b] \vee [a S b]]$. Thus if R is the relation "brother of" and S is the relation "sister of", then $[R \cup S]$ is the relation "brother or sister of". Here "$[R \cup S]$" is defined like "$[F \cup G]$".

25.5. We now state some derived introduction and elimination rules for the notions of complement, intersection, and join. Two forms are given in each case, one referring to attributes in general, the other referring to those attributes that are relations.

25.6. Rule of complement introduction ("comp int").

First form:

1	$\sim[a \epsilon F]$	hyp
2	$a \epsilon (-F)$	1, 17.20

Second form:

1	$\sim[a R b]$	hyp
2	$\sim[(ab) \epsilon R]$	1, 16.11
3	$(ab) \epsilon (-R)$	2, 17.20
4	$a (-R) b$	3, 16.10

25.7. Rule of complement elimination ("comp elim").

First form:

1	$a \epsilon (-F)$	hyp
2	$\sim[a \epsilon F]$	1, 17.19

Second form:

1	$a (-R) b$	hyp
2	$(ab) \epsilon (-R)$	1, 16.9
3	$\sim[(ab) \epsilon R]$	2, 17.19
4	$\sim[a R b]$	3. 16.12

25.8. Rule of negative complement introduction ("neg comp int").

First form:

1	$a \epsilon F$	hyp
2	$\sim\sim[a \epsilon F]$	1, neg$_2$ int
3	$\sim[a \epsilon (x \setminus \sim[x \epsilon F])]$	2, neg att int (17.35)
4	$\sim[a \epsilon (-F)]$	3, rep, def

Second form:

1	$a R b$	hyp
2	$(ab) \epsilon R$	1, 16.9
3	$\sim[(ab) \epsilon (-R)]$	2, as in first form
4	$\sim[a (-R) b]$	3, 16.12

25.9. Rule of negative complement elimination ("neg comp elim").

First form:

1	$\sim[a \,\epsilon\, (-F)]$	hyp
2	$\sim[a \,\epsilon\, (x \setminus \sim[x \,\epsilon\, F])]$	1, rep, def
3	$\sim\sim[a \,\epsilon\, F]$	2, neg att elim (17.36)
4	$a \,\epsilon\, F$	3, neg_2 elim

Second form:

1	$\sim[a \,(-R)\, b]$	hyp
2	$\sim[(ab) \,\epsilon\, (-R)]$	1, 16.11
3	$(ab) \,\epsilon\, R$	2, as in first form
4	$a \, R \, b$	3, 16.10

25.10. Rules 25.11–25.14 can be proved, respectively, like rules 25.6–25.9, and so can rules 25.15–25.18, so proofs are omitted.

25.11. Rule of intersection introduction ("intersect int"). First form (17.24): $[a \,\epsilon\, [F \cap G]]$ is derivable from $[[a \,\epsilon\, F] \,\&\, [a \,\epsilon\, G]]$. Second form: $[a \,[R \cap S]\, b]$ is derivable from $[[a \, R \, b] \,\&\, [a \, S \, b]]$.

25.12. Rule of intersection elimination ("intersect elim"). First form (17.23): $[[a \,\epsilon\, F] \,\&\, [a \,\epsilon\, G]]$ is derivable from $[a \,\epsilon\, [F \cap G]]$. Second form: $[[a \, R \, b] \,\&\, [a \, S \, b]]$ is derivable from $[a \,[R \cap S]\, b]$.

25.13. Rule of negative intersection introduction ("neg intersect int"). First form: $\sim[a \,\epsilon\, [F \cap G]]$ is derivable from $\sim[[a \,\epsilon\, F] \,\&\, [a \,\epsilon\, G]]$. Second form: $\sim[a \,[R \cap S]\, b]$ is derivable from $\sim[[a \, R \, b] \,\&\, [a \, S \, b]]$.

25.14. Rule of negative intersection elimination ("neg intersect elim"). First form: $\sim[[a \,\epsilon\, F] \,\&\, [a \,\epsilon\, G]]$ is derivable from $\sim[a \,\epsilon\, [F \cap G]]$. Second form: $\sim[[a \, R \, b] \,\&\, [a \, S \, b]]$ is derivable from $\sim[a \,[R \cap S]\, b]$.

25.15. Rule of join introduction ("join int"). First form (17.28): $[a \,\epsilon\, [F \cup G]]$ is derivable from $[[a \,\epsilon\, F] \,\vee\, [a \,\epsilon\, G]]$. Second form: $[a \,[R \cup S]\, b]$ is derivable from $[[a \, R \, b] \,\vee\, [a \, S \, b]]$.

25.16. Rule of join elimination ("join elim"). First form (17.27): $[[a \,\epsilon\, F] \,\vee\, [a \,\epsilon\, G]]$ is derivable from $[a \,\epsilon\, [F \cup G]]$. Second form: $[[a \, R \, b] \,\vee\, [a \, S \, b]]$ is derivable from $[a \,[R \cup S]\, b]$.

25.17. Rule of negative join introduction ("neg join int"). First form: $\sim[a \,\epsilon\, [F \cup G]]$ is derivable from $\sim[[a \,\epsilon\, F] \,\vee\, [a \,\epsilon\, G]]$. Second form: $\sim[a \,[R \cup S]\, b]$ is derivable from $\sim[[a \, R \, b] \,\vee\, [a \, S \, b]]$.

25.18. Rule of negative join elimination ("neg join elim"). First form: $\sim[[a \; \epsilon \; F] \vee [a \; \epsilon \; G]]$ is derivable from $\sim[a \; \epsilon \; [F \cup G]]$. Second form: $\sim[[a \; R \; b] \vee [a \; S \; b]]$ is derivable from $\sim[a \; [R \cup S] \; b]$.

25.19. The **converse** of a relation R is the relation $(\breve{R})$ such that $[b \; (\breve{R}) \; a]$ coimplies $[a \; R \; b]$. Just those couples (ab) which are such that a bears the relation R to b are the couples such that b bears the relation $(\breve{R})$ to a. Thus if R is the relation "parent of", then $(\breve{R})$ would be the relation "child of". If a is child of b, then b is parent of a; and if b is parent of a, then a is child of b. In other words, "child of" is the converse of the relation "parent of". (It would perhaps be more accurate to say that "child of" is equivalent to, or applies to the same couples as, the converse of "parent of", instead of saying that it *is* the converse of "parent of", but the former way of speaking is sufficiently accurate for present purposes of exposition.) If R is the relation "hates", then $(\breve{R})$ is the relation "is hated by", while if R is the relation "greater than", then $(\breve{R})$ is the relation "less than". The converse of the converse of a relation is equivalent to the original relation itself in the sense of relating the same things in the same way as the original relation. In other words, the converse of the converse of a relation is an attribute of exactly the same couples as is the original relation itself. We can define "$(\breve{R})$" as follows:

25.20. "$(\breve{R})$" is an abbreviation for "$(xy \setminus [y \; R \; x])$".

25.21. Rule of converse introduction ("cnv int").

1	$b \; R \; a$	hyp
2	$a \; (xy \setminus [y \; R \; x]) \; b$	1, rel int
3	$a \; (\breve{R}) \; b$	2, rep, def (25.20)

In the above proof we could equally well have started with $[a \; R \; b]$ and ended with $[b \; (\breve{R}) \; a]$. If step 2 above seems difficult to understand, the reader is advised to examine step 3 of 25.22, which is probably easier to understand, and then compare with step 2 above.

25.22. Rule of converse elimination ("cnv elim").

1	$a \; (\breve{R}) \; b$	hyp
2	$a \; (xy \setminus [y \; R \; x]) \; b$	1, rep, def (25.20)
3	$b \; R \; a$	2 rel elim

In making the transition from step 2 to step 3 above, we replace x by a and we replace y by b in $[y \, R \, x]$. This clearly gives $[b \, R \, a]$. In general, in making a transition from $[a \, (xy \setminus (\cdots)) \, b]$ to some proposition obtained from it by the rule of relation elimination, we replace x by a and y by b everywhere where the replaced things are mentioned in $(\cdots)$.

25.23. Rule of negative converse introduction ("neg cnv int"). $\sim[a \, (\breve{\ }R) \, b]$ is derivable from $\sim[b \, R \, a]$. (Proof omitted.)

25.24. Rule of negative converse elimination ("neg cnv elim"). $\sim[b \, R \, a]$ is derivable from $\sim[a \, (\breve{\ }R) \, b]$. (Proof omitted.)

25.25.

1	$a \, (\breve{\ }(\breve{\ }R)) \, b$	hyp
2	$b \, (\breve{\ }R) \, a$	1, cnv elim
3	$a \, R \, b$	2, cnv elim

25.26. We can clearly also derive $[a \, (\breve{\ }(\breve{\ }R)) \, b]$ from $[a \, R \, b]$, and we can derive $\sim[a \, (\breve{\ }(\breve{\ }R)) \, b]$ and $\sim[a \, R \, b]$ from each other. These results concerning $(\breve{\ }(\breve{\ }R))$ can all be referred to as the **rule of the double converse** ("cnv$_2$").

25.27. The **relative product** of two relations R and S is the relation $[R \mid S]$ such that $[a \, [R \mid S] \, b]$ coimplies $(\exists z)[[a \, R \, z] \, \& \, [z \, S \, b]]$. Thus $[R \mid S]$ relates a to b if and only if there is something c such that R relates a to c, and S relates c to b. For example, if R is the relation "brother of" and if S is the relation "parent of", then the relation $[R \mid S]$ holds from a to b if and only if there is somebody c such that a is a brother of c, and c is a parent of b, in other words, if and only if a is an uncle of b; so in this case $[R \mid S]$ is the relation "uncle of", that is, the relation "brother of a parent of". If R is the relation "cousin of" and if S is the relation "friend of", then the relation $[R \mid S]$ holds from a to b if and only if there is some person c such that a is a cousin of c, and c is a friend of b; so in this case $[R \mid S]$ is the relation "cousin of a friend of", while similarly $[S \mid R]$ would be the different relation "friend of a cousin of". If R is the relation "one less than" and if S is the relation "half as large as", then $[R \mid S]$ would be the relation, "one less than something half as large as", while $[S \mid R]$ would be the relation, "half as large as something one less than". We do not exclude the case where R and S in $[R \mid S]$ are the same relation. (Similarly, this case is allowed in connection with $[R \cap S]$ and

$[R \cup S]$.) For example, suppose that R and S are both chosen as the relation "parent of". Then $[R \mid S]$ is the relation "parent of a parent of", in other words the relation "grandparent of". Thus if R is the relation "parent of", then $[R \mid R]$ is the relation "grandparent of", and $[[R \mid R] \mid R]$ is the relation "great-grandparent of", and $[[[R \mid R] \mid R] \mid R]$ is the relation "great-great-grandparent of", and so on. If R is the "half of", then $[R \mid R]$ is the relation "half of a half of" and $[[R \mid R] \mid R]$ is the relation "half of a half of a half of". We call $[R \mid R]$ the (**relative**) **square** or (**relative**) **second power** of R, and we call $[[R \mid R] \mid R]$ the (**relative**) **cube** or (**relative**) **third power** of R, and we call $[[[R \mid R] \mid R] \mid R]$ the (**relative**) **fourth power** of R, and so on.

25.28. The expression "$[R \mid S]$" will be treated as an abbreviation for "$(xy \setminus (\exists z)[[x \ R \ z] \ \& \ [z \ S \ y]])$".

25.29. Rule of relative product introduction ("r p int").

1	$(\exists z)[[a \ R \ z] \ \& \ [z \ S \ b]]$	hyp
2	$a \ (xy \setminus (\exists z)[[x \ R \ z] \ \& \ [z \ S \ y]]) \ b$	1, rel int
3	$a \ [R \mid S] \ b$	2, rep, def (25.28)

25.30. Rule of relative product elimination ("r p elim"). In a similar way $(\exists z)[[a \ R \ z] \ \& \ [z \ S \ b]]$ is derivable from $[a \ [R \mid S] \ b]$.

25.31. Rule of negative relative product introduction ("neg r p int"). $\sim[a \ [R \mid S] \ b]$ is derivable from $\sim(\exists z)[[a \ R \ z] \ \& \ [z \ S \ b]]$. (Proof omitted.)

25.32. Rule of negative relative product elimination ("neg r p elim"). $\sim(\exists z)[[a \ R \ z] \ \& \ [z \ S \ b]]$ is derivable from $\sim[a \ [R \mid S] \ b]$. (Proof omitted.)

25.33.

1		$a \ [^\smile R) \mid (^\smile S)] \ b]$	hyp
2		$(\exists z)[[a \ (^\smile R) \ z] \ \& \ [z \ (^\smile S) \ b]]$	1, r p elim
3	z	$[a \ (^\smile R) \ z] \ \& \ [z \ (^\smile S) \ b]$	hyp
4		$a \ (^\smile R) \ z$	3, conj elim
5		$z \ (^\smile S) \ b$	3, conj elim
6		$z \ R \ a$	4, cnv elim
7		$b \ S \ z$	5, cnv elim

8	$[b\ S\ z]$ & $[z\ R\ a]$	6, 7, conj int
9	$(\exists z)[[b\ S\ z]$ & $[z\ R\ a]]$	8, e q int
10	$b\ [S\ |\ R]\ a$	9, r p int
11	$b\ [S\ |\ R]\ a$	2, 3–10, e q elim
12	$a\ (\smallsmile[S\ |\ R])\ b$	11, cnv int

Similarly $[a\ [(\smallsmile R)\ |\ (\smallsmile S)]\ b]$ can be derived from $[a\ (\smallsmile[S\ |\ R])\ b]$.

25.34.

1	$(z)[\sim[a\ R\ z]$ v $\sim[z\ S\ b]]$	hyp
2	z $\sim[a\ R\ z]$ v $\sim[z\ S\ b]$	1, reit, u q elim
3	$\sim[[a\ R\ z]$ & $[z\ S\ b]]$	2, d m
4	$(z)\sim[[a\ R\ z]$ & $[z\ S\ b]]$	2–3, u q int
5	$\sim(\exists z)[[a\ R\ z]$ & $[z\ S\ b]]$	4, d m q
6	$\sim[a\ [R\ |\ S]\ b]$	5, neg r p int

25.35.

1	$\sim[a\ [R\ |\ S]\ b]$	hyp
2	$\sim(\exists z)[[a\ R\ z]$ & $[z\ S\ b]]$	1, neg r p elim
3	$(z)\sim[[a\ R\ z]$ & $[z\ S\ b]]$	2, d m q
4	z $\sim[[a\ R\ z]$ & $[z\ S\ b]]$	3, reit, u q elim
5	$\sim[a\ R\ z]$ v $\sim[z\ S\ b]$	4, d m
6	$(z)[\sim[a\ R\ z]$ v $\sim[z\ S\ b]]$	4–5, u q int

25.36.

1	$\sim[a\ [(\smallsmile R)\ |\ (\smallsmile S)]\ b]$	hyp
2	$(z)[\sim[a\ (\smallsmile R)\ z]$ v $\sim[z\ (\smallsmile S)\ b]]$	1, 25.35
3	z $\sim[a\ (\smallsmile R)\ z]$ v $\sim[z\ (\smallsmile S)\ b]$	2, reit, u q elim
4	$\sim[a\ (\smallsmile R)\ z]$	hyp
5	$\sim[z\ R\ a]$	4, neg cnv elim
6	$\sim[z\ (\smallsmile S)\ b]$	hyp
7	$\sim[b\ S\ z]$	6, neg cnv elim
8	$\sim[z\ R\ a]$ v $\sim[b\ S\ z]$	3, 4–5, 6–7, cnst dil (8.25)
9	$\sim[b\ S\ z]$ v $\sim[z\ R\ a]$	8, comm dis (8.10)
10	$(z)[\sim[b\ S\ z]$ v $\sim[z\ R\ a]]$	3–9, u q int
11	$\sim[b\ [S\ |\ R]\ a]$	10, 25.34
12	$\sim[a\ (\smallsmile[S\ |\ R])\ b]$	11, neg cnv int

Similarly $\sim[a\ [(\breve{\ }R)\ |\ (\breve{\ }S)]\ b]$ can be derived from $\sim[a\ (\breve{\ }[S\ |\ R])\ b]$.

25.37.	1	$a\ [[R\ |\ S]\ |\ T]\ b$	hyp
	2	$(\exists z)[[a\ [R\ |\ S]\ z]\ \&\ [z\ T\ b]]$	1, r p elim
	3	$z\ \ [a\ [R\ |\ S]\ z]\ \&\ [z\ T\ b]$	hyp
	4	$a\ [R\ |\ S]\ z$	3, conj elim
	5	$z\ T\ b$	3, conj elim
	6	$(\exists w)[[a\ R\ w]\ \&\ [w\ S\ z]]$	4, r p elim
	7	$w\ \ [a\ R\ w]\ \&\ [w\ S\ z]$	hyp
	8	$a\ R\ w$	7, conj elim
	9	$w\ S\ z$	7, conj elim
	10	$z\ T\ b$	5, reit
	11	$[w\ S\ z]\ \&\ [z\ T\ b]$	9, 10 conj int
	12	$(\exists z)[[w\ S\ z]\ \&\ [z\ T\ b]]$	11, e q int
	13	$w\ [S\ |\ T]\ b$	12, r p int
	14	$[a\ R\ w]\ \&\ [w\ [S\ |\ T]\ b]$	8, 13, conj int
	15	$(\exists w)[[a\ R\ w]\ \&\ [w\ [S\ |\ T]\ b]]$	14, e q int
	16	$a\ [R\ |\ [S\ |\ T]]\ b$	15, r p int
	17	$a\ [R\ |\ [S\ |\ T]]\ b$	6, 7–16, e q elim
	18	$a\ [R\ |\ [S\ |\ T]]\ b$	2, 3–17, e q elim

Similarly $[a\ [[R\ |\ S]\ |\ T]\ b]$ can be derived from $[a\ [R\ |\ [S\ |\ T]]\ b]$.

25.38.

1	$\sim[a\ [[R\ |\ S]\ |\ T]\ b]$	hyp
2	$(z)[\sim[a\ [R\ |\ S]\ z]\ \vee\ \sim[z\ T\ b]]$	1, 25.35
3	$w\ \ z\ \ \sim[a\ [R\ |\ S]\ z]\ \vee\ \sim[z\ T\ b]$	2, reit, u q elim
4	$\sim[a\ [R\ |\ S]\ z]$	hyp
5	$(w)[\sim[a\ R\ w]\ \vee\ \sim[w\ S\ z]]$	4, 25.35
6	$\sim[a\ R\ w]\ \vee\ \sim[w\ S\ z]$	5, u q elim
7	$[\sim[a\ R\ w]\ \vee\ \sim[w\ S\ z]]\ \vee\ \sim[z\ T\ b]$	3, 4–6, cnst dil (8.25)
8	$\sim[a\ R\ w]\ \vee\ [\sim[w\ S\ z]\ \vee\ \sim[z\ T\ b]]$	7, ass dis (8.11)

9			$(z)[\sim[a\,R\,w] \vee [\sim[w\,S\,z] \vee \sim[z\,T\,b]]]$	3–8, u q int
10			$\sim[a\,R\,w] \vee (z)[\sim[w\,S\,z] \vee \sim[z\,T\,b]]$	9, u q dis (21.31)
11			$(z)[\sim[w\,S\,z] \vee \sim[z\,T\,b]]$	hyp
12			$\sim[w\,[S\mid T]\,b]$	11, 25.34
13			$\sim[a\,R\,w) \vee \sim[w\,[S\mid T]\,b]$	10, 11–12, cnst dil (8.25)
14			$(w)[\sim[a\,R\,w] \vee \sim[w\,[S\mid T]\,b]]$	3–13, u q int
15			$\sim[a\,[R\mid [S\mid T]]\,b]$	14, 25.34

Similarly $\sim[a\,[[R\mid S]\mid T]\,b]$ can be derived from $\sim[a\,[R\mid [S\mid T]]\,b]$.

25.39. If we let $(\text{Dm }R)$ be the domain of a relation R in the sense of 16.13, we can treat "$(\text{Dm }R)$" as an abbreviation for "$(x\setminus(\exists y)[x\,R\,y])$". It can be shown that $[a\,\epsilon\,(\text{Dm }R)]$ and $(\exists y)[a\,R\,y]$ are derivable from each other. Similarly for their denials.

25.40. If we let $(\text{Cndm }R)$ be the converse domain of a relation R in the sense of 16.14, we can treat "$(\text{Cndm }R)$" as an abbreviation for "$(y\setminus(\exists x)[x\,R\,y])$". It can be shown that $[b\,\epsilon\,(\text{Cndm }R)]$ and $(\exists x)[x\,R\,b]$ are derivable from each other. Similarly for their denials. It can also be shown that $[b\,\epsilon\,(\text{Cndm }R)]$ and $[b\,\epsilon\,(\text{Dm }(\breve R))]$ are derivable from each other, and similarly for their denials. Thus the converse domain of a relation has the same members as the domain of the converse of the relation.

25.41. If we let $(\text{Fld }R)$ be the field of a relation R in the sense of 16.15, we can treat "$(\text{Fld }R)$" as an abbreviation for "$[(\text{Dm }R)\cup(\text{Cndm }R)]$". It can be shown that $[a\,\epsilon\,(\text{Fld }R)]$ and $(\exists x)[[a\,R\,x] \vee [x\,R\,a]]$ are derivable from each other. Similarly for their denials. It can also be shown that $[a\,\epsilon\,(\text{Fld }R)]$ and $[a\,\epsilon\,(\text{Fld }(\breve R))]$ are derivable from each other, and similarly for their denials. Thus the field of a relation has the same members as the field of the converse of that relation.

25.42. Suppose that we let $[R\text{ " }F]$ be the class of things that bear the relation R to members of the class F. Then we can treat the expression "$[R\text{ " }F]$" as an abbreviation for "$(x\setminus(\exists y)[[x\,R\,y]\ \&\ [y\,\epsilon\,F]])$". If, for example, R is the relation "wife of" and if F is the class of Frenchmen, then $[R\text{ " }F]$ would be the class of wives of Frenchmen. It can be shown that $[a\,\epsilon\,[R\text{ " }F]]$ and $(\exists y)[[a\,R\,y]\ \&\ [y\,\epsilon\,F]]$ are derivable from each other. Similarly for their denials.

It would also be possible to treat "$[R$ " $F]$" as an abbreviation for "$(x \setminus [x \, [R \mid \epsilon] \, F])$". We can call $[R$ " $F]$ the R-**projection** of F.

25.43. The class $[R$ " $\{b\}]$ is the class of things that bear the relation R to the only member of $\{b\}$; in other words, the class of things that bear the relation R to b. For example, if R is the relation "square root of", then $[R$ " $\{4\}]$ would be the class of square roots of 4. The members of this class would be 2 and -2. It can be shown that $[a \, \epsilon \, [R$ " $\{b\}]]$ and $[a \, R \, b]$ are derivable from each other. Similarly for their denials. (See 17.42–17.46.)

25.44. Given classes F and G, we can form the class that has as its members all ordered couples (ab) such that a is a member of F and b is a member of G. This is called the **direct product** $[F \times G]$ of F with G. We may treat "$[F \times G]$" as an abbreviation for "$(xy \setminus [[x \, \epsilon \, F] \, \& \, [y \, \epsilon \, G]])$", since $[F \times G]$ can also be viewed as the relation of every member of F to every member of G. It can be shown that $[a \, [F \times G] \, b]$ and $[[b \, \epsilon \, F] \, \& \, [b \, \epsilon \, G]]$ are derivable from each other. Similarly for their denials. It can also be shown that $[(ab) \, \epsilon \, [F \times G]]$ and $[[a \, \epsilon \, F] \, \& \, [b \, \epsilon \, G]]$ are derivable from each other, and similarly for their denials.

25.45. The class $[F \times F]$ is the class that has as its members all ordered couples (ab) such that a and b are members of F. We will let "$[F^2]$" serve as an abbreviation for "$[F \times F]$". The propositions $[a \, [F^2] \, b]$ and $[[a \, \epsilon \, F] \, \& \, [b \, \epsilon \, F]]$ are derivable from each other. Also the propositions $[(ab) \, \epsilon \, [F^2]]$ and $[[a \, \epsilon \, F] \, \& \, [b \, \epsilon \, F]]$. Similarly for their denials. We may think of $[F^2]$ as a relation that every member of F bears to every member of F. We call $[F^2]$ the **direct square** of F.

25.46. We can treat "$[F^3]$" as an abbreviation for "$[[F^2] \times F]$", and "$[F^4]$" as an abbreviation for "$[[F^3] \times F]$", and so on. The class $[F^3]$, for example, is the class of all triples (abc) such that a, b, and c are members of F. The propositions $[(abc) \, \epsilon \, [F^3]]$ and $[[a \, \epsilon \, F] \, \& \, [b \, \epsilon \, F] \, \& \, [c \, \epsilon \, F]]$ are derivable from each other. Similarly for their denials. Analogous results hold for $[F^4]$, $[F^5]$, $\cdots$. We call $[F^3]$ the **direct cube** of F, and $[F^4]$ the **direct fourth power** of F, and so on.

25.47. If F has n members and G has m members, then the number of members of $[F \times G]$ will have to be n times m, and the number of members of $[F^k]$ will be n^k. It is also perhaps worth remarking that if F has n members and G has m members, and if F and G have no members in common, then clearly $[F \cup G]$ must have $n + m$ members. These mathematical matters will not be discussed here in further detail. The writer hopes to deal with them fully in a later volume.

25.48. If we think of U as being the class of all things (17.47), then we may think of $[\mathsf{U}^2]$ as being the class of all ordered couples, and hence as being a relation that relates all things to each other. Also we may think of $[F \times \mathsf{U}]$ as a relation that each member of F bears to everything, and of $[\mathsf{U} \times F]$ as a relation that everything bears to each member of F.

25.49. The relation $[R \cap [F \times G]]$ is the relation R with its domain restricted to F and its converse domain restricted to G. If F, for example, is the class of French people and G is the class of German people, and if R is the relation "wife of", then $[R \cap [F \times G]]$ is the relation "wife of" as between a French woman and a German man, while $[R \cap [G \times F]]$ is the relation "wife of" as between a German woman and a Frenchman. The propositions $[a\,[R \cap [F \times G]]\,b]$ and $[[a\,R\,b]\ \&\ [a\,\epsilon\,F]\ \&\ [b\,\epsilon\,G]]$ can be derived from each other. Similarly for their denials.

25.50. The relation $[R \cap [F^2]]$ is the relation R with its field restricted to F. The relation $[R \cap [F \times \mathsf{U}]]$ is R with its domain restricted to F. The relation $[R \cap [\mathsf{U} \times F]]$ is R with its converse domain restricted to F. For example, if R is the relation "half of" and F is the class of even integers, then $[R \cap [F^2]]$ is the relation between two things when both are even integers and the first is half of the second; and $[R \cap [F \times \mathsf{U}]]$ is the relation between two things when the first is an even integer and is half of the second; and $[R \cap [\mathsf{U} \times F]]$ is the relation between two things when the second is an even integer and the first is half of the second.

25.51. It is convenient to treat the relation $[= \cap [(\mathrm{Fld}\ R)^2]]$ as the (**relative**) **zeroth power** of R. (See 25.27.) Thus the zeroth power of R is taken to be the relation identity with its field restricted to the field of R. This is a relation that relates nothing but members of the field of R, and it relates each member a of the field of R to a itself and to nothing else.

25.52. Using parentheses instead of square brackets in order to avoid confusion with the abbreviations stated in 22.45 and 22.46, we can now let "(R^0)", "(R^1)", "(R^2)", "(R^3)", and so on be abbreviations, respectively, for "[$= \cap [(\text{Fld } R)^2]$]", "$R$", "[$R \mid R$]", "[[$R \mid R$] $\mid R$]", and so on. Also, we can let "(R^{-1})" be an abbreviation for "$(\breve{R})$", and in general we can let "(R^{-n})" be an abbreviation for "$((\breve{R})^n)$", where n is a positive integer. We will call (R^1), (R^2), (R^3), $\cdots$, the positive powers of R, and we will call (R^{-1}), (R^{-2}), (R^{-3}), $\cdots$, the negative powers of R.

25.53. Let (Pot R) be the class of all the positive powers of R. We can treat "(Pot R)" as an abbreviation for the following expression: "$(x \setminus (y)[[[R \ \epsilon \ y] \ \& \ (z)[[z \ \epsilon \ y] \supset [[z \mid R] \ \epsilon \ y]]] \supset [x \ \epsilon \ y]])$". It is then possible to prove the propositions $[R \ \epsilon \ (\text{Pot } R)]$, $[(R^2) \ \epsilon \ (\text{Pot } R)]$, $[(R^3) \ \epsilon \ (\text{Pot } R)]$, $[(R^4) \ \epsilon \ (\text{Pot } R)]$, and so on.

25.54. Let (R_{po}) be the relation that holds from a to b provided that a bears to b some positive power of R. For example, if R is the relation "parent of", then (R_{po}) would be the relation "ancestor of". This is because to say that a is an ancestor of b means that a bears to b one of the relations, "parent of", "grandparent of", "great-grandparent of", "great-great-grandparent of", and so on. These latter relations are the successive positive powers of the relation "parent of". We can treat "(R_{po})" as an abbreviation for the expression "$(xy \setminus (\exists z)[[z \ \epsilon \ (\text{Pot } R)] \ \& \ [x \ z \ y]])$". The relation (R_{po}) is called the **proper ancestral** of R.

25.55. Let (Potid R) be the class of non-negative powers of R, that is, the class having as its members all the positive powers of R and also the zeroth power of R. We can treat "(Potid R)" as an abbreviation for "$[(\text{Pot } R) \cup \{(R^0)\}]$". It is possible to prove the propositions $[(R^0) \ \epsilon \ (\text{Potid } R)]$, $[R \ \epsilon \ (\text{Potid } R)]$, $[(R^2) \ \epsilon \ (\text{Potid } R)]$, $[(R^3) \ \epsilon \ (\text{Potid } R)]$, and so on.

25.56. Let (R_*) be the relation that holds from a to b provided that a bears to b some non-negative power of R. We can treat "(R_*)" as an abbreviation for "$(xy \setminus (\exists z)[[z \ \epsilon \ (\text{Potid } R)] \ \& \ [x \ z \ y]])$". The relation (R_*) is called the **ancestral** of R. If R is the relation "one greater than" among integers, then (R_{po}) is the relation "greater than" among integers, and (R_*) is the relation "greater than or identical with" among integers.

25.57. The ancestral and the proper ancestral have many interesting properties. These properties will be reserved for discussion in a later volume since they are intimately related to the theory of arithmetic and require the addition of some further rules to the present system of logic. For a statement of these additional rules, see Appendix B.

EXERCISES

Prove:

1. $[a\,[R\,\cap\,S]\,b]\,\supset\,[a\,[S\,\cap\,R]\,b]$.
2. $\sim[a\,[R\,\cap\,S]\,b]\,\supset\,\sim[a\,[S\,\cap\,R]\,b]$.
3. $[a\,[R\,\cup\,[S\,\cup\,T]]\,b]\,\supset\,[a\,[[R\,\cup\,S]\,\cup\,T]\,b]$.
4. $\sim[a\,[R\,\cup\,[S\,\cup\,T]]\,b]\,\supset\,\sim[a\,[[R\,\cup\,S]\,\cup\,T]\,b]$.
5. $[a\,[R\,\cup\,R]\,b]\,\equiv\,[a\,(-\!(-R))\,b]$.
6. $\sim[a\,[R\,\cup\,R]\,b]\,\equiv\,\sim[a\,(-\!(-R))\,b]$.
7. $[a\,(-\!\epsilon)\,F]\,\equiv\,[a\,\epsilon\,(-\!F)]$.
8. $\sim[a\,(-\!\epsilon)\,F]\,\equiv\,\sim[a\,\epsilon\,(-\!F)]$.
9. $[a\,[R\,\cup\,[S\,\cap\,T]]\,b]\,\equiv\,[a\,[[R\,\cup\,S]\,\cap\,[R\,\cup\,T]]\,b]$.
10. $[a\,[R\,\cap\,[S\,\cup\,T]]\,b]\,\equiv\,[a\,[[R\,\cap\,S]\,\cup\,[R\,\cap\,T]]\,b]$.
11. $\sim[a\,[(-R)\,\cup\,(-S)]\,b]\,\equiv\,\sim[a\,(-[R\,\cap\,S])\,b]$.
12. $[a\,(\breve{\,}[R\,\cup\,S])\,b]\,\equiv\,[a\,[(\breve{\,}R)\,\cup\,(\breve{\,}S)]\,b]$.
13. $[a\,(\breve{\,}=)\,b]\,\equiv\,[a\,=\,b]$.
14. $[a\,[S\,\cap\,R]\,b]\,\equiv\,[b\,[(\breve{\,}R)\,\cap\,(\breve{\,}S)]\,a]$.
15. $[a\,[R\,\mid\,[S\,\cup\,T]]\,b]\,\equiv\,[a\,[[R\,\mid\,S]\,\cup\,[R\,\mid\,T]]\,b]$.
16. $\sim[a\,[[R\,\cup\,S]\,\mid\,T]\,b]\,\equiv\,\sim[a\,[[R\,\mid\,T]\,\cup\,[S\,\mid\,T]]\,b]$.
17. $[a\,[=\,\mid\,=]\,b]\,\equiv\,[a\,=\,b]$.
18. $[a\,[R\,\mid\,=]\,b]\,\equiv\,[a\,R\,b]$.
19. $\sim[a\,[R\,\mid\,=]\,b]\,\equiv\,\sim[a\,R\,b]$.
20. $[a\,\epsilon\,(\mathrm{Dm}\,[R\,\cap\,[F\times\mathsf{U}]])]\,\equiv\,[a\,\epsilon\,[F\,\cap\,(\mathrm{Dm}\,R)]]$.
21. $[a\,\epsilon\,(\mathrm{Cndm}\,[R\,\cap\,[\mathsf{U}\times F]])]\,\equiv\,[a\,\epsilon\,[F\,\cap\,(\mathrm{Cndm}\,R)]]$.
22. $[a\,\epsilon\,[R\,``\,F]]\,\equiv\,[a\,\epsilon\,(\mathrm{Dm}\,[R\,\cap\,[\mathsf{U}\times F]])]$.
23. $[a\,(R^0)\,b]\,\supset\,[a\,(R_*)\,b]$.
24. $[a\,R\,b]\,\supset\,[a\,(R_{\mathrm{po}})\,b]$.
25. $[a\,R\,b]\,\supset\,[a\,(R_*)\,b]$.
26. $[a\,(R^2)\,b]\,\supset\,[a\,(R_{\mathrm{po}})\,b]$.
27. $[a\,(R^2)\,b]\,\supset\,[a\,(R_*)\,b]$.

26. Inclusion

26.1. An attribute F is said to be **included in** an attribute G if everything having attribute F also has attribute G. Thus F is included in G if $(z)[[z\,\epsilon\,F]\,\supset\,[z\,\epsilon\,G]]$ is true. The relation of "being included in" is ordinarily called **inclusion**. It will be denoted by the symbol "$\subseteq$". The following definition will be used:

26.2. "$\subseteq$" is an abbreviation for "$(xy \setminus (z)[[z \; \epsilon \; x] \supset [z \; \epsilon \; y]])$".

26.3. If we were to speak in terms of classes rather than attributes, we would say that a class F is included in a class G provided that every member of F is a member of G. For example, the class of French poodles is included in the class of dogs, and the class of positive even whole numbers is included in the class of positive whole numbers. The relation of being included in must be carefully distinguished from the relation of being a member of. The class of residents of New Haven, Connecticut, is included in the class of residents of Connecticut, but it is not a member of the class of residents of Connecticut, since every member of the latter class is a person and never a class. If a class F is included in a class G, we may call F a **subclass** of G.

26.4. Rule of inclusion introduction ("incl int").

1	$(z)[[z \; \epsilon \; F] \supset [z \; \epsilon \; G]]$	hyp
2	$F \; (xy \setminus (z)[[z \; \epsilon \; x] \supset [z \; \epsilon \; y]]) \; G$	1, rel int
3	$F \subseteq G$	2, rep, def (26.2)

26.5. Rule of inclusion elimination ("incl elim").

1	$F \subseteq G$	hyp
2	$F \; (xy \setminus (z)[[z \; \epsilon \; x] \supset [z \; \epsilon \; y]]) \; G$	1, rep, def (26.2)
3	$(z)[[z \; \epsilon \; F] \supset [z \; \epsilon \; G]]$	2, rel elim

26.6. The above rules will now be used in some proofs.

26.7.

1	$a \; \epsilon \; F$	hyp
2	$F \subseteq G$	hyp
3	$(z)[[z \; \epsilon \; F] \supset [z \; \epsilon \; G]]$	2, incl elim
4	$[a \; \epsilon \; F] \supset [a \; \epsilon \; G]$	3, u q elim
5	$a \; \epsilon \; G$	1, 4, m p

26.8. Rule of reflexivity of inclusion ("refl incl").

1	$z \mid \quad [z \; \epsilon \; F] \supset [z \; \epsilon \; F]$	refl imp
2	$(z)[[z \; \epsilon \; F] \supset [z \; \epsilon \; F]]$	1–1, u q int
3	$F \subseteq F$	2, incl int

26.9. Rule of transitivity of inclusion ("trans incl").

1	$F \subseteq G$	hyp
2	$G \subseteq H$	hyp
3	$(z)[[z \; \epsilon \; F] \supset [z \; \epsilon \; G]]$	1, incl elim
4	$(z)[[z \; \epsilon \; G] \supset [z \; \epsilon \; H]]$	2, incl elim
5	$z \quad [z \; \epsilon \; F] \supset [z \; \epsilon \; G]$	3, reit, u q elim
6	$[z \; \epsilon \; G] \supset [z \; \epsilon \; H]$	4, reit, u q elim
7	$[z \; \epsilon \; F] \supset [z \; \epsilon \; H]$	5, 6, trans imp
8	$(z)[[z \; \epsilon \; F] \supset [z \; \epsilon \; H]]$	5–7, u q int
9	$F \subseteq H$	8, incl int

26.10.

1	$z \quad z \; \epsilon \; [F \cap G]$	hyp
2	$[z \; \epsilon \; F] \; \& \; [z \; \epsilon \; G]$	1, intersect elim
3	$z \; \epsilon \; F$	2, conj elim
4	$[z \; \epsilon \; [F \cap G]] \supset [z \; \epsilon \; F]$	1–3, imp int
5	$(z)[[z \; \epsilon \; [F \cap G]] \supset [z \; \epsilon \; F]]$	1–4, u q int
6	$[F \cap G] \subseteq F$	5, incl int

Similarly we can prove $[[F \cap G] \subseteq G]$, $[F \subseteq [F \cup G]]$, $[G \subseteq [F \cup G]]$, $[(-(-F)) \subseteq F]$, and $[F \subset (-(-F))]$.

26.11. A relation R will be said to be **relationally included in** a relation S if every couple having R as an attribute is a couple having S as an attribute. Thus R is relationally included in S if $(u)(v)[[u \; R \; v] \supset [u \; S \; v]]$ is true. The relation of "being relationally included in" will be called **relational inclusion.** It will be denoted by the symbol "$\subseteq_r$". The following definition will be used:

26.12. "$\subseteq_r$" is an abbreviation for "$(xy \setminus (u)(v)[[u \; x \; v] \supset [u \; y \; v]])$".

26.13. In general, if R is relationally included in S, then whenever R holds, S must hold, but not necessarily vice versa. For example, the relation "less than" is relationally included in the relation "less than or equal to". It is clear that whenever the former relation holds, the latter must hold; but the latter can hold without the former holding. As another example, the relation "brother of" is included in the relation "kin of".

26.14. Rule of relational inclusion introduction ("rel incl int").

1	$(u)(v)[[u\ R\ v] \supset [u\ S\ v]]$	hyp
2	$R\ (xy \setminus (u)(v)[[u\ x\ v] \supset [u\ y\ v]])\ S$	1, rel int
3	$R \subseteq_r S$	2, rep, def (26.13)

26.15. Rule of relational inclusion elimination ("rel incl elim").

1	$R \subseteq_r S$	hyp
2	$R\ (xy \setminus (u)(v)[[u\ x\ v] \supset [u\ y\ v]])\ S$	1, rep, def (26.13)
3	$(u)(v)[[u\ R\ v] \supset [u\ S\ v]]$	2, rel elim

26.16.

1	$a\ R\ b$	hyp
2	$R \subseteq_r S$	hyp
3	$(u)(v)[[u\ R\ v] \supset [u\ S\ v]]$	2, rel incl elim
4	$(v)[[a\ R\ v] \supset [a\ S\ v]]$	3, u q elim
5	$[a\ R\ b] \supset [a\ S\ b]$	4, u q elim
6	$a\ S\ b$	1, 5, m p

26.17. Rule of reflexivity of relational inclusion ("refl rel incl").

1	$u\vert\ v\vert\ \ [u\ R\ v] \supset [u\ R\ v]$	refl imp
2	$(v)[[u\ R\ v] \supset [u\ R\ v]]$	1–1, u q int
3	$(u)(v)[[u\ R\ v] \supset [u\ R\ v]]$	1–2, u q int
4	$R \subseteq_r R$	3, rel incl int

26.18. Rule of transitivity of relational inclusion ("trans rel incl").

1	$R \subseteq_r S$	hyp
2	$S \subseteq_r T$	hyp
3	$(u)(v)[[u\ R\ v] \supset [u\ S\ v]]$	1, rel incl elim
4	$(u)(v)[[u\ S\ v] \supset [u\ T\ v]]$	2, rel incl elim
5	$u\vert\ v\vert\ \ (v)[[u\ R\ v] \supset [u\ S\ v]]$	3, reit, u q elim
6	$(v)[[u\ S\ v] \supset [u\ T\ v]]$	4, reit, u q elim
7	$[u\ R\ v] \supset [u\ S\ v]$	5, u q elim
8	$[u\ S\ v] \supset [u\ T\ v]$	6, u q elim
9	$[u\ R\ v] \supset [u\ T\ v]$	7, 8, trans imp
10	$(v)[[u\ R\ v] \supset [u\ T\ v]]$	5–9, u q int

11	$(u)(v)[[u\ R\ v] \supset [u\ T\ v]]$	5–10, u q int
12	$R \subseteq_r T$	11, rel incl int

26.19. Similarly to 26.10 we can prove $[[R \cap S] \subseteq_r R]$, $[[R \cap S] \subseteq_r S]$, $[R \subseteq_r [R \cup S]]$, $[S \subseteq_r [R \cup S]]$, $[(-(-R)) \subseteq_r R]$, $[R \subseteq_r (-(-R))]$, $[(\check{\ }(\check{\ }R)) \subseteq_r R]$, $[R \subseteq_r (\check{\ }(\check{\ }R))]$.

26.20. Two proofs relating inclusion to relational inclusion will now be given.

26.21.

1	$F \subseteq G$			hyp
2	$(z)[[z \in F] \supset [z \in G]]$			1, incl elim
3	u	v	$u\ F\ v$	hyp
4			$(F(uv))$	3, rep, def (15.19)
5			$(uv) \in F$	4, ϵ-int
6			$[(uv) \in F] \supset [(uv) \in G]$	2, reit, u q elim
7			$(uv) \in G$	5, 6, m p
8			$(G(uv))$	7, ϵ-elim
9			$u\ G\ v$	8, rep, def
10			$[u\ F\ v] \supset [u\ G\ v]$	3–9, imp int
11		$(v)[[u\ F\ v] \supset [u\ G\ v]]$		3–10, u q int
12	$(u)(v)[[u\ F\ v] \supset [u\ G\ v]]$			3–11, u q int
13	$F \subseteq_r G$			12, rel incl int

26.22.

1	$F \subseteq_r G$			hyp
2	$(z)[[z \in F] \supset (\exists u)(\exists v)[z = (uv)]]$			hyp
3	$(u)(v)[[u\ F\ v] \supset [u\ G\ v]]$			1, rel incl elim
4	z	$z \in F$		hyp
5		$[z \in F] \supset (\exists u)(\exists v)[z = (uv)]$		2, reit, u q elim
6		$(\exists u)(\exists v)[z = (uv)]$		4, 5, m p
7		u	$(\exists v)[z = (uv)]$	hyp
8			v	$z = (uv)$	hyp
9				$z \in F$	4, reit
10				$(uv) \in F$	8, 9, id elim

11				$u\ F\ v$	10, ϵ-elim, def
12				$(v)[[u\ F\ v] \supset [u\ G\ v]]$	3, reit, u q elim
13				$[u\ F\ v] \supset [u\ G\ v]$	12, u q elim
14				$u\ G\ v$	11, 13, m p
15				$(uv)\ \epsilon\ G$	14, def, ϵ-int
16				$z\ \epsilon\ G$	8, 15, id elim
17			$z\ \epsilon\ G$		7, 8–16, e q elim
18		$z\ \epsilon\ G$			6, 7–17, e q elim
19		$[z\ \epsilon\ F] \supset [z\ \epsilon\ G]$			4–18, imp int
20	$(z)[[z\ \epsilon\ F] \supset [z\ \epsilon\ G]]$				4–19, u q int
21	$F \subseteq G$				20, incl int

26.23. Many systems of logic possess a "principle of extensionality" according to which the classes F and G must be identical if each is included in the other. The present system does not possess this principle. Instead of saying that two such classes (or attributes) are identical, we simply say that they are related by the relation of **mutual inclusion.** Thus two classes are mutually inclusive if every member of one is a member of the other, and vice versa. Similarly, we would say that two attributes are mutually inclusive if they apply to exactly the same things. The relation of mutual inclusion will be denoted by the symbol "$\simeq$". The following definition will be used:

26.24. "$\simeq$" is an abbreviation for "$(xy \setminus [[x \subseteq y]\ \&\ [y \subseteq x]])$".

26.25. The following results concerning mutual inclusion are easily established and will be stated without proof:

26.26. $[F \simeq G]$ and $[[F \subseteq G]\ \&\ [G \subseteq F]]$ are derivable from each other.

26.27. $[F \simeq G]$ and $(z)[[z\ \epsilon\ F] \equiv [z\ \epsilon\ G]]$ are derivable from each other.

26.28. **Rule of reflexivity of mutual inclusion** ("refl mut incl"). $[F \simeq F]$ is provable.

26.29. **Rule of transitivity of mutual inclusion** ("trans mut incl"). $[F \simeq H]$ is derivable from $[F \simeq G]$ and $[G \simeq H]$.

26.30. Rule of symmetry of mutual inclusion ("sym mut incl"). $[G \simeq F]$ is derivable from $[F \simeq G]$.

26.31. $[F \subseteq H]$ is derivable from $[F \subseteq G]$ and $[G \simeq H]$.

26.32. $[F \subseteq H]$ is derivable from $[F \simeq G]$ and $[G \subseteq H]$.

26.33. $[F \subseteq G]$ is derivable from $[F \simeq G]$, and so is $[G \subseteq F]$.

26.34. $[a \; \epsilon \; G]$ is derivable from $[a \; \epsilon \; F]$ and $[F \simeq G]$.

26.35. $[a \; \epsilon \; F]$ is derivable from $[a \; \epsilon \; G]$ and $[F \simeq G]$.

26.36. There is also a relation of **mutual relational inclusion** which relates R to S provided that R and S are relationally included in each other. This relation of mutual relational inclusion will be denoted by the symbol "$\simeq_r$". The following definition will be used:

26.37. "$\simeq_r$" is an abbreviation for "$(xy \setminus [[x \subseteq_r y] \; \& \; [y \subseteq_r x]])$".

26.38. The results stated below concerning mutual relational inclusion can be easily established.

26.39. $[R \simeq_r S]$ and $[[R \subseteq_r S] \; \& \; [S \subseteq_r R]]$ are derivable from each other.

26.40. $[R \simeq_r S]$ and $(u)(v)[[u \; R \; v] \equiv [u \; S \; v]]$ are derivable from each other.

26.41. Rule of reflexivity of mutual relational inclusion ("refl mut rel incl"). $[R \simeq_r R]$ is provable.

26.42. Rule of transitivity of mutual relational inclusion ("trans mut rel incl"). $[R \simeq_r T]$ is derivable from $[R \simeq_r S]$ and $[S \simeq_r T]$.

26.43. Rule of symmetry of mutual relational inclusion ("sym mut rel incl"). $[S \simeq_r R]$ is derivable from $[R \simeq_r S]$.

26.44. $[R \subseteq_r T]$ is derivable from $[R \subseteq_r S]$ and $[S \simeq_r T]$.

26.45. $[R \subseteq_r T]$ is derivable from $[R \simeq_r S]$ and $[S \subseteq_r T]$.

26.46. $[R \subseteq_r S]$ is derivable from $[R \simeq_r S]$, and so is $[S \subseteq_r R]$.

26.47. $[a \; S \; b]$ is derivable from $[a \; R \; b]$ and $[R \simeq_r S]$.

26.48. $[a \; R \; b]$ is derivable from $[a \; S \; b]$ and $[R \simeq_r S]$.

26.49. $[F \simeq_r G]$ is derivable from $[F \simeq G]$. (Compare with 26.21.)

26.50. $[F \simeq G]$ is derivable from $[F \simeq_r G]$ and $(z)[[z \,\epsilon\, [F \,\cup\, G]] \supset (\exists u)(\exists v)[z = (uv)]]$. (Compare with 26.22.)

26.51.

$$
\begin{array}{lll}
1 & (xy \setminus \phi xy) \subseteq_r (xy \setminus \psi xy) & \text{hyp} \\
2 & (z)[[z \,\epsilon\, (xy \setminus \phi xy)] \supset (\exists u)(\exists v)[z = (uv)]] & 24.15 \\
3 & (xy \setminus \phi xy) \subseteq (xy \setminus \psi xy) & 1, 2, 26.22
\end{array}
$$

26.52. From 26.51 and 26.21 we see that $[(xy \setminus \phi xy) \subseteq_r (xy \setminus \psi xy)]$ and $[(xy \setminus \phi xy) \subseteq (xy \setminus \psi xy)]$ are derivable from each other. Similarly it can be shown that $[(xy \setminus \phi xy) \simeq_r (xy \setminus \psi xy)]$ and $[(xy \setminus \phi xy) \simeq (xy \setminus \psi xy)]$ are derivable from each other.

26.53. If we let "Refl" denote the class of reflexive relations (16.17), we can regard "Refl" as an abbreviation for "$(x \setminus [(x^0) \subseteq_r x])$". The propositions $[R \,\epsilon\, \text{Refl}]$ and $[(R^0) \subseteq_r R]$ are then derivable from each other. Similarly for their denials. The propositions $[R \,\epsilon\, \text{Refl}]$ and $(x)[[x \,\epsilon\, (\text{Fld } R)] \supset [x \,R\, x]]$ can also be derived from each other.

26.54. If we let "Sym" denote the class of symmetrical relations (16.18), we can regard "Sym" as an abbreviation for "$(x \setminus [(x^{-1}) \subseteq_r x])$". The propositions $[R \,\epsilon\, \text{Sym}]$ and $[(R^{-1}) \subseteq_r R]$ are then derivable from each other. Similarly for their denials. The propositions $[R \,\epsilon\, \text{Sym}]$ and $(x)(y)[[x \,R\, y] \supset [y \,R\, x]]$ can also be derived from each other.

26.55. If we let "Trans" denote the class of transitive relations (16.19), we can regard "Trans" as an abbreviation for "$(x \setminus [(x^2) \subseteq_r x])$". The propositions $[R \,\epsilon\, \text{Trans}]$ and $[(R^2) \subseteq_r R]$ are then derivable from each other. Similarly for their denials. The propositions $[R \,\epsilon\, \text{Trans}]$ and $(x)(y)(z)[[[x \,R\, y] \,\&\, [y \,R\, z]] \supset [x \,R\, z]]$ can also be derived from each other.

26.56. We can let "Irrefl", "Asym", and "Intrans", respectively, serve as abbreviations for "$(x \setminus [(x^0) \subseteq_r (-x)])$", "$(x \setminus [(x^{-1}) \subseteq_r (-x)])$", and "$(x \setminus [(x^2) \subseteq_r (-x)])$", where "Irrefl" denotes the class of irreflexive relations (16.20), "Asym" denotes the class of asymmetrical relations (16.21), and "Intrans" denotes the class of intransitive relations (16.22).

EXERCISES

Prove the various results left unproved in this section.

27. The Consistency of the Extended System

[This section is of an advanced nature.]

27.1. In Section 20 it was shown that the system of logic developed in Sections 1–19 is free from contradiction. Subsequently the system has been extended by adding to it rules concerned with universality and existence. We now wish to show that the system in this extended form is still consistent.

27.2. The universality and existence rules will be restated below as rules R32–R40 and in a different form as compared with that originally given. The original form of each rule, however, is derivable from the form given below by making use of the various other rules listed in 20.2 and 27.4.

27.3. The notion of generality explained in 21.5 will now be somewhat revised. A proof S will be said to be general with respect to a if for each entity b we can obtain a valid proof by replacing a by b everywhere in S and by making, if necessary, a finite number of changes that replace a propositional item of the form $[c = d]$ by the corresponding denial of it, $\sim[c = d]$, or vice versa. These changes can be made to various propositional items of S or of proofs subordinate to S, but in each case the original reason for the item must be identity introduction or negative identity introduction, and the final reason must be whichever of these two the original reason was not. The purpose of revising the notion of generality in this way is to make it possible to have general subordinate proofs which use identity introduction and negative identity introduction and which do not require the derived rules of identity elimination and excluded middle for identity. If the previous account of generality were retained, then generality would have to be regarded as destroyed if the subordinate proof had to be written in different forms to correspond to the different cases, for example, considered in 19.7 and 19.8. Under the present account of generality, the second proof given in 19.8 can be regarded as general with respect to a. This is because if a is replaced throughout by something different from b, the proof is still valid, while if a is replaced by b, we have only to make one further change for the proof to be valid, and this is to change step 3 from $\sim[b = b]$ to $[b = b]$. Of course the reason for step 3 is then given as identity introduction, and the reason for step 4 is given as repetition or as hypothesis.

The second proof in 19.8 can in the same way be regarded as general with respect to b. The sort of changes mentioned in 24.5 will also still be allowed.

27.4. Rules to be added to the list of rules given in 20.2:

R32. Universality introduction (21.6, 27.2). (AF) is a d.c. of a categorical subproof that is general with respect to x and has (Fx) as its last item.

R33. Universality elimination (21.3, 27.2). (Fa) is a d.c. of (AF).

R34. Special elimination rule relating universality and disjunction (21.31, 27.2). r is a d.c. jointly of three subordinate proofs: The first is a categorical subproof that is general with respect to x and has $[p \lor (Fx)]$ as conclusion. The second is a hypothetical subproof with hypothesis p and conclusion r. The third is a hypothetical subproof with hypothesis (AF) and conclusion r. (It is, of course, assumed here that p does not mention x.)

R35. Negative universality introduction (22.30, 27.2). $\sim(AF)$ is a d.c. of $(E(-F))$.

R36. Negative universality elimination (22.31, 27.2). $(E(-F))$ is a d.c. of $\sim(AF)$.

R37. Existence introduction (22.3, 27.2). (EF) is a d.c. of (Fa).

R38. Existence elimination (22.4, 27.2). p is a d.c. of (EF) and a subordinate proof which is general with respect to x, has (Fx) as its only hypothesis, and has p as its last item. (It is, of course, assumed here that p does not mention x.)

R39. Negative existence introduction (22.32, 27.2). $\sim(EF)$ is a d.c. of $(A(-F))$.

R40. Negative existence elimination (22.33, 27.2). $(A(-F))$ is a d.c. of $\sim(EF)$.

27.5. The restriction stated in 18.6 and further elaborated in 22.57 must be understood as applying as follows in connection with the revised form of existence elimination (R38): If a subordinate proof has (Fx) as its hypothesis and is general with respect to x, and if some item is treated as being a direct consequence of it and of a proposition (EF) by R38, then there cannot be an item (Fa) which is a resultant of that subordinate proof. We continue to use the notion of resultant explained in 18.5 and 22.58.

27.6. Let S_0 be the system obtained by using rules R1–R32, and let S be the system obtained by using rules R1–R40. We will suppose that all the entities dealt with by S (and by S_0) can be enumerated, so that we can say that h_1 is the first of them, h_2 the second of them, h_3 the third of them, and so on. There is no last one, since they are infinitely many. The assumption that this enumeration can be made is justified by the fact that the totality of *expressions* employed in formulating S can easily be enumerated and by the fact that the *things designated* by the expressions can then be enumerated in the same way as the expressions themselves. Furthermore, the enumeration can be made *effective* in the sense that it can be set up in such a way that it is always possible, for any given positive integer n, to find the entity h_n.

27.7. Let S′ be a system that is like S except that in S′ we can have a whole sequence of items written in a horizontal row at one and the same step in a proof. Such a sequence will even be allowed to be infinite if there is an effective way of finding the nth member of it for each positive integer n. Thus in S′ we could have a proof of this form:

$$
\begin{array}{ll}
1 \mid \quad \mathsf{A}F & \text{hyp} \\[4pt]
2 \mid \ ^{-} \ Fh_1,\ Fh_2,\ Fh_3,\ \cdots,\ Fh_i,\ \cdots & \text{1, univ elim}
\end{array}
$$

Here step 2 is supposed to contain an infinite sequence of propositions and in fact every proposition (Fh_i), where i is chosen successively as 1, 2, 3, 4, and so on. Notice that we may omit outer parentheses of such expressions as "$(\mathsf{A}F)$" and "(Fh_1)" when no ambiguity results from so doing. Hereafter a group of three dots will be regarded as indicating that a sequence continues without cessation, unless a last member of the sequence is specified. Another example of a proof in S′ is as follows:

$$
\begin{array}{lll}
1 \mid \quad [(Fh_1) \supset p],\ [(Fh_2) \supset p],\ \cdots & & \text{hyp} \\[4pt]
2 \mid \quad \mathsf{E}F & & \text{hyp} \\[4pt]
3 \mid \quad \mid\ Fh_1 \qquad\qquad \mid\ Fh_2 & & \text{hyp} \\[4pt]
4 \mid \ ^{-} \mid\ (Fh_1) \supset p \quad \mid\ (Fh_2) \supset p \quad \cdots & & \text{1, reit} \\[4pt]
5 \mid \quad \mid\ p \qquad\qquad\quad \mid\ p & & \text{3, 4, m p} \\[4pt]
6 \mid \quad p & & \text{2, 3–5, exist elim} \\[4pt]
  & & \qquad\quad \text{(R38′ below)}
\end{array}
$$

27.8. Instead of R32, R34, and R38, the system **S′** will employ the following three rules:

R32′. Universality introduction for **S′**. (AF) is a d.c. jointly of the infinitely many propositions (Fh_1), (Fh_2), (Fh_3), $\cdots$.

R34′. Special elimination rule relating universality and disjunction for **S′**. r is a d.c. jointly of the infinitely many propositions $[p \vee (Fh_1)]$, $[p \vee (Fh_2)]$, $[p \vee (Fh_3)]$, $\cdots$, and two subordinate proofs, one with hypothesis p and conclusion r, the other with hypothesis (AF) and conclusion r.

R38′. Existence elimination for **S′**. p is a d.c. jointly of (EF) and infinitely many subordinate proofs having (Fh_1), (Fh_2), (Fh_3), $\cdots$, as their respective hypotheses and each having p as its conclusion.

27.9. Except for the differences noted in 27.7 and 27.8, the system **S′** is exactly like the system **S**. In particular, each proof in **S′** must have a *finite* number of steps and hence must be of *finite* length. At any one step, however, infinitely many items may be located, provided that a way is indicated for finding the nth item so located, for each positive integer n.

27.10. In **S′** the proposition (AF) acts as the infinite conjunction of the propositions (Fh_1), (Fh_2), (Fh_3), $\cdots$, while (EF) acts as their infinite disjunction. The consistency of **S′** can be established in essentially the same way as the consistency of **S₀**, because the infinite conjunction (AF) and the infinite disjunction (EF) can be handled in the demonstration of consistency in essentially the same way as ordinary finite conjunctions and disjunctions. The details of this are almost exactly the same as in the procedure outlined in 29.22–29.26 for the system **S₂** there being considered. Observe, however, that **S₂** permits proofs of infinite length, while **S′** does not.

27.11. In order to be able to form direct reductions of proofs in **S′** we must allow that at a given step in a proof there can be not merely infinitely many items, but different kinds of items, some perhaps being propositional items of the main proof, others being subordinate proofs or items of subordinate proofs. Suppose for example we wish to form a direct reduction of the following proof:

27.12.

| 1 | $h_1 = h_1$ | id int |
| 2 | $\{h_1\}h_1$ | 1, att int, def (17.42, 16.5) |

3	$\mathsf{E}\{h_1\}$		2, exist int

4	$\underline{\{h_1\}h_1}$	$\underline{\{h_1\}h_2}$	hyp
5	$(x \setminus (\{h_1\}x))h_1$	$(x \setminus (\{h_1\}x))h_2$ $\cdots$	4, att int
6	$\mathsf{E}(x \setminus (\{h_1\}x))$	$\mathsf{E}(x \setminus (\{h_1\}x))$	5, exist int

7	$\mathsf{E}(x \setminus (\{h_1\}x))$	3, 4–6, exist elim (R38′)

27.13. The respective hypotheses of the infinitely many subordinate proofs at steps 4–6 of 27.12 are $\{h_1\}h_1$, $\{h_1\}h_2$, $\{h_1\}h_3$, $\{h_1\}h_4$, and so on. We can form a direct reduction of 27.12 as follows:

27.14.

1	$h_1 = h_1$			id int
2	$\{h_1\}h_1$			1, att int, def
3	$\mathsf{E}\{h_1\}$			2, exist int
4	$\{h_1\}h_1$ 2, rep	$\underline{\{h_1\}h_2}$	$\underline{\{h_1\}h_3}$ $\cdots$	hyp
5	$(x \setminus (\{h_1\}x))h_1$	$(x \setminus (\{h_1\}x))h_2$	$(x \setminus (\{h_1\}x))h_3$	
6	$\mathsf{E}(x \setminus (\{h_1\}x))$	$\mathsf{E}(x \setminus (\{h_1\}x))$	$\mathsf{E}(x \setminus (\{h_1\}x))$	

27.15. In 27.14 the reasons for items at steps 5 and 6 are respectively the same as in 27.12, namely "4, att int" and "5, exist int". Notice that 27.14 is a proof of $\mathsf{E}(x \setminus (\{h_1\}x))$ and does not use existence elimination.

27.16. It is easy to see that any proposition provable in **S** is provable in **S′**. In particular, whenever we have

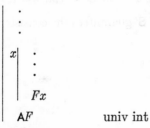

in **S**, we can have

$$Fh_1, Fh_2, Fh_3, \cdots$$

$\mathsf{A}F$ univ int (R32′)

in **S**'. And whenever we have

$$
\begin{array}{ll}
\vdots & \\
\mathbf{E}F & \\
x\ \big|\ \ Fx & \text{hyp} \\
\quad\ \ \vdots & \\
\quad\ \ p & \\
p & \text{exist elim}
\end{array}
$$

in **S**, we can have

$$
\begin{array}{lllll}
\vdots & & & & \\
\mathbf{E}F & & & & \\
\big|\ Fh_1 & \big|\ Fh_2 & \big|\ Fh_3 & \ \cdot\cdot & \text{hyp} \\
\ \ \vdots & \ \ \vdots & \ \ \vdots & & \\
\ \ p & \ \ p & \ \ p & & \\
p & & \text{exist elim (R38')} &
\end{array}
$$

in **S**'. Similarly whenever we use R34 in **S** we can use R34' in **S**'.

27.17. Hence the consistency of **S**' guarantees the consistency of **S**, and **S** is therefore consistent.

APPENDIX

Appendix A

COMBINATORY OPERATORS

28.1. In the *Timaeus* Plato attempts to treat all geometrical forms as built up out of certain ultimate simple triangles, and perhaps he also hoped to regard *all* his "ideas" or "forms" as thus built up out of some ultimate ideas or forms. Now it is possible in the system of logic of the present book to treat in some such way all the logical concepts with which we deal. If we start with the concepts denoted by the symbols "$\supset$", "&", "$\vee$", "$\sim$", "$\square$", "$\diamond$", "$=$", "ϵ", "A", and "E", together with some further logical concepts denoted by "T", "B", "W", and "K", and combine these in all possible ways by repeated use of the operation of ordered coupling (Section 15), we get a class of concepts to which belong all the logical concepts with which we deal. In particular, it will be shown that from this standpoint we can dispense with the abstracts of Section 17, or at least treat them as mere abbreviations. There will be no need now to assume the rules for attribute introduction and attribute elimination, or the corresponding negative rules.

28.2. From now on, much use will be made of the abbreviations stated in 15.18 and 15.19. These abbreviations will be assumed without mention.

28.3. The following rules will now be assumed in place of the rules for attribute introduction and attribute elimination:

Left-triple introduction. (abc) is a d.c. of $(a(bc))$.
Left-triple elimination. $(a(bc))$ is a d.c. of (abc).
T-introduction. $(\mathsf{T}abc)$ is a d.c. of (bac).
T-elimination. (bac) is a d.c. of $(\mathsf{T}abc)$.
B-introduction. $(\mathsf{B}abcd)$ is a d.c. of $(a(bc)d)$.
B-elimination. $(a(bc)d)$ is a d.c. of $(\mathsf{B}abcd)$.
W-introduction. $(\mathsf{W}ab)$ is a d.c. of (abb).
W-elimination. (abb) is a d.c. of $(\mathsf{W}ab)$.
K-introduction. $(\mathsf{K}ab)$ is a d.c. of a.
K-elimination. a is a d.c. of $(\mathsf{K}ab)$.

28.4. We also assume corresponding negative rules for left triples, T, B, W, and K. For example, the rule of negative T-introduction asserts that $\sim(\mathsf{T}abc)$ is a d.c. of $\sim(bac)$. The other negative rules are constructed analogously. These negative rules take the place of the rules for negative attribute introduction and negative attribute elimination, 17.35 and 17.36.

28.5. From the rule of ϵ-introduction and the rule of left-triple introduction the following second form of ϵ-introduction is easily obtained: (ϵab) follows from (ba). Similarly, from ϵ-elimination and left-triple elimination we get the following second form of ϵ-elimination: (ba) follows from (ϵab). There are also corresponding second forms of the negative ϵ-rules. These various second forms give rise to and are equivalent to the original forms.

28.6. In virtue of the rules for left triples, the following explanations of T, B, W, and K can be offered: We may regard T as the class of triples $(a(bc))$ such that $(b(ac))$ is true. This is because $(\mathsf{T}(a(bc)))$ and $(\mathsf{T}abc)$ are derivable from each other by repeated uses of the left-triple rules and because $(b(ac))$ and (bac) are derivable from each other by the left-triple rules, so that $(\mathsf{T}(a(bc)))$ and $(b(ac))$ are derivable from each other. Similarly $(\mathsf{B}(a(b(cd))))$ and $(a((bc)d))$ are derivable from each other, so that we may regard B as the class of quadruples $(a(b(cd)))$ such that $(a((bc)d)$ is true. Similarly $(\mathsf{W}(ab))$ and $(a(bb))$ are derivable from each other, so that we may regard W as the class of couples (ab) such that $(a(bb))$ is true. Finally, $(\mathsf{K}(ab))$ and a are derivable from each other, so that we may regard K as the class of couples (ab) such that a is true. Thus K is the class of those couples (ab) where a is true (and hence a true proposition) and where b is anything at all. Finally, ϵ is the class of those couples (ab) such that (ba) is true.

28.7. Some examples now follow: Since $(=(aa))$ is true, being otherwise written as $[a = a]$, we know that the triple $(a(=a))$ is a member of T. Since $(=((bc)(bc)))$ is true, we know that $(=(b(c(bc))))$ is a member of B. Since $(=(cc))$ is true, we know that $(=c)$ is a member of W and that $((=(cc))b)$ is a member of K.

28.8 The concepts ϵ, T, B, W, and K may be called **combinatory operators**. The ideas involved in using these operators are closely related to ideas that have been developed by H. B. Curry.[1]

---

[1] See, for example, his paper, "A Revision of the Fundamental Rules of Combinatory Logic", *Journal of Symbolic Logic*, vol. 6 (1941), pp. 41–53.

28.9. We may regard the symbols out of which we build up the expressions of our logic to be of two kinds, **improper symbols** and **proper symbols.** The left-hand parenthesis, "(", and the right-hand parenthesis, ")", are the only two improper symbols. The proper symbols are the following: "⊃", "&", "v", "∼", "□", "◊", "A", "E", "ϵ", "T", "K", "B", "W", and infinitely many further symbols "J_1", "J_2", "J_3", ⋯. The latter infinity of symbols may be thought of as denoting physical objects, persons, empirical qualities, and whatever else we might want to have names for in this system of logic. We are not considering here those symbols which we use only as parts of abbreviations, nor are we considering abstracts, since the operators "ϵ", "T", "K", "B", and "W" will make it possible to dispense with abstracts or at least to treat all abstracts as abbreviations for expressions which are not abstracts.

28.10. Among those expressions which we will call **proper expressions** are to be included all proper symbols and all expressions built up from proper symbols by combining them two-by-two within a pair of parentheses, and then (if we wish) by similarly combining *those* expressions with themselves or with other expressions obtained in the same way or with proper symbols, and by continuing the process as far as we like. Thus every proper symbol is a proper expression, and if "a" and "b" are proper expressions, so are "(ab)", "(aa)", and "(bb)". For example, "&", "v", and "ϵ" are proper expressions, and so are "(&v)", "(vv)", "(vϵ)", "((&v)(vv))", and "(((&v)(vv))ϵ)". The last two expressions, incidentally, could, by 15.18, be abbreviated respectively as "(&v(vv))" and "(&v(vv)ϵ)". Expressions which are not proper symbols and which have not been built up out of proper symbols by this process are not regarded as proper expressions.

28.11. We turn now to the task of showing that every abstract can be treated as an abbreviation for some proper expression.

28.12. First observe that the following coimplications can easily be proved from 28.3 and 28.4 by use of 15.18, 15.19, and 16.5:

$$[c \ \epsilon \ (\mathsf{T}ab)] \equiv [c \ \epsilon \ (ba)]$$
$$\sim[c \ \epsilon \ (\mathsf{T}ab)] \equiv \sim[c \ \epsilon \ (ba)]$$
$$[d \ \epsilon \ (\mathsf{B}abc)] \equiv [d \ \epsilon \ (a(bc))]$$
$$\sim[d \ \epsilon \ (\mathsf{B}abc)] \equiv \sim[d \ \epsilon \ (a(bc))]$$

$$(Wab) \equiv (abb) \qquad [b \ \epsilon \ (Wa)] \equiv [b \ \epsilon \ (ab)]$$
$$\sim(Wab) \equiv \sim(abb) \qquad \sim[b \ \epsilon \ (Wa)] \equiv \sim[b \ \epsilon \ (ab)]$$
$$(Kab) \equiv a \qquad [b \ \epsilon \ (Ka)] \equiv a$$
$$\sim(Kab) \equiv \sim a \qquad \sim[b \ \epsilon \ (Ka)] \equiv \sim a$$

28.13. From the first of the above coimplications we see that (Tab) and (ba) must have the same members, if any. We will call the expression "(Tab)" the **T-transform** of the expression "(ba)". From the third of the above coimplications we see that (Babc) and ($a(bc)$) must have the same members. We will call the expression "(Babc)" the **B-transform** of the expression "($a(bc)$)".

28.14. Not every proper expression has a T-transform, but only proper expressions of the form (ba). For example, "&", "=", and "⊃" do not have T-transforms. The T-transform of "(&B)" is "(TB&)". The T-transform of "(&B&)" is "(T&(&B))", since "(&B&)" is really an abbreviation for "((&B)&)" and since the T-transform of "((&B)&)" is clearly "(T&(&B))". In the following list the expression on the right is the T-transform of the corresponding expression on the left:

(ab)	(Tba)
(abc)	(T$c(ab)$)
($a(bc)$)	(T$(bc)a$)
($abcd$)	(T$d(abc)$)
($abc(de)$)	(T$(de)(abc)$)
($abc(def)$)	(T$(def)(abc)$)

28.15. Not every proper expression has a B-transform, but only proper expressions of the form "($a(bc)$)". For example, "(&(&&))" has a B-transform, namely "(B&&&)"; and "(⊃(BT))" has a B-transform, namely "(B⊃BT)". But "(&&)" has no B-transform, nor does "&", "B", "T", "⊃", or "=". Every proper expression of the general form "($a(bc)$)" does have a B-transform, even if "a", "b", and "c" are themselves complex expressions. Thus "($=d(\&d)$)" has a B-transform. To see this, we first write "($=d(\&d)$)" in its unabbreviated form as "(($=d$)($\&d$))". It is then clear that its B-transform is "(B($=d$)$\&d$)". In general, the B-transform of "($ab(cd)$)" must be "(B(ab)cd)". Similarly the B-transform of "($abc(de)$)" must be "(B(abc)de)". In seeking the B-transform of "($ab(cde)$)", we first note that "($ab(cde)$)" may be rewritten as "((ab)((cd)e))". It is then seen that the required B-transform is "(B(ab)(cd)e)". In the following list the expression on the right is the **B**-transform of the corresponding expression on the left:

$$(a(bc)) \qquad\qquad (\mathsf{B}abc)$$
$$(ab(cd)) \qquad\qquad (\mathsf{B}(ab)cd)$$
$$(a(bcd)) \qquad\qquad (\mathsf{B}a(bc)d)$$
$$(abc(de)) \qquad\qquad (\mathsf{B}(abc)de)$$
$$(ab(cde)) \qquad\qquad (\mathsf{B}(ab)(cd)e)$$
$$(abc(def)) \qquad\qquad (\mathsf{B}(abc)(de)f)$$
$$(abc(de(fg))) \qquad\qquad (\mathsf{B}(abc)(de)(fg))$$
$$(abc(def(ghi))) \qquad\qquad (\mathsf{B}(abc)(def)(ghi))$$

28.16. If "a" and "b" each occur only once in "(ab)", so that "a" does not occur in "b", and "b" does not occur in "a", then the only occurrence of "a" in "(ab)" will be called the **left section** of "(ab)", and the only occurrence of "b" in "(ab)" will be called the **right section** of "(ab)". If "a" occurs more than once in "(ab)", and so occurs in "b", then the leftmost occurrence of "a" in "(ab)" will be called the **left section** of "(ab)". If "b" occurs more than once in "(ab)", and so occurs in "a", then the rightmost occurrence of "b" in "(ab)" will be called the **right section** of "(ab)".

28.17. We now give some examples of left and right sections. In all cases except the first, the expression is written in two different forms. The second form is to show more clearly the separation between left and right sections.

Expression	Left Section	Right Section
$(= \supset)$	The only occurrence of "$=$".	The only occurrence of "$\supset$".
$(\&\&\&)$ $((\&\&)\&)$	The only occurrence of "$(\&\&)$".	The third occurrence of "$\&$".
$(\mathsf{TBB}(\&\mathsf{B}\supset))$ $((\mathsf{TBB})(\&\mathsf{B}\supset))$	The only occurrence of "(TBB)".	The only occurrence of "$(\&\mathsf{B}\supset)$".
(BBBBBB) $((\mathsf{BBBBB})\mathsf{B})$	The only occurrence of "(BBBBB)".	The sixth occurrence of "B".
$(\mathsf{B\&}(\mathsf{B\&}(\mathsf{B\&})))$ $((\mathsf{B\&})(\mathsf{B\&}(\mathsf{B\&})))$	The first occurrence of "$(\mathsf{B\&})$".	The only occurrence of "$(\mathsf{B\&}(\mathsf{B\&}))$".

28.18. We may also speak of the "right section of the right section", "the left section of the left section", and so on, where such sections exist. Thus the second occurrence of "**A**" in "(**AAA**)" is the right section of the left section of "(**AAA**)", since "(**AAA**)" is really an abbreviation for "((**AA**)**A**)". The second occurrence of "**B**" in "(**BA**(**BABA**))" is the left section of the left section of the left section of the right section of "(**BA**(**BABA**))". This is seen more clearly if we write "(**BA**(**BABA**))" in its unabbreviated form, "((**BA**)(((**BA**)**B**)**A**))".

28.19. Definition of the **principal transform** of an expression "a" with respect to an expression "b" occurring within "a".

CASE 1. Suppose that the rightmost occurrence of "b" in "a" is the left section of "a" or is within the left section of "a". Then the principal transform of "a" with respect to "b" is by definition the **T**-transform of "a". Thus "(**TA**(⊃**E**))" is the principal transform of "(⊃**EA**)" with respect to "(⊃**E**)", with respect to "⊃", and with respect to "**E**", but not with respect to "**A**".

CASE 2. Suppose that the rightmost occurrence of "b" in "a" is within the right section of "a" and does not constitute the whole right section of "a". Then the principal transform of "a" with respect to "b" is by definition the **B**-transform of "a". Thus "(**B**(**&A**)**A&**)" is the principal transform of "(**&A**(**A&**))" with respect to "**A**" and with respect to "**&**", but not with respect to "(**&A**)" or with respect to "(**A&**)".

CASE 3. Suppose that the rightmost occurrence of "b" in "a" is the whole right section of "a". Then there is no principal transform of "a" with respect to "b". In this case we say that "a" is in "b"-**normal form.** Thus "(**&A**(**A&**))" is in "(**A&**)"-normal form and has no principal transform with respect to "(**A&**)". Its principal transform with respect to "(**&A**)" is "(**T**(**A&**)(**&A**))" by case 1 above.

28.20. Suppose that a proper expression "b" occurs within a proper expression "a_1". Let us now form as long a sequence as possible of expressions "a_1", "a_2", $\cdots$, "a_n", starting with "a_1" and such that each successive term of the sequence is the principal transform of the preceding term with respect to "b". This sequence will be found to be uniquely determined, and it must finally come to an end with an expression of the form "(cb)", that is, with an expression that is in "b"-normal form. This is because the rightmost occurrence of "b"

in "a_1" gets moved further to the right in "a_2", and still further to the right in "a_3", and so on, until we come to the last term of the sequence. In this last term "b" is as far to the right as it can be, so this term is in "b"-normal form and has no principal transform with respect to "b". (This description of the rightmost occurrence of "b" as getting moved successively further and further to the right is accurate, strictly speaking, only if all expressions are written with as few parentheses as possible by making use of 15.18.) For example, let "a_1" be "(&&K)" and let "b" be "&". Then the sequence is as follows: "(&&K)", "(TK(&&))", "(B(TK)&&)". When parentheses are inserted in the last expression we see that it is "(((B(TK))&)&)" and that it is in "&"-normal form. In case "a_1" is so chosen as to be already in "b"-normal form, then we regard "a_1" as the only member of the sequence.

28.21. The last member of the sequence "a_1", "a_2", $\cdots$, "a_n" described in 28.20 will be said to be the "b"-**normal form** of "a_1". Thus "(B(TK)&&)" is the "&"-normal form of "(&&K)". If an expression is in "b"-normal form, then it is its own "b"-normal form. If "a_1" and "b" are any two proper expressions such that "b" occurs within "a_1", then we can always find the "b"-normal form of "a_1". As another example, suppose that we wish to find the "E"-normal form of "(EAA)". We form a sequence that starts with "(EAA)" and is such that each successive term of it is the principal transform of the preceding term with respect to "E". The sequence is as follows:

$$(EAA)$$
$$(TA(EA))$$
$$(B(TA)EA)$$
$$(TA(B(TA)E))$$
$$(B(TA)(B(TA))E)$$

Notice how the occurrence of "E" gradually moves to the right as we pass from one term of the sequence to the next. The last term of the sequence is the required "E"-normal form of "(EAA)". Its whole right section is an occurrence of "E".

28.22. We will say that a proper expression "a" is **congruent with** a proper expression "b" if $[[c \,\epsilon\, a] \equiv [c \,\epsilon\, b]]$ is provable for every c. Thus every proper expression is congruent with itself, since $[[c \,\epsilon\, a] \equiv [c \,\epsilon\, a]]$ is provable for every c and every a. (Recall 21.9 in this connection.) If "a" is congruent with "b", then "b" is clearly congruent with "a". If "a" and "b" are both congruent with a third expression, then they are clearly congruent with each other. If "a" has a T-transform, then "a" is congruent with its T-transform, as we see from 28.12. Similarly, if "a" has a B-transform, then "a" is congruent with its B-transform. Hence, if "a" has principal transform with respect to "b", then "a" must be congruent with such a principal transform, and if "a" has a "b"-normal form, then "a" must be congruent with that "b"-normal form. This is because the expressions "a_1", "a_2", $\cdots$, "a_n" of 28.20 must be congruent with each other. In particular, "(&&K)" is congruent with its "&"-normal form, "(B(TK)&&)", and "(EAA)" is congruent with its "E"-normal form, "(B(TA)(B(TA))E)".

28.23. It should now be clear that if "$(\cdots b \cdots)$" is any proper expression within which a proper expression "b" occurs, then the expression "$(\cdots b \cdots)$" has a unique "b"-normal form and is congruent with it. This "b"-normal form is some formal expression "(db)" that has "b" as its whole right section. Since "$(\cdots b \cdots)$" and "(db)" are congruent with each other, we can prove $[[c \ \epsilon \ (\cdots b \cdots)] \equiv [c \ \epsilon \ (db)]]$ for every c.

28.24. If "b" occurs within "$(\cdots b \cdots)$" and if "(db)" is the "b"-normal form of "$(\cdots b \cdots)$", then we call "d" the **first** "b"-**residue** of "$(\cdots b \cdots)$". Since "(B(TA)(B(TA))E)" has been shown to be the "E"-normal form of "(EAA)", we see that "(B(TA)(B(TA)))" is the first "E"-residue of "(EAA)". Similarly, since "(B(TK)&&)" has been shown to be the "&"-normal form of "(&&K)", we see that "(B(TK)&)" is the first "&"-residue of "(&&K)". If "d" is the first "b"-residue of "$(\cdots b \cdots)$", then we know that $[[c \ \epsilon \ (\cdots b \cdots)] \equiv [c \ \epsilon \ (db)]]$ is provable for every c.

28.25. If "d_1" is the first "b"-residue of "$(\cdots b \cdots)$", and if "d_2" is the first "b"-residue of "(Wd_1)", then we call "d_2" the **second** "b"-**residue** of "$(\cdots b \cdots)$". Similarly if "d_3" is the first "b"-residue of "(Wd_2)", then we call "d_3" the **third** "b"-**residue** of "$(\cdots b \cdots)$". And so on. The general principle is that if "d_n" is the nth "b"-residue of "$(\cdots b \cdots)$" and if "d_{n+1}" is the first "b"-residue of "(Wd_n)", then "d_{n+1}" is the $(n + 1)$th "b"-residue of "$(\cdots b \cdots)$".

28.26. Suppose that the proper expression "b" occurs exactly n times within the proper expression "$(\cdots b \cdots)$". Then there will be first, second, third, $\cdots$, nth "b"-residues of "$(\cdots b \cdots)$". Let "d_1", "d_2", "d_3", $\cdots$, "d_n" be these respective "b"-residues. Since by 28.23 we have, for every c,

$$[c \; \epsilon \; (\cdots b \cdots)] \equiv [c \; \epsilon \; (d_1 b)], \tag{1}$$

we can prove, in particular,

$$[b \; \epsilon \; (\cdots b \cdots)] \equiv [b \; \epsilon \; (d_1 b)]. \tag{2}$$

As in 28.12 we have,

$$[b \; \epsilon \; (d_1 b)] \equiv [b \; \epsilon \; (Wd_1)], \tag{3}$$

and hence,

$$[b \; \epsilon \; (\cdots b \cdots)] \equiv [b \; \epsilon \; (Wd_1)]. \tag{4}$$

By a similar argument,

$$[b \; \epsilon \; (Wd_1)] \equiv [b \; \epsilon \; (Wd_2)], \tag{5}$$

so that

$$[b \; \epsilon \; (\cdots b \cdots)] \equiv [b \; \epsilon \; (Wd_2)], \tag{6}$$

and similarly,

$$[b \; \epsilon \; (\cdots b \cdots)] \equiv [b \; \epsilon \; (Wd_3)]. \tag{7}$$

Continuing in this way, we finally get,

$$[b \; \epsilon \; (\cdots b \cdots)] \equiv [b \; \epsilon \; (Wd_n)]. \tag{8}$$

Now let "$(\cdots e \cdots)$" be the result of replacing "b" by "e" throughout "$(\cdots b \cdots)$", where "e" is any formal expression. Let "g_i" be the result of replacing the last $n - i$ occurrences of "b" in "d_i" by occurrences of "e". (In case "b" does not involve any of the expressions "T", "B", and "W", there will be exactly $n - i$ occurrences of "b" in "d_i", so in this case "g_i" will be the result of replacing all occurrences of "b" in "d_i" by occurrences of "e".) We assume here that $i = 1, 2, \cdots, n$. Now since we can get from "$(\cdots e \cdots)$" to "$(g_1 e)$" by exactly the same sequence of T-transforms and B-transforms that took us from "$(\cdots b \cdots)$" to "$(d_1 b)$", we know that "$(\cdots e \cdots)$" must be congruent with "$(g_1 e)$" and hence that

$$[e \; \epsilon \; (\cdots e \cdots)] \equiv [e \; \epsilon \; (g_1 e)]. \tag{9}$$

Paralleling the procedures of (1)–(8) above we can then prove successively,

$$[e \; \epsilon \; (\cdots e \cdots)] \equiv [e \; \epsilon \; (Wg_1)], \tag{10}$$

$$[e \; \epsilon \; (\cdots e \cdots)] \equiv [e \; \epsilon \; (Wg_2)], \tag{11}$$

and so on, until we finally get

$$[e \,\epsilon\, (\cdots e \cdots)] \equiv [e \,\epsilon\, (\mathsf{W}g_n)], \tag{12}$$

which is the same as

$$[e \,\epsilon\, (\cdots e \cdots)] \equiv [e \,\epsilon\, (\mathsf{W}d_n)]. \tag{13}$$

More generally, we could have chosen some fixed number m that is not greater than n, and we could have let "$(\cdots e \cdots)$" be the result of replacing the last m occurrences of "b" in "$(\cdots b \cdots)$" by occurrences of "e", while at the same time letting "g_i" be the result of replacing the last $m - i$ occurrences of "b" in "d_i" by occurrences of "e". Then we could show successively,

$$[e \,\epsilon\, (\cdots e \cdots)] \equiv [e \,\epsilon\, (\mathsf{W}g_1)], \tag{14}$$

$$[e \,\epsilon\, (\cdots e \cdots)] \equiv [e \,\epsilon\, (\mathsf{W}g_2)], \tag{15}$$

and so on, until we finally get

$$[e \,\epsilon\, (\cdots e \cdots)] \equiv [e \,\epsilon\, (\mathsf{W}g_m)], \tag{16}$$

which would be the same as

$$[e \,\epsilon\, (\cdots e \cdots)] \equiv [e \,\epsilon\, (\mathsf{W}d_m)]. \tag{17}$$

28.27. Suppose that the proper expression "b" occurs exactly k times within a proper expression "$(---b---)$". Let "d_k" be the kth "b"-residue of "$(\mathsf{K}(---b---))$". Let "$(---e---)$" be the result of replacing "b" by "e" throughout "$(---b---)$". Then "$(\mathsf{K}(---e---))$" is the result of replacing the last k occurrences of "b" in "$(\mathsf{K}(---b---))$" by occurrences of "e". If "b" is different from "K", then we have

$$[e \,\epsilon\, (\mathsf{K}(---e---))] \equiv [e \,\epsilon\, (\mathsf{W}d_k)] \tag{18}$$

by (13), choosing "$(\cdots e \cdots)$" as "$(\mathsf{K}(---e---))$", and choosing n as k. If "b" is the same as "K", then we can get (18) as a special case of (17), choosing "$(\cdots e \cdots)$" as "$(\mathsf{K}(---e---))$", choosing n as $k + 1$, and choosing m as k. From 28.12 we have,

$$[e \,\epsilon\, (\mathsf{K}(---e---))] \equiv (---e---). \tag{19}$$

From (18) and (19) we finally get,

$$(---e---) \equiv [e \,\epsilon\, (\mathsf{W}d_k)]. \tag{20}$$

28.28. If "x" is a proper expression that occurs exactly n times in a proper expression "$(\cdots x \cdots)$", and if "d" is the nth "x"-residue of "$(\mathsf{K}(\cdots x \cdots))$", we will call "$(\mathsf{W}d)$" the "$x$"-**abstract** of "$(\cdots x \cdots)$"

and we will use the expression "$(x \setminus (\cdots x \cdots))$" as an abbreviation for "$(\mathsf{W}d)$". If "$(\cdots a \cdots)$" is the result of replacing "x" by "a" throughout "$(\cdots x \cdots)$", then by (20) above we have

$$(\cdots a \cdots) \equiv [a \;\epsilon\; (x \setminus (\cdots x \cdots))]. \tag{21}$$

By similar methods we can also show,

$$\sim(\cdots a \cdots) \equiv \sim[a \;\epsilon\; (x \setminus (\cdots x \cdots))]. \tag{22}$$

This method of defining abstracts clearly gives the same effect as the use of the rules of attribute introduction and attribute elimination (17.4 and 17.5) and the corresponding negative rules (17.35 and 17.36). If "x" is so chosen as not to involve any occurrence of "T", "B", "W", or "K", then "x" does not occur in the expression for which the expression "$(x \setminus (\cdots x \cdots))$" serves as an abbreviation. We always can suppose "x" to be chosen in this way, and we thus conform to the requirement that x is not to be mentioned by the attribute $(x \setminus (\cdots x \cdots))$. This was discussed in 17.9.

28.29. Under the present treatment of abstracts, we do not ever have two different abstracts denoting the same attribute, so the problem discussed in 19.2 and 19.3 no longer arises.

28.30. The system of logic of this book may be developed in a purely syntactical way by restricting attention to proper expressions (28.10), by treating proper expressions as uninterpreted expressions, and by treating formal proofs as sequences of proper expressions and, more generally, as sequences involving subordinate sequences that correspond to subordinate proofs. The rules of direct consequence would then have to be restated as rules concerned with proper expressions and with sequences of proper expressions, rather than with propositions and sequences of propositions. The rules of direct consequence, together with this revised concept of "formal proof", would then serve to define the class of "formally provable" proper expressions, or "theorems".

Appendix B

A FURTHER EXTENSION OF THE SYSTEM

29.1. The system can be further extended so as to provide consistent foundations for a large part of mathematical analysis. The procedures involved in making such an extension will be briefly described below.

29.2. Instead of treating "(Pot R)" as an abbreviation as was done in 25.53, we will regard "(Pot R)" as an undefined expression, but as still having as its meaning the class of positive powers of R. Thus the proposition $[S \,\epsilon\, (\text{Pot } R)]$ is to be thought of as true if S is one of the relations R, $[R \mid R]$, $[[R \mid R] \mid R]$, and so on. Also, instead of using the notation "$[S \,\epsilon\, (\text{Pot } R)]$", it will be more convenient to write "$[R \text{ Pot } S]$", so that "Pot" will denote the relation of R to S such that S is a positive power of R, and we can read "$[R \text{ Pot } S]$" as "R has S as one of its positive powers".

29.3. We now form an extended system S_1 from the system S of 27.6 by adding to R1–R40 of S the further rules R41–R45 stated below. It seems likely that R45 is derivable from the other rules of S_1 and so could be omitted. The statement made in 27.3 about propositional items of the form $[c = d]$ and about identity introduction and negative identity introduction is now to be extended to apply also in the same way to propositional items of the form $[c \text{ Pot } d]$ and to the rules of power introduction (R41) and negative power introduction (R42).[1]

---

[1] The need for this extension and also the possibility of deriving R45 from the other rules of S_1 were both pointed out to me by Dr. John R. Myhill. It should also be remarked that even R44 is derivable from R1–R43, but the derivation is such that the length of the proof of ϕc varies with the choice of S. This fact ordinarily makes it impossible for a proof to be general with respect to S if it uses R44 as a derived rule for obtaining ϕc. The difficulty does not arise if R44 is treated as an underived rule of S_1, and it does not arise for S_2 below, since S_2 makes no essential use of general proofs as such. Hence in S_2 we treat R44 as a derived rule.

can be paralleled by a process according to which the shorter proofs are first shown to satisfy the fundamental theorem, and then $\mathfrak{I}$ itself is seen to satisfy it. The essential task is therefore to show that if 29.19 is true for every proof shorter than $\mathfrak{I}$, then it is true for $\mathfrak{I}$ itself.

29.21. We now proceed to demonstrate 29.19 for a categorical proof $\mathfrak{I}$ in S_2, assuming 29.19 true for all categorical proofs in S_2 that are shorter than $\mathfrak{I}$. If $\mathfrak{I}$ has only one step, we can argue as in 20.12. If $\mathfrak{I}$ has more than one step and has a last step, we let $\mathfrak{s}$ be the shorter proof that results if the last step of $\mathfrak{I}$ is dropped. Since we are assuming that 29.19 is satisfied by every proof shorter than $\mathfrak{I}$, we can conclude that $\mathfrak{s}$ is consistent and has a consistent normal reduction $\mathfrak{s}'$ which is no longer than $\mathfrak{s}$. Every proposition that serves as a propositional item of $\mathfrak{s}$ also serves as a propositional item of $\mathfrak{s}'$, and every propositional item of $\mathfrak{s}'$ has an introduction rule as its reason. There are various cases to consider, depending on the nature of the last item of $\mathfrak{I}$, if $\mathfrak{I}$ has a last step. We must also consider the case in which $\mathfrak{I}$ does not have a last step (29.27).

29.22. CASES 1–24 are exactly similar to Cases 1–24 of 20.14–20.37. See 20.38 regarding rules R24–R31.

29.23. CASE 25. The last item of $\mathfrak{I}$ is by R32'. (This case is the infinite analogue of 20.22.) Let the last item of $\mathfrak{I}$ be (AF). Let $\mathfrak{I}'$ be the proof that results from adding (AF) to $\mathfrak{s}'$. If $\mathfrak{I}'$ were inconsistent, $\mathfrak{I}'$ would have to have an item $\sim(AF)$ by an introduction rule, specifically by R35 (in 27.4), and so it would have to have an item $(E(-F))$ by an introduction rule, specifically by R37, and this entails that it must have an item $((-F)a)$ by an introduction rule, for some a. The introduction rule would have to be R20 (in 20.2) as we see from the definition of "$(-F)$" given in 17.18. Hence $\sim[a \; \epsilon \; F]$ must be an item of $\mathfrak{I}'$, and its reason must be negative ϵ-introduction (R18), and so $\sim(Fa)$ must be an item of $\mathfrak{I}'$ and hence also of $\mathfrak{s}'$. But since the reason for (AF) in $\mathfrak{I}$ is R32', $\mathfrak{I}$ must have as items (Fh_1), (Fh_2), $\cdots$, and so on, and hence must have (Fc) as an item for every entity c that is considered in the system S_2, and in particular it must have (Fa). Then (Fa) and $\sim(Fa)$ would both be items of $\mathfrak{s}'$, and $\mathfrak{s}'$ would be inconsistent. But we know that $\mathfrak{s}'$ must be consistent. Hence the assumption that $\mathfrak{I}'$ is inconsistent must be rejected as false, and we see that $\mathfrak{I}'$ is the required consistent normal reduction of $\mathfrak{I}$ and that $\mathfrak{I}$ itself is consistent.

R41. Power introduction. If the expression "S" is one of the expressions "R", "$[R \mid R]$", "$[[R \mid R] \mid R]$", "$[[[R \mid R] \mid R] \mid R]$", and so on, then $[R \; \text{Pot} \; S]$ is an axiom.

R42. Negative power introduction. If the expression "S" is not one of the expressions "R", "$[R \mid R]$", "$[[R \mid R] \mid R]$", "$[[[R \mid R] \mid R] \mid R]$", and so on, then $\sim[R \; \text{Pot} \; S]$ is an axiom.

R43. Special rule for powers. The propositions $[R \; \text{Pot} \; S]$ and $[[R = S] \vee (\exists z)[[(uv \setminus [[u \mid R] = v]) \; \text{Pot} \; z] \; \& \; [R \; z \; S]]]$ are direct consequences of each other. Their denials are also direct consequences of each other.

R44. Rule of induction. ϕc is a d.c. of $(y)[[b \; R \; y] \supset \phi y]$, $[R \; \text{Pot} \; S]$, $[b \; S \; c]$, and $(x)(y)[[[x \; R \; y] \; \& \; \phi x] \supset \phi y]$.

R45. Axiom of infinity. $[[[(xy \setminus (\exists z)[[x \cup z] = y]) \; \text{Pot} \; R] \; \& \; [(-\cup) \; R \; a]] \supset (\exists w)\sim[w \; \epsilon \; a]]$ is an axiom. (See 17.47.)

29.4. We can define the expressions "(R_{po})", "$(\text{Potid} \; R)$", and "(R_*)" as in 25.54–25.56. And we can regard the propositions $[S \; \epsilon \; (\text{Pot} \; R)]$ and $[R \; \text{Pot} \; S]$ as coimplying each other in virtue of the ϵ-rules (16.5), the left-triple rules of Appendix A, and the abbreviations of 15.19. Similarly we can regard $[S \; \epsilon \; (\text{Potid} \; R)]$ and $[R \; \text{Potid} \; S]$ as coimplying each other provided that we first define "Potid" as "$(uv \setminus [[u \; \text{Pot} \; v] \vee [(u^0) = v]])$", rather than defining "$(\text{Potid} \; R)$" in the manner of 25.55. We would still be able to show that $(\text{Potid} \; R)$ and $[(\text{Pot} \; R) \cup \{(R^0)\}]$ have the same members.

29.5. The following three rules of induction are easily derivable in the system S_1:

29.6. First derived rule of induction. ϕc follows from $(y)[[b \; R \; y] \supset \phi y]$, $[b \; (R_{\text{po}}) \; c]$, and $(x)(y)[[[x \; R \; y] \; \& \; \phi x] \supset \phi y]$.

29.7. Second derived rule of induction. ϕc follows from ϕb, $[b \; (R_*) \; c]$, and $(x)(y)[[[x \; R \; y] \; \& \; \phi x] \supset \phi y]$.

29.8. Third derived rule of induction. ϕS follows from ϕR, $[R \; \text{Pot} \; S]$, and $(x)[\phi x \supset \phi[x \mid R]]$.

29.9. In order to derive the fundamental theorems of mathematical analysis in the system S_1 we need the two following results, where "D_1" is being used as an abbreviation for "$(z \setminus (x)[[x \; \epsilon \; z] \vee \sim[x \; \epsilon \; z]])$":

$$[[F \; \epsilon \; D_1] \; \& \; [F \subseteq D_1]] \supset [(x \setminus (\exists y)[[x \; \epsilon \; y] \; \& \; [y \; \epsilon \; F]]) \; \epsilon \; D_1],$$

$$[[F \; \epsilon \; D_1] \; \& \; [F \subseteq D_1]] \supset [(x \setminus (y)[[x \; \epsilon \; y] \vee \sim[y \; \epsilon \; F]]) \; \epsilon \; D_1].$$

These two results can be obtained without great difficulty. They are important for proving the existence of least upper bounds and greatest lower bounds in the theory of real numbers. The following result, important in deriving the Heine-Borel theorem, is also easily obtained:

$$(x)(y)[[x \; R \; y] \lor \sim[x \; R \; y]] \supset (x)(y)[[x \; (R_{\mathrm{po}}) \; y] \lor \sim[x \; (R_{\mathrm{po}}) \; y]].$$

The relevance of these various results to mathematical analysis can be seen from the procedures used in my papers, "The Heine-Borel Theorem in Extended Basic Logic" (*Journal of Symbolic Logic*, vol. 14, pp. 9–15) and "A Demonstrably Consistent Mathematics" (*ibid.*, vol. 15, pp. 17–24; vol. 16, pp. 121–24).

29.10. In what follows we will assume that all the entities with which S_1 is concerned can be enumerated, so that we can call h_1 the first of them, h_2 the second of them, h_3 the third of them, and so on as in 27.6.

29.11. A method for establishing the consistency of S_1 will now be presented in outline. The same method could also be applied if S_1 were extended by adding to it the rules stated in 28.3 and 28.4. Let S_2 be a system exactly like S_1 except for three differences: The first difference is that S_2 permits proofs of infinite length provided that the steps of each such proof form a well-ordered series (see 29.12). The second difference is that the rules R43–R45 can be omitted in defining S_2 since they are derivable in S_2. The third difference is that R32, R34, and R38 are replaced in S_2 by the stronger rules R32′, R34′, and R38′ as stated in 27.8.

29.12. The requirement that every infinite proof in S_2 have a well-ordered series of steps merely means that if the series is broken at any point, there will always be a step that *immediately* follows the break, though there may or may not be a step that *immediately* precedes the break. When there is no step immediately preceding such a break, this is because there is no last step among the various steps that do precede the break. Without the requirement of well-ordering, the reasoning in 29.20 could not be considered valid.

29.13. The restriction stated in 18.6 is of course retained in S_2. There is no need to employ here the more complicated forms of the restriction stated in 22.57 and 27.5. This is because S_2 does not make any essential use of general proofs.

29.14. It will now be shown that S_2 is free from contradiction. From this it will follow that the weaker system S_1 is also free from contradiction.

29.15. Since proofs in S_2 are well-ordered with respect to their steps, we can assign infinite as well as finite ordinal numbers in numbering the steps. For this purpose, however, we use only the ordinal numbers of the first and second number classes, that is, only finite and denumerably infinite ordinal numbers. This because we consider only proofs of denumerably infinite length. The demonstration of the consistency of S_2 will not involve any essential use of these ordinal numbers, though it could be presented as proceeding by a transfinite induction over them.

29.16. If we wish to avoid altogether the use of ordinal numbers in S_2, then in giving a reason for an item in a proof we merely specify the rule used without mention of numbers referring to preceding items. If this leaves some ambiguity as to which preceding items are being used, we are free to resolve the ambiguity in any way that leaves the proof in conformity with the restriction 18.6.

29.17. A proof $\mathfrak{I}$ in S_2 will be said to be an **extension** of a proof $\mathfrak{R}$ in S_2 if $\mathfrak{I}$ results from adding one or more steps to $\mathfrak{R}$.

29.18. Two proofs $\mathfrak{I}$ and $\mathfrak{R}$ in S_2 will be said to be of **equal length** if the steps of $\mathfrak{I}$ and $\mathfrak{R}$ can be paired up by means of a one-to-one correspondence that does not destroy their order. We will say that $\mathfrak{R}$ is **shorter than** $\mathfrak{I}$, and that $\mathfrak{I}$ is **longer than** $\mathfrak{R}$, if $\mathfrak{I}$ is an extension of a proof that is of the same length as $\mathfrak{R}$.

29.19. Fundamental theorem concerning categorical proofs in S_2. Every categorical proof $\mathfrak{I}$ in S_2 is consistent and has at least one reduction which is consistent and normal and which is no longer than $\mathfrak{I}$. (This theorem is eventually proved only after a further change is made in S_2, as indicated in 29.27. It is convenient to postpone making this change until later.)

29.20. The method for establishing the above theorem is first to show that it is true for all proofs of minimum length (this we at once assume done as in 20.12), and second to show that if it is true for all proofs shorter than $\mathfrak{I}$, then it is true for $\mathfrak{I}$ itself. Thus any process by which a proof $\mathfrak{I}$ is built up from proofs of which it is an extension

29.24. CASE 26. The last item of $\mathfrak{I}$ is by R33 (in 27.4). (This case is the infinite analogue of 20.23 and is somewhat similar to it.) The method is in outline as follows: (Fc) must be an item of $\mathfrak{S}'$ for every c, since $(\mathsf{A}F)$ is an item of $\mathfrak{S}'$ by an introduction rule, specifically by R32′. Hence if (Fa) is added to $\mathfrak{S}'$ to give $\mathfrak{I}'$, we know that some other item (Fa) already appears as an item of $\mathfrak{S}'$ and of $\mathfrak{I}'$. The reason for this last item of $\mathfrak{I}'$ can then be the same introduction rule that serves as the reason for the previous (Fa). Any inconsistency in $\mathfrak{I}'$ would clearly entail an inconsistency in $\mathfrak{S}'$. Thus $\mathfrak{I}'$ is the required consistent normal reduction of $\mathfrak{I}$.

29.25. CASE 27. The last item of $\mathfrak{I}$ is by R34′. Let this last item be r. Then the infinitely many propositions $[p \vee (Fh_1)]$, $[p \vee (Fh_2)]$, $\cdots$, are items of $\mathfrak{S}$ and so are two subordinate proofs, one with hypothesis p and conclusion r, the other with hypothesis $(\mathsf{A}F)$ and conclusion r. Clearly either p is an item of $\mathfrak{S}'$ or else (Fh_1), (Fh_2), $\cdots$, are all items of $\mathfrak{S}'$; and either r itself is an item of $\mathfrak{S}'$ or else both subordinate proofs are items of $\mathfrak{S}'$. If r is an item of $\mathfrak{S}'$ the required consistent normal reduction of $\mathfrak{I}$ is obtained by adding r to $\mathfrak{S}'$ as a redundant item. If r is not an item of $\mathfrak{S}'$ we form a direct reduction of $\mathfrak{S}'$ with respect to one of the two subordinate proofs. In the case of the subordinate proof that has hypothesis $(\mathsf{A}F)$ this procedure is somewhat unusual, since $(\mathsf{A}F)$ may not already be an item of $\mathfrak{S}'$, but this makes no trouble as the subordinate proof can be replaced by the sequence of all its items, including its hypothesis, and the direct reduction can be arranged in such a way that R32′ can be given as a reason for $(\mathsf{A}F)$. (This is because by 18.6 and 22.58 no one of (Fh_1), (Fh_2), $\cdots$, can be a resultant of any subordinate proof having $(\mathsf{A}F)$ as hypothesis.) If r is added to this direct reduction as a redundant item, we have the required consistent normal reduction of $\mathfrak{I}$.[2]

29.26. CASES 28–33. The last item of $\mathfrak{I}$ is by one of the rules R35–R37, R38′, R39, R40. These cases are the infinite analogues of 20.24–20.29. Details will be omitted for brevity. The reader can supply the missing details by noting the analogy of Case 25 to 20.22 and of Case 26 to 20.23.

---

[2] The "direct reduction" here referred to does not really conform to the notion of direct reduction defined in 20.7; but we can suppose 20.7 to be modified in such a way that p of 20.7 need not already be an item of the main proof, and we can allow the subordinate proof in such a case to be replaced by $p, q_1, \cdots, q_n$, instead of $q_1, \cdots, q_n$.

29.27. Case 34. In this case $\mathfrak{I}$ does not have any last step. Each proof of which $\mathfrak{I}$ is an extension is consistent and has a consistent normal reduction no longer than itself. In order to provide a consistent normal reduction of $\mathfrak{I}$, the simplest method seems to be to allow proofs to have a finite or infinite number of items at each step, instead of just one item as heretofor. Then by "superposing" all the consistent normal reductions of proofs of which $\mathfrak{I}$ is an extension, we obtain a proof $\mathfrak{I}'$ which is the required consistent normal reduction of $\mathfrak{I}$. (In "superposing" two or more proofs, we simply place them next to each other in parallel so that the nth step of each is on a level with the nth step of each of the others. Some items at the nth step of the resulting proof might be items of the main proof itself, others might be items of various subordinate proofs.) Cases 1–33 can still be handled in very much the same way as before more than one item was allowed to a step. If the proof $\mathfrak{I}$ in Cases 1–33 has more than one item at its last step, we take the various $\mathfrak{I}'$ proofs corresponding to each of these items and superpose them to give the required consistent normal reduction of $\mathfrak{I}$. In this process we can disregard those items which are located at the last step but which are items of subordinate proofs rather than of the main proof. The present case, Case 34, of course also allows $\mathfrak{I}$ to have many items per step.

29.28. By allowing more than one item per step in proofs in S_2 we have obtained a system at least as strong as the original system S_2. The consistency of this modified form of S_2 can now be established by methods like those used in 20.44–20.46. The original form of S_2 is therefore also consistent. Since all the rules used to define S_1 can be shown to be derivable in both forms of S_2, the consistency of S_1 is guaranteed.

Appendix C

SELF-REFERENCE IN PHILOSOPHY [1]

A theory always has a particular subject matter associated with it. We say that the theory is "about" its subject matter. For example, Darwin's theory of natural selection is about living organisms, and species of living organisms, and genetic relationships among such species. Newton's theory of universal gravitation is about particles of matter and about certain relationships of attraction between such particles. In so far as a theory is vague, the exact extent of its subject matter tends to be hard to specify. A precisely stated theory, on the other hand, tends to have a clearly delineated subject matter. We may ordinarily regard the subject matter of a theory as consisting of some class of entities, together with certain subclasses of that class and certain relations among its members. The notion of "subject matter" could be more carefully analyzed, but this concept should be clear enough in the light of the informal examples just given.

Some theories are about theories. Others are not. Theories which do not include theories in their subject matter will be said to be of *ordinal level zero*. A theory which includes in its subject matter some theories of ordinal level zero, but none of higher ordinal level, will be said to be of *ordinal level one*. And so on. In general: A theory of ordinal level $n + 1$ includes in its subject matter no theories of ordinal

---

[1] This is a slightly revised form of an article which I published under the same title in *Mind*, vol. 55, n.s. (1946), pp. 64–73. It is reprinted here in order to indicate more fully my motives for rejecting the Russell-Whitehead theory of types and in order to emphasize the philosophical importance of self-referential propositions and the need for a logic, such as the present one, which can handle such propositions. I have not discussed Russell's theory of "typical ambiguity" as constituting a possible reply to my objections, but I do not believe that such a theory can be developed in detail without encountering type difficulties of an insuperable sort at the semantical level. I wish to thank the Editor of *Mind* for permission to reprint this material. See also, in connection with some of these problems, the article by Weiss referred to in the first footnote of the Foreword, and the remarks by W. M. Urban on p. 209 of his book *Humanity and Deity* (London, 1951).

level greater than n, but it does include some of ordinal level n. Here n may be thought of as any finite or infinite ordinal number. Many theories proposed in the empirical sciences can be seen to be of some fairly low finite ordinal level. This is because empirical science is not generally concerned with framing theories about all theories.

A different situation prevails in philosophical research. Here extreme comprehensiveness is sought for. Theories are constructed which purport to deal with all entities whatsoever and which therefore have an unrestrictedly extensive subject matter. In dealing with all entities, such theories in particular deal with all theories, since theories are themselves entities of a special sort. In philosophy we thus encounter theories about the general nature of theories. If a theory has an ordinal level, its ordinal level must be greater than the ordinal levels of all theories occurring within its subject matter. Hence a theory about the general nature of theories can have no ordinal level, for its ordinal level would have to be greater than itself. Theories having no ordinal level will be said to be "vertical" or "non-ordinal" theories. Theories having ordinal levels will be said to be "horizontal" or "ordinal" theories.

If a theory is included in its own subject matter, we say that it is a *self-referential* theory. Since no ordinal level can be assigned to a self-referential theory, every self-referential theory is vertical and non-ordinal. The converse, however, is not true, because a theory might contain vertical theories in its subject matter without containing itself in its subject matter. Such a theory would be vertical but not self-referential.

An example of a vertical and self-referential theory is Whitehead's philosophical system as presented in *Process and Reality*. Among the entities considered in his system are not only actual occasions, eternal objects, prehensions, nexūs, contrasts, and multiplicities, but also propositions or theories. His whole doctrine of these entities is itself a theory. Since it is a theory about all theories, it includes itself in its subject matter.

Whitehead's identification of propositions with theories raises the question as to whether theories should be treated as classes of propositions or as individual propositions. Either view seems equally tenable. For present purposes Whitehead's view will be accepted. This means that every proposition is a theory, and conversely, so that every proposition is regarded as having a subject matter. One might say that all entities mentioned by a proposition belong to the subject matter of the proposition, and that if a class or a relation is among the entities that belong to the subject matter so are all members of the class and so are all entities related by the relation.

Some writers attempt to abandon the notion of "proposition" altogether, and to replace it by the notion of "statement" or "sentence", regarding the latter as a mere string of symbols. Such a procedure is useful as a matter of method in the field of syntax, where the meanings of symbols are not of interest so much as the symbols themselves. When questions of meaning are raised, however, this sort of nominalism seems very inadequate. Even Carnap, who formerly advocated some such nominalism, has now largely relinquished it.

Any system of philosophy which takes a position on the nature of theories or propositions is itself a vertical self-referential theory. Particular views as to what constitutes a valid or acceptable theory are also themselves vertical self-referential theories. For example, consider the view that every valid theory must be obtained from observed empirical data. This is a theory about theories and their validity. Incidentally it is a theory which does not seem to conform to its own criterion as to what constitutes a valid theory, at least not unless it can itself be shown to have been obtained as a generalization from observed empirical data. A vertical theory is always open to just this sort of danger. It may not itself conform to some principle that it lays down concerning theories in general. A horizontal theory, on the other hand, is open to no such danger. It may be internally inconsistent, or it may be inconsistent with known facts, and hence "externally" inconsistent, but it cannot be inconsistent with its own nature in the way that a self-referential theory can. If a self-referential theory T implies that T has the property P, and if T in fact does not have the property P, then we shall call T self-referentially inconsistent.

Self-referential inconsistency is important in at least two respects. In the first place, a standard method for attempting to refute a philosophical view is to show that it is self-referentially inconsistent. This is a method which can be applied only to vertical, or at least self-referential, theories. Hence it is a method which is for the most part peculiar to philosophy and philosophical logic. In the second place, self-referential inconsistency, or something almost the same, is at the heart of many important problems in logic and mathematics. Some of the most interesting problems of modern logic center around the paradoxes of set theory and the closely analogous semantical paradoxes. All these paradoxes involve propositions which refer directly or indirectly to themselves. Any system of mathematics or logic in which such paradoxes can arise is both vertical and inconsistent, though it might not be actually self-referential itself. The vertical or non-ordinal aspect would arise from the fact that self-referential propositions would be part of its subject matter. There exist restricted vertical systems of logic and mathematics which seem to be free from the paradoxes of set theory, though consistency has not yet been definitely established in the case of the most important and useful of such systems. Even within such restricted systems it is possible to prove certain fundamental theorems due to Cantor and Gödel which are closely similar to the paradoxes of set theory both with respect to the presence of something analogous to self-reference (or even self-reference itself, in the case of Cantor's theorem) and with respect to the role played by the concept of negation. More will be said about these mathematical matters later. First let us consider the importance of the notion of self-reference in philosophical methodology.

It may be that nobody has ever seriously proposed or tried to defend a system of philosophy which was actually self-referentially inconsistent, though many systems of philosophy superficially *seem* (to those attacking such systems) to be self-referentially inconsistent. For example, consider the skeptical point of view according to which nothing is "absolutely" true. This view casts some element of doubt on every proposition. According to it no proposition can be asserted as true for certain. All theories are open to some doubt, it holds. But this view is itself a theory about all theories, and the doubt it casts on all theories it casts equally well upon itself. If it is really a valid theory, then it is wrongly questioning its own validity in questioning the validity of all theories. Therefore, if it is valid it is self-referentially inconsistent and hence not valid after all. Therefore it cannot be valid. A similar situation is to be found in Descartes' method of doubt. He could not doubt that he was doubting, and hence he found something indubitable. Complete doubt of everything led to a self-referentially inconsistent view and so had to be abandoned. We thus get the positive result that some propositions may be affirmed with certainty. In fact we can conclude that doubt "presupposes" certainty.

The notion of "presupposition" suggests various sorts of philosophical idealism and related types of philosophy. In such philosophies a "presupposition" often seems to mean some hypothesis that cannot be systematically denied without in some sense being already assumed. The very denial itself, or some important aspect of it, or some assumption or method involved in presenting and defending it, constitutes an exception to the denial. A presupposition might be defined as an assumption whose denial is self-referentially inconsistent. For example, any systematic consideration of and rejection of the accepted principles of logic already involves the use of at least some of those principles of logic. Hence it is a presupposition that at least some of the principles of logic are valid. Similarly, any attempt to reduce the principles of logic to mere conventions regarding the use of symbols must already employ those principles themselves in carrying out the reduction. Hence the reduction is really a reduction of logic to *conventions-plus-logic*, and logic is not completely "analyzed away" into something else.

The concept of presupposition may also be considered in connection with the theory of value. This is because value judgments enter into the theory of value, or rather into specific theories of value, not only as part of the subject matter but also as part of the intellectual apparatus used for defending or attacking particular theses concerning value. For example, one value theorist might attack the scientific or philosophical methodology of another value theorist as "bad" or "unsound" methodology. But the attacking theorist might be assuming a theory of value according to which the phrase, "X is bad", should always be replaced by a phrase of the form, "Y dislikes X", and nevertheless might be unwilling to restate his attack in the form of a mere statement of personal dislike. If so, the attack becomes self-referentially inconsistent, inasmuch as it is based on a theory to which it does not itself conform. The rejection of the demand that phrases of the form, "X is bad", be restated in the form, "Y dislikes X", is a presupposition of every theory which makes value assumptions ("good" and "bad") about methodology and fails to treat such value assumptions as mere matters of personal like or dislike.

The type of argument in which one accuses one's opponent of self-referential inconsistency is really a very ancient type of argument. It has often been called the *ad hominem* type of argument, since it may involve the pointing out of some fact about the opponent himself which contradicts or is an exception to the view he propounds. It is perhaps best understood as a request that the opponent clarify his position sufficiently to destroy some superficial appearance of self-referential inconsistency. A solipsist, for example, might be expected to hold the view that his solipsism needs no defence against the attack of an opponent, since the solipsist maintains that nobody else, and hence no opponent, exists. Thus solipsism seems to presuppose the existence of other minds insofar as the solipsist takes the trouble to reply to objections to his view. But this is perhaps a superficial interpretation of solipsism, and a careful solipsist might state his position in such a way that it would be evident that he was stating his position for the benefit of no other mind but his own.

The *ad hominem* type of argument is probably more liable to stir up the resentment of an opponent than any other type of argument. This is because it has the appearance of being directed at the opponent himself, as well as against his thesis. It may therefore be treated as if it were a personal insult of some sort, involving even ridicule and irony. The opponent is made to look like very much of a fool when the *ad hominem* argument is well presented, because the exception to the opponent's view is found to exist not in some distant situation but, of all places, in some situation or fact immediately involving the opponent himself. Not only does self-referential inconsistency involve a definite sort of irony, but consideration seems to reveal that all cases of irony, conversely, have in them some element of self-referential inconsistency, or something approximating to it.

The personal aspect of the *ad hominem* type of argument tends to cause it to be regarded as an "unfair" type of argument, and indeed unsound. The present writer, however, regards it as a very important sort of argument, and one that is perfectly valid against certain kinds of vertical theories. The mere fact that it cannot be used in connection with horizontal theories arising in the special sciences does not mean that it can have no application in philosophy. On the contrary, the possibility of using it in philosophical speculation and in the criticism of systems of philosophy is a mark which distinguishes philosophy from the empirical sciences. W. M. Urban in his book, *The*

Intelligible World, makes repeated use of the *ad hominem* argument. On page 45 he quotes Lowes Dickinson as holding that in ultimate matters the *argumentum ad hominem* is "the only argument possible and, indeed, the only one in which anyone much believes".

Although no *ordinal* level can be assigned to a theory which is about all theories, still we may speak of its "level" in some broader sense. A theory about all theories may be said to have attained the level of maximum theoretical generality. At such a level all other levels may be dealt with. There is no level which is higher in the sense that it can deal with theories not dealt with on the level of maximum theoretical generality. To deny that there is such a level is already to be proposing a theory about all theories and hence to be presenting a theory which is itself of the level of maximum theoretical generality. Thus an *ad hominem* argument can be used against the contention that no such level is to be found. It is characteristic of philosophy to reach this maximum level and to be able to use the self-referential sorts of reasoning which are possible on this level.

An analogous situation is to be found in the classical theory of real numbers. The real numbers can be defined as classes of rational numbers. We thus obtain numbers (namely, the irrational real numbers) having various properties not possessed by the rational numbers. If we attempt to go a step further and define some other sort of number in terms of classes of real numbers in exactly the same way that the real numbers are defined as classes of rational numbers, then nothing essentially new or different is obtained. This is because the class of real numbers has a sort of "level of maximum numerical generality", just as a theory about all theories has a level of maximum theoretical generality. The analogy can be seen from the fact that on the classical theory of real numbers it is permissible for an individual real number to be defined in terms of the class of all real numbers. This is similar to the situation where we have a theory dealing with all theories. On the classical theory of real numbers, generally speaking, it is permissible for an entity to be defined in terms of a class (e.g., the class of real numbers) having that entity as a member. Such a definition is not "circular" in the objectionable sense of defining an entity in terms of itself, but it is nevertheless circular in a secondary sense, since a class having the definiendum as a member is a factor in the definiens. Real numbers defined in terms of the class of all real numbers are thus circularly defined (in a secondary sense of "circularity") and involve self-reference. Cantor's proof that the class of real numbers cannot be put into a one-to-one correspondence with the class of rational numbers consists in supposing that the correspondence has been set up and then in defining *in terms of the correspondence* (and hence in terms of the whole class of real numbers) a particular real number that must have been omitted from the correspondence. The particular real number, of course, involves a sort of self-reference. Russell's "branched" or "ramified" theory of types of the first edition of *Principia Mathematica* was designed to do away with all self-reference in logic and mathematics in order to provide protection against the paradoxes of set theory and the paradoxes of semantics, since Russell believed these paradoxes to be due to a "vicious" circularity. Russell proposed the Axiom of Reducibility, however, as a device to moderate (in effect, if not in theory) the elimination of all circularity and to permit the sort of secondary circularity required for Cantor's theorem. (A similar effect is obtained more simply by replacing the branched theory of types by the "simplified theory of types". This method, however, can be safely used only where semantical concepts are not being assigned type.) Unless some appropriate sort of circularity and self-reference is allowed, Cantor's theorem no longer holds and the real numbers no longer represent a genuine maximum level. In order to get enough real numbers for mathematical purposes without some such circularity, it becomes necessary to keep proceeding to higher and higher levels (or "orders") without ever reaching a final level on which all the real numbers may be handled. For this reason the branched theory of types, unless moderated by the required reducibility principle (or, equivalently, transformed into the simplified theory of types), is not held in esteem by most mathematicians. Something very much like the branched ("ramified") theory of types, not too much moderated by a reducibility principle, has often been urged for avoiding the paradoxes of semantics in those theories which are concerned with *semantical* as well as mathematical concepts. The ramified theory of types, however, cannot be taken as laying down ultimate restrictions which eliminate all sorts of self-reference whatsoever. Not only would the theory of real numbers be crippled, but all theories about the totality of theories would be eliminated. Furthermore, such a ramified theory of types could not even be stated. Its sweeping restrictions against self-reference would apply to every theory, including itself, and so it would be self-referential in violation of its own edicts. A similar criticism can be made even against the more moderate simplified theory of types, if regarded as universally applicable. This sort of criticism is clearly just another instance of a use of the *ad hominem* argument. One way of attempting to meet this objection to the ramified or simplified theory of types is to assert that a formulation of a theory of types is simply the formulation of certain more or less arbitrary or conventional stipulations about the permitted ways of combining symbols. This answer seems to be all right so long as one is restricting oneself to the realm of uninterpreted symbols, but as soon as one enters the realm of semantical concepts it becomes necessary to apply distinctions of "type" to *meanings* of symbols as well as to symbols themselves, and the element of self-reference reappears. For example, the ramified theory of types cannot assign a type to the meaning of the word "type", and yet it must do so if the theory applies to all meanings. In a similar way, no "order" (in the sense used in the ramified theory of types) can be assigned to a proposition which is about all propositions, hence no order can be assigned to the proposition which states the ramified theory of types.

The problem is to find a logic which eliminates the "vicious" sorts of self-reference that lead to the mathematical and semantical paradoxes but not those sorts of self-reference that seem to be such an important part of philosophical logic, or are required in developing the theory of real numbers. The system of logic of this book seems to satisfy these demands. On the other hand, Russell's theory of types, in its various forms, excludes the sort of self-reference that is essential to philosophy. At the same time the theory of types requires for its own statement the sort of inclusive generality that it treats as meaningless. It is therefore self-referentially inconsistent.

INDEX OF NAMES

References are to paragraph numbers except references in italics which are to page numbers.

INDEX OF SUBJECTS

References are to paragraph numbers except references in italics which are to page numbers.

INDEX OF SPECIAL SYMBOLS

References are to paragraph numbers. For abbreviations of names of logical principles and rules, see Index of Subjects.

Trans, 26.55

U, 17.47

[U²], 25.48

W, 28.1–28.9

Y, 18.3

Z, 18.8

The italic letters *p*, *q*, *r*, *s*, and *t* refer to propositions.

The italic letters *F*, *G*, and *H* refer to attributes or classes.

The italic letters *R*, *S*, and *T* refer to relations.

The italic letters *a*, *b*, *c*, *d*, and *e* refer to things of all sorts, including propositions, attributes, classes, relations, physical objects, and persons.

The italic letters *x*, *y*, *z*, *u*, *v*, and *w* refer to things of all sorts, but they serve a special purpose in connection with abstracts (17.17) and also in connection with quantifiers, since the latter are defined in terms of abstracts. See also the last two sentences of 21.6.